WILLIAM F. (BILL) HOLTROP stands out as the best man to revise this famous decorator-finisher's "bible" for the wood craftsman. Author of several leading textbooks in woodworking, he is also a professor of industrial education—holding a doctor's degree.

No book is perfect. But here the authors have tried to marshall the facts, pigeon-holed and discussed in full —every conceivable formula and bit of know-how information that the craftsman needs, to improve his performance and quality of the job. To make the book the best of its kind, Dr. Holtrop has updated the entire coverage yet retained the older materials and methods necessary in renewing or applying special finishes that require care and techniques of a fine old tradition.

Coloring Finishing and Painting Wood

By **Adnah Clifton Newell** • Late Professor of
Industrial Arts, Illinois State Normal University

Revised by **William F. Holtrop,** Author of
WOODSHOP TOOL MAINTENANCE

Associate Professor, Industrial Arts
University of California, Santa Barbara College,
Santa Barbara, California

CHAS. A. BENNETT CO., INC.
Peoria, Illinois

Acknowledgments

In the preparation of this revision I was ably assisted by many firms and persons connected with the finishing industry. I wish to express my appreciation to the following for supplying glossy prints and useful literature:

American Brake Shoe Company, Kellogg Division; Rochester, New York.
Behr-Manning Corporation; Troy, New York.
Cellusuede Products, Inc.; Rockford, Illinois.
Claremont Waste Manufacturing Co.; Claremont, New Hampshire.
The De Vilbiss Company; Toledo, Ohio.
Dremel Manufacturing Company; Racine, Wisconsin.
Devoe and Reynolds Company, Inc.; New York, N.Y.
W. P. Fuller and Co.; San Francisco, California, and Los Angeles, California.
Grand Rapids Varnish Corporation; Grand Rapids, Michigan.
Hillyard Sales Company; St. Joseph, Missouri.
King Paint Roller, Inc.; Detroit, Michigan.
George Koch and Sons, Inc.; Evansville, Indiana.
Mahogany Association, Inc.; Chicago, Illinois.
The Porter-Cable Machine Company; Syracuse, N.Y.
Rayon Processing Co., of R.I.; Pawtucket, R.I.
Edward A. Sheenan and Sons, Inc.; Walpole, Massachusetts.
Sherwin-Williams Co.; Cleveland, Ohio.
Sundstrand Machine Tool Co.; Rockford, Illinois.
United States Department of Agriculture, Forest Products Laboratory; Madison, Wisconsin.
United States Plywood Corporation; New York, N.Y.
William Zinsser and Co.; New York, N.Y.

I wish to make particular acknowledgment to the following persons:

Mr. Arthur Bloomquist and Mr. Edward FitzGibbon of the W. P. Fuller Laboratory, Los Angeles, California, who checked the manuscript from the chemist's standpoint.

Mr. Alex Funke, painting contractor, Santa Barbara, California, who checked the completed revision from the viewpoint of the practical painter.

Mr. Raymond Muhlethaler and Dr. Robert A. McCoy for their help in preparing many photographs placed throughout the book.

Santa Barbara, California W. F. HOLTROP

Preface

Since 1930, COLORING, FINISHING, AND PAINTING WOOD by the late Adnah C. Newell has been an excellent source of information for the amateur and professional wood finisher. However, in the span of years many changes have occurred in the finishing industry. Chemists have developed new and better formulas for paints, varnishes, and lacquers. There have been outstanding improvements in finishing equipment.

Realizing all this the publishers of this book asked me to revise and bring up-to-date the material which has served as the best source of information for so long on a complicated subject.

The revision was accomplished in two ways: the deletion of obsolete material and the addition of new, including some 195 photographs. Very little important material has been deleted except for two chapters, "Air Drying Finishes for Metal," and "Dyes Useful as Stains." This is because finishers differ considerably in what they consider acceptable modern finishing materials and practice and that which is outmoded.

Wherever feasible there are illustrations of procedures and techniques, such as those included in the chapter on "Lacquer Finishes and Lacquer Technique." Two new chapters have been added to the book, "Flock and its Application," which discusses this popular and new material, and the final chapter on "Furniture Refinishing." This latter topic is so broad that it could well be treated in a complete volume.

Contents

Chapter I

Preparing the Surface of Wood with Plane and Scraper

Wood Must Be Dry. The seasoning of wood until it contains the proper amount of moisture is an important factor in successful wood finishing. Wood that is to be used indoors should be kiln dried to about 5 per cent of moisture as a final stage in seasoning, and be allowed to stand for a time in a dry room where it will reabsorb a small amount of water from the air, thus equalizing the per cent of moisture in the wood with that of the air in the shop. A finish which would not show checks, wrinkles, or other defects would have to possess very unusual qualities of elasticity were it to be placed on a piece of wood that is too moist, and which later on shrinks as the dampness dries out. For permanence of finish and lasting qualities of construction, wood must be properly seasoned and remain in a proper shop-dry condition during the construction and finishing periods.

Articles which are made from wood that has received only air seasoning are usually unsatisfactory. The woodworker is likely to be blamed for loose joints, and the wood finisher for poor workmanship or material. The real blame should be put on the excess of moisture in the wood, but this trouble-maker always escapes and goes into thin air and possibly condenses where it may cause more damage. Tests of the moisture content of lumber which is used in shops should be made occasionally, especially when new shipments of lumber are received, because this information will show whether or not the material is safe for use. Even kiln dried lumber must be kept in a very dry place or it will reabsorb moisture to such an extent as to be unfit for any important construction.

11

1—1. Quarter-sawed red oak. A magnification of 50 diameters shows roughness and fragments of torn tissue about the large open pores or tracheal vessels which have been cut open lengthwise. Most of the roughness has been removed from the surface of this section.

Use Great Care in Preparing the Surface. Beauty of finish depends to a great extent upon knowledge of how a surface should be prepared and the skill which is used in carrying out definite plans. Knowledge of the characteristics of the woods used and of the tools that are available is like the good management at the head of a factory. If a workman knows considerable about the structure of wood, and its mechanical and chemical properties, he is not so likely to decide upon poor plans. On the other hand, he must have proper tools and equipment for preparing the surface and know how to use them skillfully. Finally, the real craftsman must have a valuable ethical quality known as honesty of purpose, and a perseverance which will bring creditable results.

If a hand magnifier or microscope, magnifying about 18 times, is turned on a piece of so-called smooth wood, the surface which was supposed to be smooth is found to be rough; sometimes very rough, in the case of ring-porous woods such as oak (Fig. 1-1). A few minutes of microscopic study will prove to any one that it really takes very great care to produce a smooth surface on a piece of wood. The broken fragments of wood cells under a strong glass sometimes look like the tree trunks of "down timber" on a burnt over area on a mountainside or great plain. The coarser defects of an improperly finished surface are easily visible and objectionable to the ordinary eye, but a microscopical examination sometimes reveals undreamed of roughness on a carelessly scraped or inadequately sanded piece of wood.

No surface is ready for the wood finisher that shows marks made by the machine planer in dressing or surfacing the board to thickness. Such marks cannot be sanded out by hand, but must be carefully removed by a smoothing plane, or scraper; or both may be used to advantage on some woods. Sometimes fragments of fibers are torn out by a machine or hand plane, leaving ragged rough spots. Such places must be scraped out, or may be removed by a sanding machine. Hand sanding will not remove such defects.

Planing the Surface by Hand. The first operation in the preparation of the surface of a piece of wood is, usually, planing with a hand plane, using a smooth plane after the rougher parts have been gone over with a jack plane. Edges are frequently finished with a jointer plane in order to have them as straight as possible. In school and home shops, where it is not practicable to have a plane for each purpose, the most satisfactory all-round plane for general use is an iron jack plane, about 14″ or 15″ in length, with a 2″ plane iron.

Plane irons for smoothing surfaces should have straight edges, with rounded corners, ground to a bevel of about 22½° (Fig. 1-2). Cutters used for very hard wood may be stiffer, and are often ground to a 25° or even 30° angle in extreme cases. If the surface is to be scraped after planing, the edge of the plane iron may be very slightly curved, as in a jack plane. The troughlike places made on a surface by such a plane can be removed later by proper scraping. Dull plane irons never cut smoothly and are a frequent cause of rough surfaces, torn out fibers, and broken flakes and knots. They sometimes do serious and almost irreparable damage before the cause of the trouble is discovered. They also require frequent sharpening when used on hard woods. The plane-iron cap sometimes requires sharpening, and should always fit perfectly on the cutter.

A smoother, sharper, and better cutting edge can be put on a plane-iron if a strop is used for the finishing touches. A very practical strop for this purpose can be made by gluing to a board a piece of leather belting about 4″ by 12″ in size (Fig. 1-3). Such a strop sharpens a tool better if very fine emery dust and cup grease are worked into the surface of the leather. If properly used on a plane-iron, the strop improves the cutting qualities.

The plane should be carefully adjusted before planing is attempted. For fine finished work the plane-iron cap should be set close to the edge, about ⅟₃₂″ back, and should be firmly clamped with the edge of the plane-iron parallel to the edge of the plane-iron cap.

The frog of the plane should be slightly advanced for smooth work, and placed so that the opening in the throat in front of the cutter is less than is ordinarily used in a jack plane. The small throat and close adjustment of the plane-iron cap prevent to some extent the tearing out of irregular fibers or those that run against the grain.

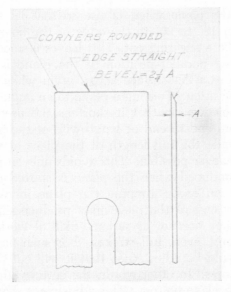

CORNERS ROUNDED

EDGE STRAIGHT

BEVEL=2¼ A

A

1—2. Sharpen plane iron like this.

1—3. Cutting edges of chisels and plane irons are sharpened to a keen edge on a leather strop.

Holding the plane when in use so that its side is at an angle of from 10° to 20° to the edge of the board causes the cutter to make a shearing cut. This leaves a smoother surface than when the parallel position of the plane is used. It is easier to secure a flat surface across grain when the plane is held in this position. Turning a plane to an angle has one disadvantage, however, in that it shortens the useful length of the plane from end to end or lengthwise of the piece.

Strokes made the full length of the piece of wood should be taken whenever possible. This avoids uneven places which are always produced when the plane is started *on* the piece instead of at an end. Stopping the plane anywhere except at the farther end of the piece may produce similar uneven places, but they are not as serious. Skillful workmen always plane with long, even, full strokes. For such finishing work, the plane should be adjusted so that it will cut thin shavings of even thickness. In other words, the cutting edge should be parallel to the plane bottom. This adjustment should be made with great care before any planing is attempted.

1—4. Remove old hook by honing the flat side on a hard honing stone.

The hand planing operation should not be omitted on any surface which is to be finished with transparent finishes, unless it is decided that a scraper plane should be substituted for the smooth plane, on account of unusual grain, such as in curly birch, bird's-eye maple, or quarter sawed oak. A scraper plane properly handled will cut against the grain more satisfactorily than a smooth plane, and is a much better and safer tool to use on twisted or unusual grain.

Inexperienced workmen sometimes get in a hurry and try to dodge the planing operation. Sometimes attempts are made to scrape a surface with a hand scraper instead of using a plane or scraper plane. The hand scraper follows the irregularities or waves of the board and does not level the surface at all. Attempts to smooth a machine-planed surface with sandpaper alone are always very time consuming and result in failure. Sandpaper follows the waves made by the machine cutter and does not smooth properly or level the surface.

Scrapers and Their Use. Scrapers when properly sharpened and used are a great source of satisfaction to a workman and perform work that is usually surprising to an amateur. In shops where machine sanders are not available to smooth and level surfaces of wood, scrapers are very important tools.

There are two different kinds of scrapers: (1) scraper planes and (2) cabinet scrapers or hand scrapers.

Scraper planes are tools which hold scraper blades or cabinet scrapers in stocks, which, in some of their forms, resemble plane stocks. With the increasing popularity of various types of sanding machines, this tool is not used nearly as much as in years past.

Scraper blades for use in scraper holders are sharpened with a beveled instead of a square edge. The procedure is as follows:

(1) Remove the old hook by honing the flat side of the blade on a honing stone. Never use a file for this purpose, as the side of the blade will become scratched, and these scratches will make nicks in the new hook (Fig. 1-4).

(2) File a bevel on the blade at an angle of about 60°, using a 10″ or 12″ mill file. Round the corners slightly, as in grinding a plane iron (Fig. 1-5).

1—5. File at 60° beveled edge on the cabinet scraper, using a mill file. Corners are slightly rounded.

1—6. Remove the wire edge by honing beveled edge first. Hone flat side next. 1—7. Turn a hook on the edge of bevel in four successive strokes. On the last stroke, the burnisher makes an angle of 85° with the flat side of the scraper blade.

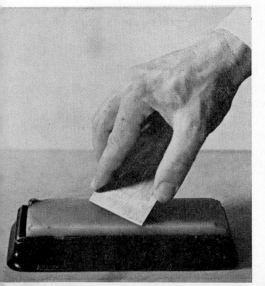

1—8. A cabinet scraper performs like this.

(3) Whet the edge with great care on an oilstone. Any feathered edge may be removed by cutting into a piece of wood, using the blade like a chisel, but drawing the edge across the fibers of the piece as with a knife. Repeat this operation until the blade is sharp and the feathered edge is removed (Fig. 1-6).

(4) Place the scraper blade in a vise. Take a burnisher made of specially hardened steel, and turn a hook on the edge of the bevel, bending the metal over toward the flat or front side. Use about four strokes, turning the hook more each time and holding the burnisher at an angle of about 85° with the face of the blade on the last stroke (Fig. 1-7).

A scraper blade sharpened as described above, if properly adjusted in the scraper holder, will cut thin, long shavings, and will plane against the grain to some extent without tearing out the fibers (Fig. 1-8). On some very hard, crooked grained woods, the smooth plane should not be used, the cabinet scraper being substituted for the entire scraping process in order to avoid tearing out fragments such as flakes in oak and the eyes in bird's-eye maple (Fig. 1-9).

A dulled scraper blade hook can be flattened out part way back with a burnisher and then turned over again as in the first turning of the hook.

The hand scraper has two square edges for cutting instead

1—9. Surface of chestnut wood showing torn fragments. Fragments of wood have been torn out because of planing against the grain. The surface was improperly scraped. Note the filler in the open pores. Magnification is about 5 diameters.

of one beveled edge. It is not possible to turn a large hook, but a very sharp fine scraping edge or burr can be secured that is excellent for finishing a surface by hand.

The method used for sharpening a square edge on a hand scraper is as follows:

(1) Hone off the old hooks by placing the scraper blade flat down on an oilstone and whetting till the old hook is gone (Fig. 1-10).

(2) With the edge that is to be sharpened up, or on top, clamp the scraper blade in a vise.

(3) File a square edge on the blade with a fine 10″ or 12″ mill file. File from edge to edge, rounding off the two corners slightly as in a plane iron.

(4) Draw file the edge by holding one end of the file in

1—10. Remove old hook on a hard honing stone. Whet flat side first. Whet square edge next.

each hand and filing back and forth toward the corners, keeping the file at right angles to the blade (Fig. 1-11).

(5) Hone the sharpened edges by holding the blade perpendicularly on an oilstone. Also hone each flat side with the blade flat down on the stone. Repeat the processes until the edges are square and sharp (Fig. 1-12).

1—11. Draw-file the edge with a mill file.

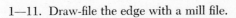

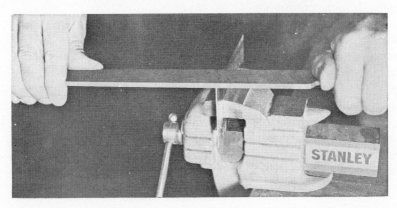

1—12. Hone edges and flat sides on an oilstone.

(6) Turn the square cutting edges down to about 85° with a large smooth burnisher, holding the blade firmly in a bench vise. Use about four strokes in turning the edge, increasing the pressure and decreasing the angle with the face side each time (Fig. 1-13).

The small, sharp burr or hook on a hand scraper will do wonders in smoothing defective places that cannot be removed with sandpaper (Fig. 1-14).

A few of the coniferous woods such as cypress and some very soft woods do not scrape well. On such woods the scraping operation should be omitted. Soft woods which cannot be scraped satisfactorily can be smoothed very effectively with a sharp plane; scraping in such cases is not important and should not be attempted.

Curved scrapers can be used to advantage especially for smoothing concave surfaces. A scraper blade may be filed or ground to the desired shape, and then sharpened with a hook similar to that put on a square scraper. A beveled-edge hook is frequently put on curved scrapers. A scraper of this kind

1—13. Turn cutting edges down in four successive strokes. On the last stroke, the burnisher makes an angle of 85° with the side of the blade.

1—14. A handscraper performs like this, cutting shavings much finer than can be made with a plane.

is often helpful in smoothing up surfaces which are made with a gouge.

In addition to the scrapers described thus far, so-called hook scrapers are on the market which do a satisfactory job of removing roughness in grain pattern. These scrapers come with replaceable blades. After the blade is resharpened a few times, it is discarded and replaced by a new one.

Plugs and Cement for Holes and Cracks. Various small defects such as wormholes, knotholes, dents, torn fibers in small spots, and places that have been injured by tools or in some other way during the process of construction, are frequently found on otherwise perfect surfaces. If the injury is large, as a knothole extending through the board, it is frequently best to insert a plug of wood and to glue it into place. Sometimes bad defects can be chiseled out, and a piece of wood having similar grain and color can be so carefully inlaid and glued into place that it will hardly show when finished. This kind of repair takes more time than other processes, but is permanent and causes less disfigurement to the piece, if done skillfully.

Another process commonly used in factories is to fill the defective place with cabinet maker's cement. This material is made for furniture factories, and comes in bricks having a color resembling wood. In use, fragments of cement are broken up, melted, and thinned with water to a thick paste which can be pressed into the defect with a putty knife. The opening should be filled slightly too full when first put in place and sanded level after it has dried. The spot of cement will usually take stains nearly the same as the wood itself. If the cement is used on a dark-colored wood, or put in a spot in a cedar chest, the cement should be stained to the proper color with dry pigments before it is used. There are also water putties on the market that can be made into paste with cold water and pressed into place with a putty knife.

An old method for repairing small defects is to secure some fine dust from sanding the surface of the wood which has the defect. This powder is then mixed with a liquid cold glue, making a paste which can be pressed into place with a putty knife. When dry the spot can be sanded. A repaired place of this kind filled with glue paste will not stain well.

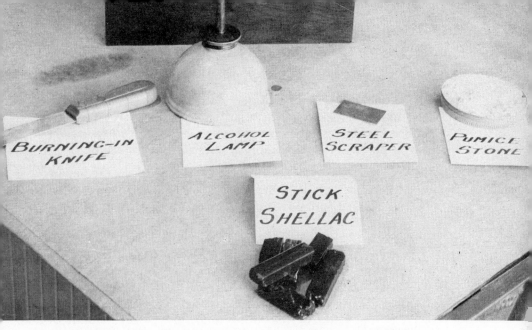

1—15. Tools and materials needed to make repairs with stick shellac.

Paste can be mixed with dry colors, however, while in the wet form and made nearer the proper color. Glue paste should be quite thick, and in use should not be spread over the surface of the wood around the defect because glue sizes wood and prevents stain from "taking" when the article is stained later on.

Repairing Surfaces with Stick Shellac: Melted wax from

1—16. Select a piece of shellac that matches the color of the wood and finish as closely as possible. 1—17. Heat the burning-in knife lightly over an alcohol flame.

shellac sticks may be run into small defects. This is usually done after the article is partly finished so that the color can be matched to better advantage. Shellac sticks in various colors can be purchased from supply houses for wood finishing.

1. Assemble the tools and materials needed to do the repair job. These include: burning-in knife, alcohol lamp, small steel scraper, pumice stone, and a variety of shellac sticks (Fig. 1-15).
2. Select a piece of shellac that matches the color of the wood and finish as closely as possible (Fig. 1-16).
3. Heat the burning-in knife lightly over an alcohol flame. Alcohol is preferred because an alcohol flame leaves no black carbon on the knife (Fig. 1-17).
4. With the point of the knife, melt off a small amount of shellac from the stick and work it into the hole that needs filling (Fig. 1-18).
5. Smooth the filled area carefully with the heated knife (Fig. 1-19).
6. When the shellac is completely dry, scrape the repaired spot with the steel scraper (Fig. 1-20). Such a scraper is sharpened like a regular hand scraper, except that the edges are not turned down with a burnishing tool.
7. After smoothing it like this, rub the repaired area with the palm of your hand, using a little pumice stone as the abrasive (Fig. 1-21).

1—18. With the knife fill the hole with molten stick shellac. 1—19. Smooth the filled area carefully with the heated knife.

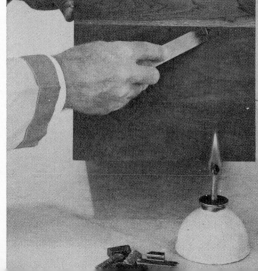

STEEL SCRAPER

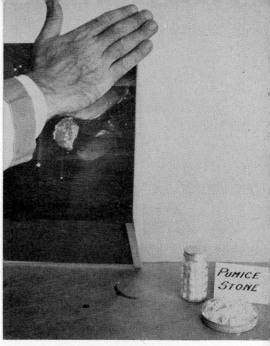
PUMICE STONE

1—20. When the shellac is completely dry, remove any excess shellac with the small steel scraper. 1—21. Smooth the repaired spot by rubbing it with pumice stone, using the palm of your hand as a polisher.

Dents can sometimes be removed by steaming with a wet cloth and a hot iron. Hot water alone if put into a dent several times will sometimes swell the compressed fibers back to normal condition and thus practically remove the unsightly spot. A putty knife, if carefully heated about as hot as a flat iron when used for ironing, will help to raise a dented spot if placed over wood that has been well moistened with water. In all of these cases the wood fibers are swelled by steam and are likely to resume nearly their original shape, thus causing the dent to disappear.

SELECTED REFERENCES, CHAPTER I

Preparing the Surface of Wood with Plane and Scraper

Browne, F. L., "Natural Finishes for Exterior Wood." *Architectural Record*, 111, pp. 196-198, Feb., 1952.
Chemical Week, 75, "Wood that Won't Warp," p. 44, Oct. 23, 1954.
Deniston, G. L., *The Science of Modern Woodfinishing*, "Cabinet, Furniture and Other Woods," Chapter I, pp. 1-25, 1949.
Feirer, John L., *Industrial Arts Woodworking*, pp. 174-186, 1960.

Feirer, John L., *Advanced Woodwork and Furniture Making*, "Wood Finishing," Section 4, pp. 138-153, 1960.

Gibbia, S. W., *Wood Finishing and Refinishing*. Introduction, Chapter I, pp. 1-15, 1954.

Hunt, G. M., "Protecting Wood from Decay and Fire." *Architectural Record*, 114, pp. 167-171, Dec., 1953.

Pelton, B. W., *Furniture Making and Cabinet Work*. "Cabinet Making," Chapter I, pp. 1-45, 1949.

Prince, R. E., "Finishes for Wood." *Paint Oil and Chemical Review*, 114, page 12, May 10, 1951.

Soderberg, G. A., *Finishing Materials and Methods*. "Methods of Procedure," Chapter XXVII, pp. 203-204, 1952.

Stamm, A. J., "Diffusion and Penetration Mechanism of Liquids into Woods." *Pulp and Paper Magazine of Canada*, pp. 54-63, Feb., 1953.

Ibid., "Recent Advances in Wood Chemistry." Paper Industry, pp. 1233-1234, Jan., 1953.

Stieri, E., *Woodworking for the Home Craftsman*. "Wood and Wood Products," Chapter I, pp. 1-28, 1950.

Tombach, H., "Special Methods of Drying Wood." *Mechanical Engineering*, page 40, Jan., 1951.

Chapter II

Surface Abrasives and Their Use

Importance of Surface Preparation. Proper surface preparation is the first operation in successful wood finishing. It is here that the actual process of finishing starts. Sanding rules, although few and simple, must be clearly understood and strictly adhered to. It is also important to know the different kinds of abrasives, their grades, structure, and particular use.

What formerly was a tedious and time-consuming operation has now been reduced to a minimum of work by the development of mechanical sanding machines. Although a certain amount of hand sanding will always be necessary, the greater share of the work is now performed by means of these mechanical devices.

Whether surfaces are prepared by hand or machines, *the proper preparation of all surfaces is of utmost importance.* No amount of filler, varnish, or lacquer will hide an underlying rough surface. On the contrary, it only magnifies dents, scratches, and other surface defects.

Inspection Before Sandpapering. Inspection of the surfaces to be sandpapered is an important preliminary which should never be overlooked. If rough spots or planer marks have been left they should be found and removed before any sanding is attempted. Hand sandpapering will not remove or cover up defects of this kind. It is a waste of time and increases the difficulty. Scraping out the unfinished places later on is harder because sandpapering always leaves sand in the pores of the wood, and this sharp grit soon dulls the edge of a scraper blade. Very frequent sharpenings of the hook on a scraper are necessary, if scraping is attempted after wood has been sandpapered.

Amateur wood finishers should learn what defects to look

29

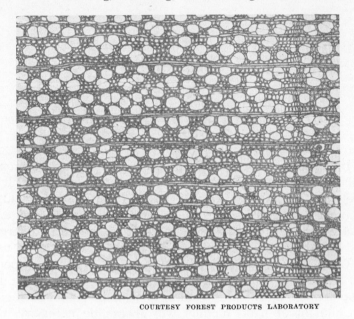

2—1. End grain of red gumwood. This cross-section of the wood of the red gum shows the porosity of the end grain of a close-grained wood. Magnification about 50 diameters.

for, and should realize that planer marks and minor blemishes that hardly show on the natural wood are greatly exaggerated on the finished piece, especially, if stain of any kind is used. Rough surfaces practically always expose more cross sections of the pores or end grain, which, when stained, will show darker than the rest of the surface. This is due to the fact that the end grain of wood is always more porous than the ordinary grain of longitudinal or transverse sections (Fig. 2-1).

Sandpaper Manufacture. Sandpapers of the present day are not made from sand and paper. The grit which looks like sand is made from quartz or flint rocks (Fig. 2-2). The red or garnet papers have a grit made from garnet ore (Fig. 2-3). Great hardness and sharpness of edges are important factors in a grit. Natural sand, while hard, has few sharp edges, as all such cutting places are soon worn off and smoothed by rubbing against each other, just as rocks on the mountain sides

2—2. Flint quartz used in the manufacture of flint paper. 2—3. Garnet, a natural abrasive, is much harder than flint quartz.

are smoothed and rounded by glacial action. Sharp grit is made from crushing hard rock and sifting in order to secure particles of uniform size. Various sizes of rock fragments, sometimes called sand, are secured in order that sandpaper of different grades of coarseness and fineness may be manufactured.

Flint and garnet are classified as natural abrasives. In addition to these natural abrasives a number of artificial ones have been perfected. Examples of this type are silicon carbide and aluminum oxide. Silicon carbide is chemically composed of carbon and silicon. Through heat treatment in an electric furnace it is formed into blue-black crystals. As an abrasive it is extensively used in the finishing field (Fig. 2-4).

Aluminum oxide is also produced by heat treatment in an electric furnace. Although not so hard as silicon carbide, it is tougher and does not fracture so easily. This reddish-brown abrasive is widely used in woodworking and finishing (Fig. 2-5).

The best grades of paper are strong, especially when made from Manila fiber, which is sometimes secured from old ropes. The strength is also increased by a crisscross or uneven arrangement. Papers which are made so that the fibers are not

COURTESY BEHR-MANNING CORPORATION

2—4. Silicon carbide is produced electrically by fusing silica sand and coke. 2—5. Aluminum oxide, reddish brown in color, is made in electric furnaces by fusing the mineral bauxite at high temperatures.

parallel with their lengths in one direction are stronger crosswise and have nearly uniform strength in every direction. Such papers are difficult to tear and, if torn, leave a rough uneven edge. Thicker papers are used when coarser grits are to be applied.

In recent years some significant changes have been made

2—6. Abrasive grains are screened by means of silk screens from very fine to very coarse.

COURTESY BEHR-MANNING CORPORATION

in the methods of covering abrasive cloth and paper (Fig. 2-6). Formerly the abrasive grains were sprinkled evenly on a previously glue-prepared surface. This method is now largely replaced by what is known as the *electrostatic process.* Here the abrasive grains are electrically imbedded into the cloth or paper surfaces. This action results in placing the particles more uniformly, in a position to give a sharper and faster cutting surface.

Waterproof paper has some excellent features very desirable in wood finishing, for it can be used to great advantage over a wet felt pad. The finer grades of waterproof sandpaper, such as the 5/0 to 8/0 sizes, are excellent for sanding varnish between coats. A varnish surface smoothed with one of these papers having the finest grit looks much like a finish rubbed with pumice stone and the operation can be completed in much less time.

Sizes of Sandpaper. Many sizes of grit are used in manufacturing sandpaper, ranging from 8/0 to 4, as follows:

(1) *Very fine or soft papers,* used by wood finishers: from 00000000, or 8/0, to 00, or 2/0.

(2) *Medium sizes,* commonly used by woodworkers: 0, or 1/0, 1/2, 1, 1½, 2.

(3) *Very coarse papers,* more commonly used on sanding machines for rapid cutting: 2½, 3, 3½, 4.

Sizes finer than 8/0 sandpaper are made by some manufacturers, but are not commonly found on the market.

For many years, sandpaper in the standard sized sheets of 9″ x 11″ was sold in quires and reams. A quire contained 24 sheets and a ream was made up of 20 quires or 480 sheets. This method of packaging was simplified in 1948. Since that year sheets of abrasives are packed in sleeves of 25, 50, and 100 sheets. Ten sleeves form a unit. Some supply catalogs list abrasives in minimum packages of 50-100 sheets and standard unit packages of 500-1000 sheets.

Use of Sandpaper. The cardinal principle in the use of sandpaper is that *all sanding must be with the grain* (Fig. 2-7). Never make circular, cross-grain, nor oblique strokes with sandpaper, as scratches always result. End grain of wood

2—7. Properly scraped and sanded surface of chestnut. The pores of the wood have been successfully filled with paste wood filler. The magnification is about 5 diameters.

must be sanded crosswise. A careful study of wood structure with a magnifier shows that the fibers are arranged like parallel tubes lengthwise of the grain. These fibers are scratched, torn, or cut through by the sharp edges of the sand grit if the strokes are in any other direction than lengthwise of the grain. Resanding with the grain in the proper way will not easily remove scratches. Such injuries should be scraped out, and after all scratches have disappeared, the surface should be sanded, pushing the sandpaper with the grain of the wood.

Blocks for holding sandpaper in order that greater pressure may be applied are used in every finishing room. The size, weight, and covering for the blocks depend upon the kind of work. For big surfaces a rather large heavy block has some advantages. A brick covered with canvas or other cloth is used in some shops for coarse work, especially where rapid cutting on large surfaces is desired. For the first sanding with coarse sandpaper, some workmen prefer a hard flat block with little or no covering. This will cut off the high spots better and help to reduce the somewhat irregular surface to a truer surface.

34

A favorite size of sandpaper for use on many kinds of wood for the first sanding is No. 1 or 1½. For the finer-grained woods one should use the No. 1, which is finer than No. 1½.

The second sanding with finer paper can best be done with a soft block or a block with a soft cover. Corks about 1″ x 3″ x 6″ in size are preferred by some; another size sold on the market for such work is 1″ x 4″ x 4″. Felt faced or cloth covered blackboard erasers can be used very satisfactorily for sanding blocks. Some finishers use rubber faced blocks. A homemade block of this kind can be prepared from a rectangular scrap of soft wood to which is tacked a piece of rubber taken from an automobile inner tube. The sizes of sandpaper used for fine sanding are about ½ or 0. Sometimes 00 paper is preferable for very fine grained hard wood.

Rounding off the corners of a piece of wood in sanding is a very common fault that must be avoided, or the appearance of the finished work will be ruined. This does not mean that the sharp feathered edges should not be slightly smoothed off to get rid of slivers, for this should always be done with fine sandpaper in the final sanding. Unless care is taken to avoid a rocking motion while sanding, corners and edges will become rounded off unevenly, and poor work is the result.

End grain sanding is just as important as sanding of the surfaces and edges. If the end grain is left too rough, additional stain will be absorbed there; consequently it will become darker than other portions of the surface.

When sanding end grain, the finisher should sand in one direction only, rather than with a back and forth motion. By lifting the sanding block off the stock after reaching the end of the stroke, he will flatten out the wood fibers more readily and make a smoother surface.

The use of sandpaper between the successive coats of finish is necessary in securing a level surface and proper adhesion of the films of shellac, varnish, or lacquer that are to be applied later on in the finishing process. The kind and size of sandpaper, and the method of using it, depend upon various conditions. Two types of sandpaper are used by wood finishers: (1) standard paper, with either flint or garnet grit; and (2) waterproof sandpaper. The standard type has already been described in previous paragraphs of this section.

Waterproof sandpapers have been developed to help solve several problems of the finishing room. The use of such papers enables a workman to sand a moist surface of wood soon after it has been sponged, thereby saving a certain amount of time. Sanding with wet paper reduces the dust in the room which helps to preserve the health of the finisher and to reduce danger of specks in varnish finishes. For sanding moist wood to remove fuzz, rather fine grades of grit, such as sizes ½, 0, or 00, should be used in most cases. Waterproof papers, which do not lose their grit when dampened and kept in that condition during several minutes, are often preferred for rubbing between coatings of varnish; and, when used over a rubber or felt block, they produce a level surface without gloss, more quickly and more satisfactorily, between the first coats especially, than does pumice stone. The sanding should all be done with the grain only, where this is possible, and fine grades of grit, such as the 5/0 to 8/0, leave an excellent surface for refinishing.

Automobile painters are using a special sandpaper which can also be used wet. Automobile finishers' sandpaper is sold by number; such as No. 280, rather coarse; No. 320, medium in grit; and No. 400, very fine. These sandpapers are used for smoothing undercoats and surfaces of lacquer which must be made level in preparation for the next coat. They scratch if they are used dry, and for this reason they are kept wet when rubbing varnished or lacquered surfaces.

Steel Wool and Its Use. Steel wool is often used in smoothing concave surfaces. The sizes of steel wool most commonly used are: 000 or 3/0, 00 or 2/0, 0, 1, and 2; 000 being the finest, and No. 2 the coarsest. Cartons or packages of steel wool in 1-pound, 5-pound, and 10-pound sizes are sold on the market by hardware stores, and paint and varnish supply houses. In use, a ball or wad of steel wool is taken in the hand, and the surface is rubbed as with sandpaper. Strokes should be made with the grain whenever possible, as scratches will result if the abrasive is used crosswise or obliquely.

Steel wool can be bought in ready-made, layer-built pads. They are easy to work with and more economical than pieces of steel wool torn from a package. Their layer-built construction enables the user to fold back each used layer, exposing a fresh, new surface. A 1-pound package contains sixteen pads. The packages are graded from No. 4/0, fine, to No. 3, course.

Sponging and Resanding. Beauty and clearness of grain can be secured by sponging with water. This is done in order to dampen and raise the grain on all surfaces that are to be finished. Sponging the surface may be done with a wool sponge, an ordinary sponge, or with a soft large brush that holds water well. The wood should be dampened enough to cover all of the wood fibers on the surface with water, yet with not enough to leave a layer or coating that takes considerable time to dry. An excess of moisture might injure glue joints particularly those of veneer.

Fuzz appears over the entire surface of any piece of wood that has been sponged and allowed to dry. The surface of a piece of wood consists of cells which are something like long tubes running lengthwise of the grain. Many of these cells are cut through, exposing the ragged walls, when the processes of planing and scraping are done (Fig. 2-8). Some of this roughness, however, is removed by sanding. The finest sandpaper does not remove all the fragments of the cell walls. Some of these particles are more or less loose after sanding, and swell up and stiffen as a result of sponging and drying, and become the fuzz that can be felt on a sponged board after it has dried. The fuzziness on the surface of wood that has been moistened can largely be removed by resanding with fine sandpaper. The best results are secured by using 2/0, 3/0, or even 4/0 sandpaper over a block, as described in the first sanding operation.

Careful use of sandpaper, using long full strokes with the grain, leaves the surface in a very smooth condition. Sponging, and resanding a second time very slightly improve the surfaces of some kinds of wood, but not enough to pay for the trouble. Sponging and resanding are always necessary if water stains are used because these operations prevent the stain from raising the grain or fuzz. If stains that do not contain water are used in the finish, the sponging and resanding operations are usually omitted on account of the cost of extra work required.

Excessive use of water in sponging, and excessive pressure on the sandpaper, should both be avoided on veneered work, or spots may be cut through which cannot be repaired without reveneering. Veneer is thin, being ordinarily about ½₀″ in thickness, and part of this is always removed in the first sanding operation. Hard pressure and coarse sandpaper should never be used in smoothing veneered wood.

Glue Sizing. Instead of sponging the wood surfaces with water, an application of glue size can be made. Normally it is done just before the final sanding. The purpose of glue sizing is to raise any loose and ruptured wood fibers which may have resulted from a previous operation. As the glue size dries, the stiffened fibers are cut off more cleanly and evenly in the final sanding.

A satisfactory glue size is prepared as follows:

1. Soak one part of hide glue in two parts of water.

2. Let it stand until all the glue has softened.

3. Heat this mixture to a temperature of from 140° to 150° Fahrenheit until a uniform liquid mixture is obtained.

4. Dilute with additional water. A satisfactory mixture is obtained by adding eight parts of water to one part of liquid glue.

A glue size may be applied either by spraying, brushing, or sponging. All surfaces must be thoroughly dry before they are sanded. The sandpaper used should not be coarser than 5/0. Paper coarser than 5/0 cuts through the glue size and in so doing eliminates the benefit of the size.

Glue sizing has been found to be useful in partly eliminating so-called "pin-holing." This difficulty is often encountered with certain kinds of mahogany. Pin holes result when air escapes from improperly filled pores. A glue size tends to plug these pores, allowing a better filling job. Although it may not completely stop this trouble, it helps to some extent.

The application of too much glue size and improper sanding afterward may cause trouble when the actual finishing starts. Stain, especially non-grain-raising stain, may not penetrate so deeply as desired. If this is the case, additional sanding is necessary. Surfaces, when properly sized and sanded, will show a slight resistance to taking up stain, but not enough to cause any difficulty.

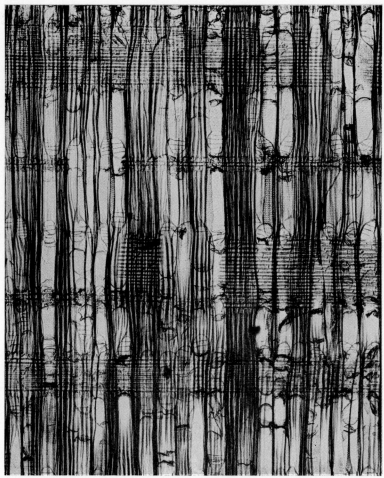

COURTESY FOREST PRODUCTS LABORATORY

2—8. Cellular structure of wood. Radial section of yellow poplar, a wood of fine grain; the edges of the cell walls have been cut through in many places, and these broken walls will leave ragged fragments of tissue on the surface. Sandpaper should be used lengthwise of the grain in order to remove all roughness from the broken cell walls. Magnification, 50 diameters.

Sanding Machines Used in Wood Finishing. Up to this point little or no mention has been made of the usefulness of various types of sanding machines. They are now extensively

2—9. Sanding flat stock on a small belt sander.

used in the furniture industry and in school and home workshops.

Actual shop experience and tests conducted have proved that a wood surface can be sanded and rubbed by mechanical means in from 50% to 70% less time than by ordinary hand sanding and rubbing.

The more commonly used sanders are the following:

Belt sanders: These machines are made in a variety of sizes and forms. They are especially useful for sanding large, flat surfaces. By changing the belt from coarse to fine, resulting surfaces need little additional attention before the actual finishing starts.

Some of the smaller belt sanders have belts that travel in a horizontal or vertical position. These machines will readily sand small pieces (Figs. 2-9 and 10). An adjustable table makes it possible to sand at different angles. Inside curves can be sanded by using the curvature formed by the pulley (Fig. 2-11).

Disk sanders: A disk sander is simply a revolving metal

COURTESY BEHR-MANNING CORPORATION

2—10. Tapered cuts are sanded smooth and straight. 2—11. Inside curves can be sanded on one of the pulleys of a small belt sander.

disk to which a sheet of abrasive paper has been fastened. The table that supports the stock can usually be tilted as much as 45°. Some tables have a fence which makes it possible to do accurate sanding on end grain (Fig. 2-12).

Spindle sander: Spindle sanders resemble a wood shaper and operate in a vertical rotary motion. Some machines have in addition an oscillatory or up and down motion. The abra-

2—12. Outside curves are readily smoothed on a disk sander. 2—13. Areas of assembled projects can be sanded with a portable belt sander. Some experience in the use of this machine is recommended.

COURTESY BEHR-MANNING CORPORATION

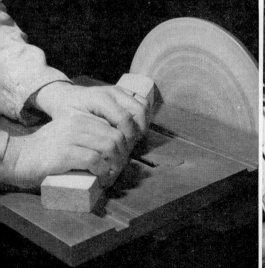

2—14. Fine finishing sanding is possible by mounting a fine belt on the portable sander.

sive sleeve is mounted either on rubber rolls or on felt covered split rolls. By tightening the nut on the spindle, the operator makes the rolls expand slightly and keep the abrasive sleeve in place. This machine is particularly useful in sanding inside curves.

When no spindle sander is available, the operations performed on this machine can be done on an ordinary *wood lathe.* To use the lathe as a sander, first make one or more wooden cylinders. Next cover these cylinders with abrasive paper. With the cylinder mounted between the live and dead center of the lathe, do inside sanding from either the top or the bottom of the cylinder.

Portable sanders: The advantage of portable sanders is that they can be taken directly to the job (Figs. 2-13, 14 and 15). They should be handled carefully and maintained according to the manufacturer's instructions. Most of them require a special grease and oil.

2—15. Portable sander with dust bag attached.   2—16. Small finishing sander with back and forth stroke.

Oscillating or Straight-Line Action Sanders: These sanders are especially useful in doing the final sanding. They are often referred to as finishing sanders, since the finest grades of sandpaper can be used on them.

The sanding action on these machines is by short forward and backward strokes (Figs. 2-16 and 17).

2—17. Polishing the top of a desk with a straight-line action sander.

43

COURTESY SUNDSTRAND MACHINE TOOL CO.

2—18. White sanding with a two-
pad straight-line action air sander.

When purchasing or using these sanders, one should be sure
that the machine has a back and forward motion only. Many
of the smaller sanders have a slight side motion. These so-
called "vibrators" leave small circular scratches, which become
quite noticeable when stain is applied to a wood surface.

Portable air sanders: In addition to these sanders there are
several portable air sanders on the market with either one or
two sanding pads. The pad motion on the two-pad machine
is straight-line, whereas that on the single-pad sander is either
straight or orbital. Single-pad sanders are used primarily for
sanding small areas; those with two pads for large, flat surfaces (Fig. 2-18).

Air sanders have various sized sandpaper and rubbing at-
tachments, all of which are interchangeable and so adaptable
to almost all types of sanding and rubbing operations. They
can be successfully used on the five steps typical in woodfinishing operations: white sanding, wash coat sanding, pad-
ding filler, sealer sanding, and rubbing final finishes.

Since these machines operate by means of compressed air, a number of accessories—such as filter and moisture trap, pressure regulator, gauge, and automatic oiler—are needed.

Dust Sanded Surfaces. The last operation in the preparation of the surface of wood should be a thorough dusting with a stiff bristle brush that will remove all dust and broken fragments and much of the sand from the pores of the wood. The brushes commonly used for this purpose are called picking brushes. If the wood is to be filled with wood-filler, the dusting operation is of considerable importance, because it cleans the surface and opens up the cavities of the cells or pores; and, at the same time, it removes any loose gum or other waste matter that may have been left in the cell lumina as end products of food growth or digestion. Picking brushes should be used on open grained woods for dusting, but close grained woods that require no filler may be dusted with any coarse dusting brush.

Dust will settle on any article in a few hours' time; consequently every piece of wood should be dusted just before any wood finishing process is started, and just before any later coat is applied.

SELECTED REFERENCES, CHAPTER II

Surface Abrasives and Their Use

American Builder, "How to Obtain Quality Work with Power Hand Sanders," page 117, Aug., 1949.

The Carborundum Co., "Coated Abrasive Products for all Purposes," Niagara Falls, N.Y.

Deniston, G. L., *The Science of Modern Woodfinishing.* "Sanding," Chapter III, pp. 40-52, 1949.

Gibbia, S. W., *Woodfinishing and Refinishing.* "Preparing the Surface for Finishing," Chapter II, pp. 16-29, 1954.

Mill and Factory, "Industrial Abrasives," pp. 87-94, Sept., 1954.

Soderberg, G. A., *Finishing Materials and Methods.* "Coated and Polishing Abrasives," Chapter XIX, pp. 119-132, 1952.

Trowbridge, Thomas, *Use of Modern Coated Abrasives in Woodworking Industries.* Behr-Manning, Troy, N.Y., 1945.

Wampler, Rollin H., *Modern Organic Finishes.* Chemical Publishing Co., N.Y., 1946, 452 pp.

Chapter III

Wood-Stains and Water-Staining

Reasons for Staining. 1. Color harmony of the woodwork with the furnishings of a home requires staining, for wood in its natural tones does not usually harmonize with textiles and wall colors. Changing a garish, unpleasant color to a softer more attractive one that will take a place in a color scheme is an important reason for staining.

2. Greater beauty in a particular article can often be secured by staining. This can sometimes be obtained by changing an inferior or cheap wood to make it look like an expensive, beautiful one, such as imitation mahogany finish on birch through staining; or, the coloring may bring out unsuspected qualities and beauty in the wood itself, by accentuating contrasts and bringing before the eye attractive natural characteristics which are not emphasized in the unstained material. The reaction of the stain upon flakes or cells of the medullary rays, its effect upon the mass of wood fibers, and its greater absorption by the open pores or broken cell cavities, are all elements of great surprise that are very interesting and vary with different kinds of wood.

3. Staining often tones down natural wood colors that are displeasing to the eye. Sometimes only part of a board needs to be changed in color, as in staining a streak or edge of sapwood to match the general color of the rest of the wood.

4. Sometimes staining is resorted to as a means of giving new wood an aged effect, as in weathered oak.

5. Greater durability can be obtained, where wood is exposed to the weather, through preservative stains made with creosote oil. No other finish is applied over creosote stains. Oil stains, if they contain certain quantities of drying oils such as linseed oil, will protect or preserve wood through the varnishlike film which is left as a covering after the oil has dried.

46

Definition of Wood Staining. Wood finishers are begining to give a very definite and narrow meaning to the word staining, and, at present, generally exclude all materials that add an opaque pigment to the surface, calling such coatings, which remain largely or partly upon or outside the surface, paints, lacquers, or enamels. With this exclusion in mind, staining is a changing of hue or tone which is due to a chemical reaction or to the application of a liquid that enters to some extent into the interior, and with coloring matter changes the color of a layer of wood near the surface while still allowing the grain with its different cell arrangements to be seen clearly. Staining should leave a transparent effect instead of obscuring the surface with opaque material such as pigments. The coloring matter in stains should be in a thoroughly dissolved condition, instead of being in a turbid muddy paste, when it is applied to the wood.

Classification of Wood Stains. So many kinds of stains are used for wood that any intelligent and useful classification of them is difficult. The problems which are apt to be met in applying a stain depend to a very large extent upon the solvent which is used to dissolve the coloring matter. For this reason stains are generally classified according to the solvents used in making them.

The five classes of stains for wood are:

1. Water stains.
2. Oil stains.
3. Spirit stains.
4. Non-grain raising stains.
5. Chemical stains.

Two other classes of so-called stains are found on the market: varnish stains and wax stains. These are not transparent, as they obscure the grain and leave a layer of pigment on the surface. Wax stains and varnish stains are really in a class midway between true stains and enamels or paints. They are not often used in furniture making, but are occasionally suitable for a home repair job where the transparency of the grain of the wood is not considered. Colored varnishes are not popular with expert wood finishers because they always leave muddy, unattractive effects.

The five classes of stain—water, oil, spirit, chemical, and non-grain raising—may be subdivided generally into two classes, acid and alkaline, depending upon their chemical reaction with other substances.

Water soluble acid stains are very often made of coal-tar dyes, which dissolve in water, and can be used in an acid bath; or they may be produced from some of the weak acids, such as tannic or pyrogallic, which give little color unless used in connection with an alkali. Chromic acid which comes in red crystals was formerly used; but on account of its corrosive action, its expense, and uncertain effects, it has largely been replaced by its well-known salt, bichromate of potash. Picric acid which produces a good yellow on wood is also sometimes used with a water soluble nigrosine to produce an olive black tone known as Early English. The strong acids are little used by the wood finisher.

Alkaline stains which were quite commonly used a few years ago were frequently preceded or followed by an acid treatment. A volatile alkali, such as ammonia, or some fixed alkali, like caustic soda, caustic potash, or bichromate of potash, when used alone or in mixtures where practicable, was generally the alkaline element employed in producing the so-called alkaline stains.

Water Stains. Many wood finishers consider coloring matter dissolved in water the most satisfactory stain to use on wood. Water passes easily from cell to cell in the growing tree. Wood that has become thoroughly dry will quickly reabsorb moisture; and, if used in a wet place, it will take up water until its cell walls are at the saturation point; then, with still more moisture, it will become water soaked as the cell lumina or cavities are gradually filled. This great readiness with which wood absorbs water is very important in wood finishing, and is one reason for the great popularity of water stains.

Stain powder for mixing with water can now be secured in practically any shade of color desired for making water stains.

Formerly, the colors used in mixing water stains were fugitive, and the stains faded; but, at present, water stains made from acid coal-tar dyes are much more permanent than spirit stains or water stains made from basic dyes, and also more permanent than oil-soluble dyes. Quite permanent acid coal-tar dyes are at present used almost exclusively in making water stains. Vegetable extracts are still made to some extent from various color-giving woods such as fustic, logwood, Brazilwood, and more recently from the osage orange. The ground-up barks from camwood and ground red sanders are also quoted on the market, and are usually cheaper than the other dyewoods.

Advantages of Water Stains. The principal advantages of water stains may be enumerated and discussed briefly as follows:

1. Water stains penetrate much more deeply into the wood than do either oil or spirit stains. The preliminary treatment for water staining is sponging and resanding. Sponging opens up the fibers of the wood, and sanding removes the broken fragments of cell walls that have become matted into the cell cavities through scraping and sanding. Water stains enter very easily into the open pores of wood that has been sponged and resanded. Wood substance also seems to be more permeable to water than to other solvents used in making stains.

2. Water stain powders are very soluble, especially in hot water. They generally are moderately soluble in cold water, but for deeper colors hot water is preferable. Some water stains are improved by straining through filter paper or cloth having a fine mesh.

3. The dipping process can be used safely with water stains, whereas dipping in a spirit or oil stain is dangerous, and greatly increases the fire risk of a building. Many furniture factories have large vats filled with water stains. Chairs, tables, and other articles are completely immersed in the liquid for a short time, and then removed and wiped in order to secure as even a tone as possible.

Water stains can also be applied successfully with a spray gun.

4. It is very easy to secure darker or lighter shades and tints with water stains. For a lighter tone all that is necessary is to dilute the stain with water. For darker shades more powder may be added to the stain. In case additional powder

will not dissolve, one or more coats of stain may be put over the first attempt at staining, each application making a darker effect or tone. It is possible to secure very dark or deep effects with water stains.

5. The color of a water stained article can be changed to a large extent by applying a coat of a different color over a stain that is not suitable or which does not match the required color. Mottled effects or uneven tones of the same color, can be produced by adding color with a brush before the first coat is absolutely dry. A similar effect can usually be produced by wetting a water-stained surface with a brush or sponge and then applying more color before the dampened surface dries out.

6. It is possible and safe to apply water stains hot, thus securing greater penetration.

7. The greatest possible variety in colors, shades, and tints is obtainable in water colors since the advent of water soluble coal-tar dyes. Fewer colors, and less delicate hues, are obtainable in oil and spirit than in water stains.

8. Permanency, at least equal to that of other stains, is now secured with coal-tar water stains. Some authorities state positively that coal-tar water soluble stains are more permanent than oil soluble colors of similar origin. A large proportion of all the stains used for wood is now made from aniline and non-aniline dyes which are coal-tar products. The dye manufacturers recommend acid colors that are water soluble coal-tar dyes for use in wood staining, as they are far more permanent in light than are basic colors which are frequently very brilliant, but, unfortunately, quite fugitive.

9. More transparent, clear effects can be secured with water stains than with any other kind, with the exception of some of the chemical stains, and possibly a few of the volatile oil stains. When water stains are used, no visible pigments remain on the surface of the wood to obscure and spoil the beauty of the grain. Clear, brilliant effects can be obtained with water stains which penetrate into the wood fibers and change the color of the wood to an appreciable depth.

10. Brushes are much more easily cleaned and taken care of when water stain is used, because they can be washed out in water; while brushes used in oil or spirit stains require

cleaning in turpentine or alcohol, a more expensive and slower process.

11. In general, water stains are cheaper, gallon for gallon, than any other kind, because the solvent, water, costs less than turpentine, alcohol, and other solvents used to dissolve oil or spirit stains.

12. Water stains dry quickly.

13. Water stains will usually penetrate through one coat of linseed oil, or will even darken a filled surface to some extent. The grain is not usually raised appreciably when water stains are applied to surfaces that have already been oiled or filled. Much less water stain is absorbed by the wood, however, under such conditions.

14. After they are applied and allowed to dry properly, water stains do not "bleed" into subsequent finishing coats. Bleeding can often be prevented or eliminated by the application of an intermediate coat of wash shellac or lacquer sanding sealer.

Disadvantages of Water Stains. The chief disadvantages of water stains are:

1. The use of water stains requires sponging and resanding as a preliminary preparation in order to avoid the fuzziness that would appear on the surface of the wood without this treatment.

2. The extra expense resulting from the sponging and resanding operations adds to the labor cost.

3. Sandpapering cannot be done over a water stained surface without great danger of cutting through the stained layer, leaving streaks or spots of the natural color of the wood which show in a very objectionable manner. If there is fuzz on a water stained surface it is best to apply a wash coat of shellac, using liquid shellac diluted with about seven parts of alcohol. Sanding can be done more easily, and with less danger, over a coat of thin shellac; but fine sandpaper (3/0 or 4/0) should be used, and great care must be taken to avoid cutting through the stain at the corners and other exposed places.

The proper procedure is to sponge, allow to dry, and then resand, whenever water stains are to be applied. If this method

is followed little or no sanding will be necessary after staining with water stains.

4. The use of water in sponging and in the staining process
may have a tendency to loosen glued joints. This difficulty can
usually be overcome if care is taken to avoid long immersion
while dipping, and also through prompt wiping to prevent
too great absorption, if the water stain is applied with a brush.
The greatest danger comes from using water stains on thin
veneers which may loosen at the joints.

5. It is difficult to apply water stains with a brush and
secure an even tone on a large surface. More care and skill
are needed in brushing on water stains than is the case with
oil stains. Water stains dry rapidly, and unless a rather wet
brush, full of stain is used, the edge of one brush stroke of
stain may dry before the next is put on adjacent to it. The
brush strokes should be made with the grain wherever possible. The use of a brush that has little stain in it is to be
avoided. Dip the brush in the stain very often, and always
before it begins to dry.

A large surface may be tipped slightly. In this case, if
one begins at the back of the surface, which should be highest
up, and brushes the stain on crosswise, the excess of liquid
will run to the lower edge of the brush stroke and keep it wet
until the next application of stain is made. Streaks and laps
can usually be avoided entirely by this method, if the workman applies the stain rapidly.

Another method of avoiding laps is to sponge the article
with water and apply the stain to the damp surface. The color
is likely to be slightly lighter when the last method is used;
but stronger stain can be used safely, or a second application
of the coloring liquid can be made after the first coat has
dried.

6. Water stains of the most permanent character, made
from coal-tar dyes, frequently have an acid reaction, and
therefore should be kept in glass or earthenware containers
when in a liquid form. Brushes with hard rubber ferrules are
best because metal bindings on brushes may be affected by
acids.

7. Sapwood streaks are apt to take up too much stain;
and, on some of the lighter kinds of wood, they may become

darker than the heartwood. This trouble can largely be avoided by sponging the sapwood with water, thus weakening the absorptive power of that part of the wood; the stain is then quickly applied evenly over the whole surface. Another method is to use weaker stain on sapwood, which absorbs more color than the rest of the wood and thus becomes too dark.

Woods with strong contrast between the sapwood and heartwood, or kinds that are not very porous, usually require an entirely different treatment. In such cases the sapwood requires more stain than the remainder of the wood. A coat of stain is applied to the light streaks, and after it dries the entire surface may be stained. Stain may also be put on the sap streaks after the object has been stained as a whole. Blending, by dampening the line at the edge of the sapwood, is often helpful in securing a soft lap.

Helpful Hints on Water Staining.

1. End grain takes too much stain; consequently it becomes too dark unless care is taken to prevent this extra absorption. The open ends of the tracheal vessels, or the tracheids in some woods, absorb very avidly water and stains in general. Sometimes sponging the end grain, and applying the stain while this part of the wood is wet, will even up the color as it may do on sapwood. Some wood finishers prefer to apply a coat of very thin glue sizing to the end grain and sapwood, after experiments are made to determine the proportions of sizing glue and water which are needed in the mixture. End grain usually requires more glue in the sizing mixture than does sapwood. The stain should not be applied until the sizing has dried in the pores of the wood and resanding has been done where necessary.

2. Knots and different kinds of wood which are laid side by side sometimes require special treatment, but some variation of the methods suggested for end grain and sapwood are ordinarily used.

3. The end grain of woods with large open pores especially is sometimes treated with a coat of paste wood filler to prevent the stain from soaking in too much. None of the filler

should run over on the faces and edges, or lighter spots or streaks will show where they are not wanted.

4. Brushes should not be kept standing in water stains, because soaking will cause the bristles to become too soft and "moppy" for good work. They can be washed in water and dried, and thus kept in better condition for future work. A fitch brush about 2½″ wide, set with a rubber ferrule, is frequently used. Polar bear bristles, which should be rubber set, are also preferred for some kinds of work. A rather soft brush will do good work in staining a close-grained wood; but, for wood with large open pores, a stiff bristle brush is superior as the bottoms of the cell openings are reached and covered to better advantage. Stiff brushes give a flatter or more even tone than flaccid brushes in staining a porous wood.

5. A soft brush, if used on wood with large open pores, leaves light specks in the cell cavities because stain thus applied does not penetrate sufficiently into the tiny openings. Glue set brushes cannot be used for any length of time in water stains, because the bristles will come out. Either oval or flat brushes are satisfactory, but in any case a rather large size is preferable. On large work a 3″ or 4″ brush should be used, as it holds more stain.

6. Brushes used in applying water stains should be kept quite wet or full of stain, because dry brushes are apt to cause streaks, laps, and an uneven tone. Too wet a brush, which is dripping with stain, will bring trouble through drops falling where stain is not wanted at that time. After dipping the brush into stain, it is best to get rid of any excess wettness by wiping one side of the bristles against the rim of the container, or on a drip wire placed across the top for that purpose.

7. Work should be done rapidly and with great care that stain may not run over the edges or drop on surfaces which are to be stained later on. Careless work is apt to leave spots that will show after the staining operation is completed. The workman should also be very careful as to where he places the stain container, if he would avoid spots where they are not wanted.

8. The proper places for beginning and ending, when applying water stain to an article of furniture, are worth consideration before work is begun. The most important surfaces

should always be stained last, if possible. The parts to stain first are the bottom, back, or under portions which are less seen than the front or top of most articles.

9. Hot water stains penetrate deeper and dry faster, both when the dipping process is used and when the stain is applied with a brush.

10. When the dipping process is used the article should remain completely immersed only a moment; then it should be withdrawn quickly, and after standing on the dripping board for a few moments for the excess stain to run off, the entire piece should be wiped to even the depth of the stain.

11. Veneers are quite apt to appear lighter than solid wood after staining. Usually, a thin stain applied as a second coat to the veneer only will even up the color. Veneer is very thin; and the glue which is used in gluing it to its place may, to a slight extent, size the surface thus leaving its penetrability reduced more or less.

3—1. Before applying water stain, sponge all surfaces with water to raise the grain of the wood. When surface is dry, sand carefully with No. 5/0 finishing paper.

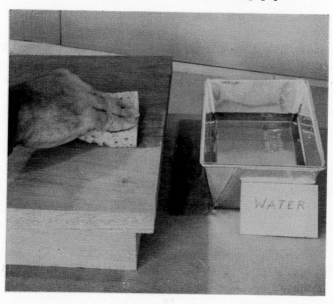

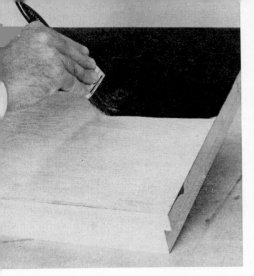

3—2. With a well-loaded brush, apply the stain with the grain of the wood. Avoid dripping stain on endgrain surfaces. 3—3. With a fairly dry brush, brush out any wet spots on the stained surface.

12. Greater evenness of tone can be secured in using water stains by applying two or three coats of thin stain than by the use of one application of strong color. The second coat lessens any defects of the first, to some extent, and laps or streaks are much fainter than when strong stain is used.

Procedure in Applying Water Stain: Apply water stain by any one of several methods—brushing, wiping, sponging, dipping, or spraying. The first and last methods are used most commonly.

When applying water stain with a brush, proceed as follows:

1. Sponge all surfaces. Allow them to dry and resand carefully (Fig. 3-1), page 55.

2. Select a reasonably stiff nylon brush, two to four inches wide.

3. Determine which parts should be stained first. In general, begin with the most inconspicuous parts, such as the back and the inside of shelves.

4. Fill the brush well with stain.

5. Apply the stain in sweeping strokes with the grain of the wood. Avoid dripping stain on endgrain surfaces (Fig. 3-2).

6. Brush rapidly back and forth without lifting the brush until it becomes too dry to stain the surface.

7. Refill the brush and apply the stain as before until the entire surface is covered.

8. Remove any excess stain from the brush on the edge of the container or drip wire.

9. Before the stain has set thoroughly, brush out any wet spots until all surfaces assume a dull appearance (Fig. 3-3).

10. Allow the stain to dry. Water stain air-dries in twelve hours, or force-dries in two to four hours.

To avoid excessive penetration on endgrain reduce the strength of the stain with water, or by first sizing all endgrain with a coat of wash shellac or thin glue.

Speed in application is essential to successful water staining. Speed secures uniform color and helps prevent laps and streaks.

SELECTED REFERENCES, CHAPTER III

Wood Stains and Water Staining

Carpenter, A., "Stains; their Cause, Cure and Removal." *American Dyestuff Reporter*, page 560, Sept. 3, 1951.

Cox, R. M. and Millarg, E. G., "Non-Grain Raising Stains." *Paint Oil and Chemical Review*, 112, pp. 14-15, Aug. 17, 1950.

Deniston, G. L., *The Science of Modern Woodfinishing*, Chapters V-VII, pp. 70-104, 1949.

Gibbia, S. W., *Wood Finishing and Refinishing*. "Staining," Chapter III, pp. 30-54, 1954.

Hogstrom, E., "Woodfinishing Procedures." *Industrial Finishes*, page 86, Sept., 1945.

Leil, W. B., "Staining." *Industrial Finishes*, pp. 70-73, Nov., 1949.

Mattiello, J. J., *Protective and Decorative Coatings*, Volume 3, Chapter XXV, pp. 769-813, 1943.

McGee, R. A., and Brown, A. G., *Instructional Units in Woodfinishing*, "To Prepare and Apply Wood Stains," Chapter I, pp. 9-15, 1950.

Soderberg, G. A., *Finishing Materials and Methods*. "Stains," Chapter XV, pp. 104-107, 1952.

Chapter IV

Oil Stains

There are several kinds of oil stain on the market, each of which is intended for a distinct purpose, and should not be confused with the others. The most distinctive types are:

1. *Pigment stains.*
2. *Preservative stains.*
3. *Volatile oil stains.*

Pigment Oil Stains. Colors or pigments which are ground in raw linseed oil were formerly much used as stains. They can be thinned with turpentine, or a mixture of turpentine and linseed oil, or even with benzine with a little japan drier. After soaking into the wood fibers for a few minutes, such stains are wiped off and allowed to dry for several days before any other finishing is attempted. Vandyke brown, burnt and raw sienna, the umbers, ultramarine blue, and yellow ochre are examples of colors ground in oil that can be purchased at any paint shop.

Asphaltum black, which is an asphaltum varnish, is another material that can be thinned with turpentine and used as an oil stain. It is permanent when exposed to light and is especially good as a stain for finishing cypress, as it produces a dark brown tone similar to mission oak in color.

Dry pigment colors do not dissolve well in turpentine, and are not as satisfactory when used as stains as are colors which are ground in oil.

Colors which are ground in oil are used as coloring matter to mix with paints. They produce more brilliant effects in paint than do dry pigment colors, and keep the mixture more liquid so that it will spread better with a brush.

When dark pigment colors are used with oil as a stain they

have a covering effect instead of the transparency of water colors. These somewhat opaque results are desired for silver gray or "driftwood" stains.

Preparation of Pigment Oil Stains. All pigments ground in oil are not equally permanent when exposed to light. The three primary colors—red, yellow, and blue (plus black) provide nearly any desired tone or hue if you know how to mix colors. The following ready-mixed colors are dependable:

PIGMENTS PERMANENT IN LIGHT

Ivory Black	Light Red
Vandyke Brown	Madder Lake Red
Burnt Ochre	Burnt Sienna
Yellow Ochre	Raw Sienna
French Yellow Ochre	Burnt Umber
Venetian Red	Raw Umber
Indian Red	Ultramarine

The above colors are not all equal in chroma or brilliance of hue, some of them being weak in coloring power.[1] A pigment which is low in chroma must be used in a greater amount than is the case where the color is strong and brilliant. On account of the variations in strength of various colors the amount by weight that is required to produce desired tones also varies. The following formula is suggestive of the approximate composition of a pigment oil stain for use on the trim of a house or in staining furniture:

To each gallon:
1 part boiled linseed-oil
2 parts turpentine
1 to 2½ pounds of pigment colors ground in oil

Advantages of Pigment Oil Stains:

1. They are easily prepared.

2. They are very easy to apply, because of their slow drying.

3. They do not raise the grain, consequently sponging and resanding are unnecessary, and two operations are saved.

4. They may be used on thin veneers without danger of loosening the glue.

5. They are cheaper to apply than water stains, conse-

[1] See Chapter VII, pp. 84-85 for definition of such terms as *chroma, brilliance,* and *hue.*

quently they are used on cheap furniture, and frequently in house finishing.

6. They are good to use on the interior of case goods where raising the grain and resanding are difficult.

7. They generally contain a certain amount of drying oil, such as linseed oil, and in drying leave a thin varnish-like film which protects the wood.

8. A drying oil, such as linseed oil, unless it is bleached, darkens the wood even without being mixed with any colors.

9. Oil colors can be mixed with wood filler, and this combination stains and fills in one operation.

10. Oil stains can be used successfully on certain very absorptive woods, such as cypress which becomes very rough and porous when water staining is attempted.

11. Stains containing a drying oil, such as linseed oil, do not penetrate as deeply into the wood as they do when turpentine is used. Stains with drying oils as the vehicle give an even, flat tone, however, because they do not penetrate unevenly in spots on account of irregular wavy or end grain around or near knots.

12. Attractive effects can be produced with several of the pigment oil stains on some of the close grained woods, such as poplar, cherry, maple, white pine, and even on walnut which is somewhat porous.

Disadvantages of Pigment Oil Stains:

1. Oil stains do not penetrate deeply, and as a result they are easily cut through by sandpaper, or are quickly worn off by use.

2. Restaining is difficult with oil stains, therefore the proper color must be secured with one coat. (If the stain is raised with benzine, another darker color can be applied with some success.)

3. Oil stain pigments are opaque and remain on the surface to some extent; they obscure the grain and cause a loss of transparency.

4. Oil stains are more expensive than water stains, and do not cover as much surface gallon for gallon.

5. If it is applied too slowly, or if it is not rubbed soon

enough, an oil stain may go into the pores too deeply to dry promptly; later on, it may ooze out and cause trouble.

6. Oil stains require several days for proper drying.

7. Oil stains are likely to "lift" or come off to some extent with a filler.

8. The shades of color available in pigment oil stains are more limited in number than in water stains.

9. Oil stains have a tendency to "bleed" into subsequent finishing coats. This is particularly true when applying a lacquer finish. Bleeding can be prevented by applying a coat of wash shellac over the oil stain. Additional drying time will also help eliminate this difficulty.

Use of Pigment Oil Stains. The use of pigment oil stains for coloring the wood of furniture has diminished during recent years because better stains have been placed on the market. Oil stains are still in general use for architectural work. It is easier to apply oil stains than water stains on wood used for the inside finish or trim of a house, especially if the wood is nailed in place before the stain is applied. Whenever it is difficult to raise the grain of wood and resand in order to remove the fuzz caused by sponging, it is usually best to color the wood with an oil stain rather than with water stain.

Application of Pigment Oil Stains.

1. Select a suitable brush to apply the stain.
2. Apply the stain by brushing with the grain of the wood. Stain the inside corners and recessed surfaces first (Fig. 4-1).
3. When staining end grain, wipe immediately to avoid excessive penetration and darkening of the wood. End grain may first be coated with turpentine or linseed oil just before staining.
4. After the stain dries for a few minutes, wipe all the surfaces with a clean rag to produce an even shade (Fig. 4-2).
5. Allow the surface to dry for at least twelve to twenty-four hours.

Wiping Stains (Pigmented Type). It is generally best to stain close-grain or soft woods by using pigmented wiping stains which are prepared with a higher percentage of pig-

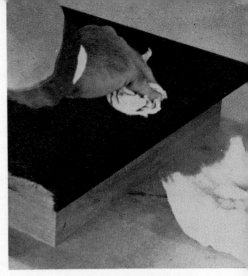

4—1. In staining, it is good practice to stain inside corners and recessed surfaces first. 4—2. After the stained surface takes on a dull appearance, wipe the surface with a clean rag.

ments than used in oil stains. These woods do not require as much filling as open-pore woods. Wiping stain will stain and fill, both in one operation. One of the advantages of this stain is that through wiping it emphasizes certain uniformity of figure and character of the grain.

Apply pigment wiping stains either by brush, spray, or dip. These stains are supplied in concentration and may be reduced up to 100% with mineral spirits or naphtha depending upon weather conditions. They should be allowed to set from five to ten minutes or until the surface turns dull or gray. Evaporation of the thinner causes this. Control the depth of the color by the amount of stain wiped off. Allow pigmented stains to dry four hours before applying a sealer. Oil stain may be used for this purpose according to the instructions on the label.

Creosote Oil Stains. Stains for use out-of-doors are frequently made with one of the creosote oils as a vehicle for carrying the coloring matter to the wood. Shingle stains which are made from coal tar creosote, or water gas tar creosote, together with colors are in common use. The shingles are usually dipped for a few minutes, then placed on a draining board to dry. Creosote oil stains are put on for a one coat finish. Paints and varnishes do not adhere properly over creosote oil.

Creosote oil stains can be used best in warm weather. In cold seasons certain so-called "creosote salts" are likely to settle, leaving part of the stain in a conditon that cannot be used.

Creosote oil is an excellent preservative of wood from decay fungi, which makes it valuable for outside use. A preservative oil is not really needed for furniture or for the inside finish of a house where the wood is not exposed to dampness. *Creosote oil*, when used in stains for articles requiring several coats of finish, is harmful when applied to furniture, on account of its dark color, lack of rapid evaporation, and tendency to prevent other finishes from adhering properly.

The pigments commonly used in creosote shingle stains are chrome green, and the red and brown iron oxides.

A creosote shingle stain contains about 1½ pounds of pigment to the gallon, and a vehicle and solvent consisting of 2 parts of creosote oil, 2 parts of heavy benzene, and 1 part of benzene japan drier.

Volatile Oil Stains. On the market at present are so-called oil stains which are largely made from coal-tar dye powders dissolved in volatile oils, such as turpentine, benzol, light and heavy naphthas, and various turpentine substitutes mostly of a mineral nature. These stains, called penetrating stains, are put up in both dry and liquid form and are popular, because they penetrate deeply into the wood and do not require the preliminary treatments of raising the grain and resanding that are so necessary with water stains; also, because the aniline and other coal-tar dye powders are more soluble than pigment colors, and do not obscure the grain as such colors mixed with drying oils always do to some extent.

Volatile oil stains are made in a variety of colors, especially for use on oak, walnut, and mahogany. They should be wiped before they dry in order to produce an even tone, and must be handled with more speed and care than is necessary with ordinary pigment stains, because the solvents used evaporate more rapidly than do the drying oils, such as linseed oil, used with pigment stains or colors ground in oil. Volatile oil stains are really in a class by themselves, because they have many of the advantages of pigment oil stains and not many of the disadvantages.

Volatile oil stains sold in a liquid form are apt to contain benzol, at least in part, as a solvent. Benzol and coal-tar dyes are coal-tar products; and being of a somewhat similar nature chemically, the liquid is an excellent solvent of the powders. Benzol alone is recommended by some manufacturers as a solvent for some of their oil-soluble colors.

Many oil-soluble aniline and other coal-tar dry powders sold for oil stains are preferably dissolved in turpentine; in fact, the manufacturers recommend this solvent. Turpentine substitutes, especially if they contain benzol, can be used successfully instead of turpentine. Benzene or benzol, naphtha, gasoline, kerosene, and carbon tetrachloride, are also used as solvents for oil-soluble coal-tar dyes.

Permanency of Oil-Soluble Coal-Tar Stains. Some dealers in wood-stains say that aniline and other coal-tar oil and spirit stains fade out more than water-soluble coal-tar dyes do. This statement is especially true, as far as spirit stains are concerned, because they are made of fugitive basic dyes, which manufacturers and chemists admit are not fast to light and permanent, though brilliant when first used. Oil-soluble coal-tar dyes now made are often more permanent than basic dyes which are used for spirit stains, and are recommended for use on wood by some reliable manufacturers.

Shellac Wash over Volatile Oil Stains. Lifting of the stain by after treatments of filler or shellac is a common fault of volatile oil and spirit stains. Volatile oil stains are not much changed by a filler, however, if a thin coat of shellac, mixed in the proportion of one part of liquid shellac to seven or eight parts of alcohol, is applied over the stain and allowed to dry before filling. Shellac in its full strength from the can should not be used on porous woods that require a filler until after the filling is finished. A very thin shellac coat, called a shellac wash, may be used over a stain without filling the pores to such an extent that a filler will not have proper anchorage to hold it in place.

Varnishes cannot be applied directly over any of the oil stains without probable loss in clearness of tone, because the solvents used in all cases are the same or similar. Some of the coloring matter may be "lifted" and mixed with the varnish coat, thus producing a muddy or cloudy effect, and a loss of transparency.

Volatile oil stains, especially those containing benzol as a solvent, penetrate very deeply into the wood in comparison to pigment oil stains, and do not dry as readily as is indicated by appearances on the outside. It is best to allow at least 24 hours for drying before a shellac wash is applied over a volatile oil stain.

Sometimes, in order to secure certain tone or color effects, the shellac wash is omitted between the coats of stain and filler. In all cases, in order to prevent "bleeding" of the coal tar oil stains into the varnish-coats, it is important that one or more coats of shellac be applied to the stained or stained and filled wood before any varnishing is done.

SELECTED REFERENCES, CHAPTER IV

Oil Stains

Campbell, M. L., *Campbell Finish Repair Specialties*, Chapter VII, page 23.

Feirer, John L., *Advanced Woodwork and Furniture Making*, Section 4, pp. 147-148, 1960.

Fryklund, Verne C. and La Berge, Armand J., *General Shop Bench Woodworking*, Fourth Edition, Unit 49, pp. 82-83, 1955.

Gibbia, S. W., *Wood Finishing and Refinishing*, Chapter III, pp. 30-52, 1954.

Scharff, Robert, *Improve Your Home with Built-Ins,* Chapter XII, pp. 229-230, 1951.

Sherwin-Williams Handbook, "Furniture Finishing Facts," pp. 7, 10, 15, and 18. Sherwin-Williams Co., 1954.

Soderberg, George A., *Finishing Materials and Methods*, Chapter XV, pp. 104-107, 1952.

Wall, William E., *Graining Ancient and Modern*, Chapter VII, pp. 24-27, 1948.

Yates, Raymond W., *New Furniture from Old*, Chapter IX, pp. 89-126, 1951.

Chapter V

Spirit Stains and

Non-Grain-Raising Stains

Characteristics of Spirit Stains. Colors or dyes used today are almost entirely spirit-soluble basic coal-tar dyes.

Spirit stains dry fast, and do not penetrate deeply into the wood. Laps, streaks, and brush marks are likely to disfigure any large surface stained with spirit stain. The trouble is due entirely to the rapid evaporation of the alcohol which is used as the solvent for the colors.

Spirit stains are more expensive than water stains, because the solvent, alcohol, costs much more than water.

Spirit stains are sometimes used for quick work, especially for touching up spots and streaks, and in making repairs or renewing old finishes. The expert can occasionally use them to advantage, but the beginner always has trouble with them.

Another difficulty with spirit stains is that they may "lift" with the filler coat, or with the application of shellac which is a spirit varnish cut with alcohol. Such stains are liable to mix with the shellac under the brush, and produce a muddy effect which spoils the transparency and beauty of the finish.

Mixed Spirit Stains and Volatile Oil Stains. Some manufacturers of spirit stains have changed their formulas, and do not use alcohol exclusively as a solvent. Turpentine and benzol are sometimes used as solvents or thinners in addition to alcohol, and these oils slow down the rapidity of drying of the spirit stain. Benzol also causes the stain to penetrate more deeply than if alcohol alone is used. These stains can be thinned with either alcohol or turpentine, but turpentine is preferable on account of its slower evaporation.

Some of the best liquid stains on the market today are

really a combination of volatile oil and spirit stains, and these mixtures are giving very satisfactory results though they are rather expensive on account of the high cost of the solvents. Water is also sometimes used as a thinner for spirit stains, reducing the rapidity of drying.

Evaporation and Fire Risk. Spirit stains cannot be left in open vats in factories on account of the rapid evaporation of the solvents used, and because this practice would increase the fire risk. Such stains should be kept in tightly-closed glass bottles.

Method of Application. More even tones and brilliant effects can be obtained from spirit stains by wiping and spreading any excess of color soon after the dye is applied with a brush. The best results are secured (1) by working rapidly with a brush loaded with color, rather than with an almost dry brush; and (2) by evening up, by wiping before the stain has set or dried.

Spirit Stains Fade. Spirit stains made from aniline or other coal-tar dyes are considered by many experts to be the most fugitive of all stains, although they are much more permanent than they were a few years ago. Their tendency to fade, and difficulty in application, have caused them to be used much less than are either water or oil stains. Spirit stains are made from basic coal-tar dyes which the manufacturers know to be fugitive. Where a temporary brilliant effect is desired, and fastness to light is not a requisite, such stains may be used to advantage. Whenever spirit stains are used on articles of furniture the fresh colors should not be exposed to bright light until after coats of shellac and varnish have been applied. Such impervious finishes keep out the air and prevent fading to a large extent.

Non-Grain-Raising Stains.[1] During recent years these stains have helped revolutionize finishing procedures and techniques. They are becoming increasingly popular, since in addition to other advantages, they show a minimum tendency to raise the grain of wood.

Essentially N.G.R. (non-grain-raising) stains are made

---

[1] Deniston, G. L. *The Science of Modern Wood Finishing*, Ch. 5, pp. 78-82. Research Press, Inc., Dayton, Ohio.

from light-fast dyes soluble in non-aqueous vehicles. The solvent used is usually a mixture of one of the "glysol" group solvents, plus an alcohol, such as methanol. To these a coal-tar hydrocarbon is added, usually toluol. Solvents such as carbitol, cellosolve, and ketones are also used.[2]

The composition of the N.G.R. solvent is very important and manufacturers have done much research on it. It is the correct adjustment of this solvent mixture that very much determines the performance of an N.G.R. stain.

In their various forms of preparation N.G.R. stains combine the characteristics of the other types of stain. Yielding bright, transparent, and light-resistant effects, they can be formulated so that they are non-toxic and have little or no odor. In some instances certain precautions must be taken in their application.

N.G.R. stains are supplied by the manufacturer either as concentrated base colors or mixed ready for use. Some finishers prefer to buy the base colors and make mixed stains by their own formulas. A stain reducer accompanies the base colors. The majority of users, however, prefers to buy the stains ready mixed so that they can be brushed or sprayed on directly from the container.

N.G.R. stains have all the important advantages of other stains without their disadvantages. Containing the same dye powders, they are equal in brightness and light fastness. Dye colors may be blended and reduced with proper solvents to the desired strength.

These stains are fast drying. In fact, because of the vehicles used, brushing is difficult. Spraying is the ideal method of application. As their name implies, they do not raise the grain of wood as do water stains. This eliminates the labor and expense of wash coating and sanding. Penetration into the wood surface is uniform and moderately deep, assuring greater and more uniformly clear color tones. Soft streaks can be matched readily. The solvents used in N.G.R. stains are compatible with most sealers and subsequent finish coats.

Although the initial cost of these stains is higher than that

---

[2] Matiello, Joseph J., *Protective and Decorative Coatings*, Volume III, Ch. 25, pp. 799-803.

of water stains, it is offset by the elimination of the steps of wash coating and sanding. The use of N.G.R. stains has not only reduced the number of operations previously required, but actually raised the quality of finishes by eliminating bleeding and other difficulties associated frequently with the older types of stain.

Special Problems in Staining.[3] The inexperienced writer of stories has difficulty in deciding on "how to start" or "where to start" the writing. The novice in wood finishing has similar problems, and must decide which parts should be stained first. In general, it is best to begin with the most inconspicuous or least important parts, and to finish with the front, or parts that are most often seen. On vertical surfaces it is best to start at the top and work downward, usually with the grain. The article to be stained should be placed, whenever possible, so that no stain will drip or spatter onto an important surface, because spots will not always blend out. This trouble with spots may be serious, if the dye or color drips onto unstained portions of the article; and it is equally or more bothersome when drops fall upon surfaces already stained. Spots are not usually so troublesome with oil stains as with other kinds.

Placing the surface in an inclined position, with the operator standing at the lower long edge, and brushing from left to right, or lengthwise of the grain of the wood, are frequently helpful in preventing streaks and laps (Fig. 5-1). The brush for staining should, in general, be kept quite full of stain, but must not be wet enough to drip. Part of the liquid can be removed from the brush by wiping it on a wire strung across the can, or by using the side of the container itself to press out the excess of stain.

The inside and shelves of cases, backs of legs, under side of arms of chairs, and other parts that will be seen but little should be stained first.

Use of Brushes and Wiping. The brushes must generally be handled with care to prevent the stain from running over edges, and to avoid the drying of portions of a surface before it is entirely covered. It is best to apply the stain lengthwise or

---

[3] See also "Disadvantages of Water-Stains," p. 51; "Helpful Hints on Water-Staining," p. 53; "Advantages of Pigment Oil-Stains," p. 59; "Disadvantages of Pigment Oil-Stains," p. 60.

5—1. To avoid streaks and laps in staining, place the surface in an inclined position.

with the grain of the wood rather than across the grain. A flatter, more even tone can be secured by brushing lengthwise, especially on open-grained or porous woods, because the bristles of the brush get down into the low places of the cell lumina or openings more satisfactorily when the stain is applied with the grain. Most stains must be rubbed or wiped off with some absorbent material, such as cotton waste (Fig. 4-2). It is often best to wipe off crosswise and to finish lengthwise. The crosswise wiping rubs the stain into the pores, and the lengthwise rubbing cleans off any excess and evens up the color.

Speed in Staining. Speed in applying the coloring liquid is fundamental to success with most stains. Speed secures uniform color and helps in preventing laps and streaks. The amount of speed required varies with the kinds of stain used, depending upon the rapidity of the evaporation of the solvents which hold the coloring matter in solution. Spirit stains containing alcohol evaporate with astonishing rapidity. Volatile oil stains vary greatly in rapidity of drying; those containing gasoline evaporate almost instantly; while, if turpentine is used as a solvent, vaporization is much slower.

The manufacturers of the best volatile oil stains in liquid form ordinarily use solvents which will control the rapidity of drying and slow down the evaporation to practical workable limits. Pigment oil stains contain a certain amount of drying oil, such as raw linseed oil, and this makes them dry slowly. There is no difficulty in applying pigment oil stains, as they dry very slowly—so slowly in fact, that no other finish should be placed over them for several days.

SELECTED REFERENCES, CHAPTER V

Spirit Stains and Non-Grain-Raising Stains

Brown, S., "Staining is Easy with Brush or Spray," *Popular Mechanics,* 95, pp. 178-183, June, 1951.

Deniston, G. L., *The Science of Modern Wood Finishing,* Chapter V, pp. 78-82. Research Press, Inc., Dayton, Ohio.

Fisher, E. M., *What You Should Know About Paint,* "Interior Surface Treatments and Primers," Chapter VIII, pp. 121-128; 1953.

Gibbia, S. W., *Wood Finishing and Refinishing,* "Spirit Stain," Chapter III, pp. 40-43; 1954.

Mattiello, Joseph J., *Protective and Decorative Coatings,* Volume 3, "The Formulation and Uses of Stains," Chapter XXV, pp. 769-814; 1941.

McGee, R. A., and Brown, A. G., *Instructional Units in Woodfinishing,* Unit 1, "To Apply a Spirit Stain," page 15; 1950.

Soderberg, George A., *Finishing Materials and Methods,* "Stains," Chapter XV, pp. 104-107; 1952.

Wampler, R. H., *Modern Organic Finishes,* Chapter 3, pp. 38-39; 1946.

Waring, Ralph G., *Woodfinishing and Painting Made Easy,* "Wood Stains and Their Application," Chapter III, pp. 57-63; 1940.

Chapter VI

Chemical Stains

Some years ago certain forms of chemical stain enjoyed quite a little popularity. White oak was a suitable material for the manufacture of mission furniture which was then in vogue, and this wood with its high tannic-acid content lent itself admirably to several chemical stains, the most satisfactory of which was produced by the ammonia fuming process. Other acid and alkaline stains were used with some success, and writers of that period predicted a great future for chemical stains. The most popular stains of the present day are the result of chemical discoveries, but they are synthetic dyes instead of true chemical stains in the sense that the term is usually used by the wood finisher.

Definition of Chemical Stains. In a scientific sense, chemical stains depend upon some chemical reaction in the wood resulting in the formation of new colored compounds. One of the chemicals is sometimes contained in the wood itself. In other cases one chemical may be applied to the surface of the wood and be absorbed or produce some chemical change. Later on, another chemical which may be in the form of a gas or liquid, may come in contact with the first and bring about a chemical change in the wood itself, thereby causing a change in color. True chemical staining, therefore, is the result of chemical action in the wood which produces a new color. Often chemical staining depends upon the changing of coloring matter already in the wood to a new or different color, because of a chemical reaction, rather than to the application of a dye or pigment. Woods differ greatly in their chemical composition; consequently they react very differently to chemical treatment.

Waning Popularity of Chemical Stains. Oak, which years

ago was so much used for furniture, has partly been replaced by other woods which are not so easily stained by chemical processes. Another reason for the decline of chemical staining is that a uniform tone cannot usually be secured on an article of furniture, even when made of oak which is one of the best woods for this kind of staining. This unevenness is due to the fact that sapwood is not changed to a tone to match heartwood, and boards from different trees do not take equal amounts of color.

Considerable "doctoring" of spots and streaks was a common aftermath of chemical staining. Some factories gradually came to the practice of giving a light chemical stain, following this treatment with a water-soluble or other coal-tar dye coating to even up the color and produce a flat uniform tone. The hardest blow of all to chemical stains came from the great improvements in coal-tar dyes that are as permanent as any stains. These synthetic dyes are very convenient to use, and last, but not least, they can be found in almost any color, shade, and tint desired.

Chemicals Used in Staining. Chemical stains are generally acid or alkaline in reaction. A combination of the two is usual in producing colors that have been most popular recently.

Acid stains are very commonly dependent upon either tannic or pyrogallic acid as a base, especially where shades of brown are produced. Strong acids are not often used. Acetic acid has been tried, but its benefit is quite doubtful. Chromic acid and salts are useful in connection with alkalies and other stains, and emphasize or brighten the resultant colors. Picric acid is useful where a decided yellow is desired, and can be used in connection with acid water-soluble coal-tar colors, such as nigrosine, in producing Early English and other dyes. Such chemicals as sugar of lead, potassium chromate, and magnesium sulphate, are valuable in use with acid aniline and other coal-tar colors.

Tannic acid used in connection with other substances produces interesting, valuable, and sometimes troublesome colors. When it is used in connection with iron salts and ammonia, a ferric ammonium tannate having a blue-black or olive-green color is formed. This combination is occasionally used as a wood stain. It sometimes appears unexpectedly where it is not wanted, if tannic acid is used in contact with iron, as in a tin can.

Sulphate of iron in dried form and chloride of iron can be used with tannic acid, and various tones of gray are the result. The water-soluble coal-tar dye called nigrosine can be used with tannic acid alone or with iron salts added. A still different color can be secured by applying a five-percent solution of tannic acid and water, and following with a weak solution of logwood extract in hot water which may be mixed with various amounts of copper sulphate in a five-percent solution.

The tannins are complex compounds, and vary in composition depending upon their origin. Solutions of tannins in water are liable to absorb oxygen from the air and change in composition. The action is rapid with alkaline solutions. For this reason mixtures containing tannic acid should be made up fresh. Solutions of tannic acid and water, if kept in a covered glass jar or bottle, will remain in good condition for several days.

Various alkalies are used to produce stains on wood. Frequently the alkalies are applied following an acid treatment and react with the acid to produce a new color. One of the most satisfactory chemicals to use in staining is bichromate of potash, which is dissolved in water in the proportion of one quart of water to a half ounce of the crystals. It makes a yellowish or golden brown stain, and is sometimes used with vegetable mahogany dyes, and also with carbonate of potash or soda following a treatment of tannic acid, thus making an orange brown color. Coniferous woods, such as pine, and many of the broad leafed hardwoods, contain little tannin and should not be stained with potassium bichromate, because the stain which shows at first will fade unless there is a union with tannin to form a tannate and produce a color that is permanent and brown in tone.

Potassium permanganate crystals dissolved in various proportions in cold water make another useful chemical stain. The crystals are of a violet hue, and make a solution of a similar color. The liquid should be sponged on the wood because the permanganate will soon destroy a bristle brush. The wood will have a violet tone when the solution is first applied, but this gradually changes to an interesting brown, which varies with the strength of the stain and the kind of wood. Darker shades can be secured by the use of more than one coat, just as with water stains. The lignocellulose of which wood is composed gradually and sometimes rapidly reacts with the potassium permanganate, leaving a brown deposit of hydrated manganese dioxide.

Volatile and fixed are the two types of alkalies that are used in chemical staining. Strong ammonia (26°) in a solution of water is the volatile alkali found effective for staining, while the fixed alkalies are represented by caustic potash or caustic soda, and by potassium bichromate, copper sulphate, and potassium carbonate.

Necessary Precautions When Using Chemical Stains. Brushes, preferably of the type called rubber-set, are generally used in applying stains to wood. For coarse woods rather stiff bristles are needed to force the stain down into the open pores. Strong alkalies and some of the acids may affect the bristles and soon ruin a brush. Some of the alkalies in common use that affect brushes to some extent, especially when used in strong solution, are potassium hydroxide, ammonia, sodium hydroxide, and the carbonates. A brush cannot be used with any of the strong acids. Weak acids in common use, such as tannic acid and pyrogallic acid, can be applied successfully with a rubber-set brush. The brushes should be cleaned with water and allowed to dry when not in use. Brushes made of vegetable fibers instead of bristles can be used in staining wood.

When a sponge is used in applying a chemical stain, the hands are apt to become badly stained, or the skin may be eaten out in tender spots such as the backs of the fingers and under the nails. Cylinder oil, or some other mineral oil, vaseline, or similar heavy grease, may be coated over the hands in such a manner as to protect them from weak acids or alkalies when using a sponge to apply stains. For best protection, wear rubber gloves (Fig. 6-1), page 76.

Preparation of the Surface Before Applying Chemical Stain. The same care must be used in preparing the surface of wood for chemical staining as for water staining; see Chapters I and II. All glue must be carefully removed, or light spots will appear about or under the adhesive.

6—1. When applying a chemical stain with a sponge, protect your hands with rubber gloves.

Fumed Oak Color with Fixed Alkalies. A color very much like that produced on white oak by fuming with ammonia can be obtained on certain varieties of oak, chestnut, mahogany, gum, pine, and some other woods, by preparing the surface with a tannic acid or pyrogallic acid solution, and later on giving a coat of fixed alkalies in an aqueous solution instead of fuming. The procedure is as follows:

1. Raise the grain by sponging with water, allow to dry, and resand.

2. Coat the wood with No. 1 solution, made up of ½ oz. tannic acid powder in one quart of water; or ⅓ oz. pyrogallic acid powder in one quart of water. (The solutions may be mixed in these proportions in any quantity.) Allow the wood to dry.

3. Sand lightly with No. 000 sandpaper.

4. Apply a coat of No. 2 solution, made up of:
    1 quart water,
    1 oz. bichromate of potash,
    ½ oz. caustic potash.

5. When dry, rub with diluted linseed oil, made up of:
   1 part boiled linseed oil,
   3 parts turpentine.

On white oak the above procedure will produce a color almost identical with that obtained by ammonia fuming. It is very important, however, that each of the two solutions shall be thoroughly worked into the wood. A stiff, rather coarse, rubber bound bristle brush is best. On porous woods, such as oak, the stain solutions may not be forced well down into the open pores unless the brush is kept quite wet, and applied with vigorous strokes with the grain. Unless care is taken in applying the solutions, many light specks will show in the open pores where the solutions did not penetrate properly.

Stains produced by acids and fixed alkalies penetrate about as deeply as water stains, while those obtained by the fuming process with ammonia are better in that they enter into the wood much more deeply.

A slightly different, but pleasing color, can be produced on many woods by substituting for the No. 2 solution a mixture of about one ounce of bichromate of potash to the quart of water. The latter solution seems to be more effective when applied quite warm. A lighter tint of brown is obtained by using part carbonate of potash instead of all bichromate of potash in the solution.

The Ammonia Fuming Process. The fuming process has been much used to produce a rich brown tone on white oak commonly known as fumed oak. Chestnut is another wood that is quickly and beautifully stained by this process because it contains a large amount of tannin in a form that readily reacts with ammonia gas. These chemicals quickly change the surface of this wood to a dark rich brown hue when fumed and rubbed with linseed oil.

Certain other American woods can be changed in color to some extent by the fuming process. Walnut and mahogany may be browned by fuming because they contain quite a little tannin. Doubtless some of the foreign woods that contain an unusual amount of tannin can be fumed successfully.

The woodworker should not mix red oak with white oak in articles that are to be stained by this process, for the former does not react to ammonia as readily as the latter, since it contains much less tannin.

A chemical reaction takes place when ammonia gas unites with tannic acid, and a new compound is formed called ammonium tannate which is of a rich reddish or yellowish brown color.

Success in fuming wood to produce stain comes from technical knowledge and proper equipment. The finisher must know what woods can be fumed, and how to prepare and treat them before and after fuming.

The Fuming Process on White Oak. White oak, the wood that is most commonly used when the fuming process is attempted, requires proper preliminary treatment. Fuming a finished and sanded article made of white oak may seem disappointingly slow. It can be hastened by sponging with water before putting the article in the fuming box. The sponged wet wood can be fumed at once and sanded later on after removal from the box, or it can be dried and resanded to remove the fuzz and then fumed. Raising the grain of the wood with water opens up the pores and speeds up the chemical action of the ammonia fumes.

Weak solutions of tannic or pyrogallic acid, or a mixture, applied to the surface of the wood, will greatly speed up the fuming process. For the mixture of tannic acid, use one ounce of tannin powder to one quart of water; for the pyrogallic acid solution, which will produce a more reddish brown than can be secured from tannin alone, the mixture should be weaker, in general, with about ¾ oz. of pyrogallic acid powder to the quart of water.

A mixture of the two solutions is excellent, and produces a color in the final finish slightly different from that produced by either acid used alone. None of the above mixtures should be put in tin containers, or a blue-black color will result from the action of the acid on iron. Glass or earthen containers and rubber-set brushes should always be used.

Sapwood streaks and boards from different trees are brought to a much flatter and even tone by the use of one of the acid solutions before fuming. This reduces the amount of "blending in" with stain to color the light places to the general tone of the piece. Wood that has been treated with one of the acid mixtures has a more uniform acid content on the treated surfaces, and after fuming has a much less varying and more even tone.

The Fuming Box. A fuming box is the special article required for staining with ammonia. Large factories use a specially-built, practically air-tight room, which has an outside window for ventilation, to clear out the gas fumes as soon as possible, and to keep them from other parts of the factory. Of the various ways of introducing the ammonia gas into the fuming chamber or box, the simplest and commonest is to use aqua ammonia in concentrated form, which is known to the druggist as varying from 26 to 35.7 per cent in strength. It should have a specific gravity between .906 and .880, the latter being the strongest of all. Household ammonia is too weak to secure good results. Usually, the liquid ammonia is placed in a tank and allowed to run into one shallow pan after another by slowly dripping. The ammonia gas is gradually liberated leaving water in the pans.

A fuming box for the school shop can easily be built by students, using matched lumber, and making the tight or face joints on the inside of the box. A practical size is about 4′ x 4′ x 8′, as such a box will take a table, or any other article of furniture which is apt to be made in a school shop. A removable partition should be placed so as to make two boxes of about 4′ x 4′ x 4′, as one box of this size is ample for most school work, and less ammonia is required for a small box. About ¼ pint of strong ammonia (26° or 28°) is required to charge the box. The inside of the box may be papered to close up the small cracks. The doors of the box should be fitted so that they will close perfectly over felt strips around the joints.

Articles to be fumed must be placed in such a way that the ammonia gas can reach all the surfaces to be stained. If one article is laid upon another, the gas will not properly color the surfaces that are in contact, and light unstained places will be the result. All surfaces that are to be stained should be separated. Small articles can be leaned against the sides of the box in such a way that all surfaces will be exposed. Ammonia can be poured into a large flat dish or pan which is placed near the door on the bottom of the box. In pouring out the ammonia care must be taken not to splatter the liquid on any of the articles, or disagreeable spots that cannot be removed will be the result. A person should be careful not to breathe the fumes of ammonia when charging the box.

Time Required for the Fuming Process. The length of time required for fuming to a given shade of brown varies with a number of conditions, such as the species of wood, the preparation of the surface, the strength of the ammonia, and the size and tightness of the box. In a commercial fuming room, in which concentrated ammonia drips from one warmed pan to another, articles of white oak that have been sponged with a tannic or pyrogallic solution, as described in a previous paragraph, will fume in about twelve hours. In the box described for the school shop, furniture treated with a tannin solution will fume in about 18 to 24 hours from ammonia in a flat pan. If the surface of the wood is simply sponged with water to open up the pores instead of being treated with one of the above acids, the time for fuming is generally doubled. Articles made of chestnut will usually fume in about one-half the time required for white oak. Chestnut wood does not usually require the preliminary coat of tannic acid; and care must be taken, or the color will be too dark.

Testing for Color. The color of fumed wood is not a rich brown when it comes from the fuming box; but is gray, like an old weathered fence post. A test for color can be made by wetting the finger or a piece of waste with linseed oil and touching the wood in some inconspicuous place. The oil will instantly change the gray to the rich brown color so much admired. If the resultant color after application of the oil to a small spot is too light, the article can be returned to the fuming box and refumed by adding new ammonia. If the color is too dark, allow the article to stand a few weeks before oiling, and let it fade out.

To avoid opening a fuming box before the fuming process is completed, some operators use a sample piece of the same kind of wood, prepared in the same manner, which is inserted through a small opening in the box, and removed for testing.

After removal from the box, the fumed surfaces should be sanded lightly with No. 000 sandpaper. The stain penetrates quite deeply into the wood, much deeper than water stain;

therefore, there is little danger of sanding through the stained layer and causing streaks or spots. Reasonable care should be taken on the corners.

Securing Uniform Results. Sap streaks and light spots are a bugbear to the wood finisher who uses the fuming process. Boards taken from different trees of the same species vary in the amount of tannin content; consequently, an article made from several boards will be uneven in color, or tone at least, after the fuming process. Various methods of blending or touching up are used to secure a more uniform tone. One of the best procedures for correcting the trouble is to "blend in" a fumed oak water stain of a color similar to that of the darker parts of the article. The line of demarcation between the light and dark tones should be dampened with a soft brush and water, and before this dries the stain in diluted form should be applied to the lighter areas. The same process may be repeated, if necessary, to secure a still darker tone over any portion of a surface. When whole boards or large portions of the article are lighter than other portions, the darker parts may be covered with diluted linseed oil; the lighter parts may be coated with the tannin solution a second time; refuming will greatly darken the unoiled portions and only slightly affect the oiled wood.

Some finishers prefer a stain made of bichromate of potash and water-soluble jet black. Only a little of the jet black is needed to give a brownish tone. The bichromate of potash is a fixed alkali, and, with tannic acid, produces on oak a color similar to that secured by the volatile alkali, ammonia. This staining process can be repeated, if necessary. It is a little easier to tell what the resultant colors are going to be if the surface containing the uneven tones is moistened with naphtha and allowed to dry before applying the bichromate of potash solution. Colored shellac may also be used if the article has already been shellacked and shows an uneven tone. The shellac should be thin, and the amount of color added must not be great, or the effect will be muddy. The grain will be much obscured and the shellacked portion may be too dark.

Use the following mixture if it is necessary to add a considerable amount of color:

½ pint liquid white shellac,
½ pint denatured alcohol, with ¼ oz. Bismarck brown spirit soluble aniline dye dissolved in it,
½ pint denatured alcohol, with ¼ oz. (or less) of alcohol soluble black dye.

Each solution should be mixed separately before pouring together, gradually adding the black solution, until the correct color is obtained. Other spirit soluble colors may be used to produce a more accurate tone when applied to the light portions. The chief objections to this method of evening up tones are that spirit soluble stains are somewhat fugitive, and the grain is obscured. The effect is like that produced with varnish stains.

Oiling with boiled linseed oil is the next step after sanding and staining sap streaks, and this brings out the real color which is clear and transparent with no pigment to obscure the beauty of the grain. The oil should be diluted with about three parts of turpentine or naphtha. Raw linseed oil warmed or heated can be used to great advantage, but it dries very slowly, and slows up the finishing process. The diluted boiled linseed oil penetrates the wood deeply and leaves no gum or residue in places that are difficult to rub.

Better results can be obtained by giving the fumed wood two or more coats instead of one of the diluted boiled oil, rubbing it well into the wood first with an oil-soaked pad and later with dry or nearly dry rags, waste, or other cleaning material. The oil should be allowed to dry two or three days between coats, and even longer, if possible, before any other finish is applied over it.

Procedure for Fumed Oak Finish. The steps in finishing an article of white oak, in chronological order, are as follows:

1. Raise the grain of the wood, by sponging the surface with water. Allow it to dry.

2. Resand the entire sponged surface, to remove all fuzz.

3. Apply a coat of a tannic acid solution, containing about ½ oz. of tannic acid powder to the quart of water. (Use part or all pyrogallic acid solution for a more reddish tone.) If none of these acids is at hand, open the pores by sponging with water, and fume longer.

4. Fume in a tight fuming box or room for 6 to 48 hours,

depending upon the box, the strength of the ammonia, the wood used, and the shade of brown desired. Use approximately ¼ pint of 26° ammonia in charging a box having 64 cubic feet of space.

5. Test for color with a spot of oil in an inconspicuous place on the article. Another coat of tannin solution may be applied and the article refumed for a darker color.

6. Stain all sap streaks to even up the color. Slightly stain any boards or portions that are too light.

7. Sand the surfaces lightly with No. 000 sandpaper.

8. Apply one or two coats of diluted boiled linseed oil (1 part oil to about 3 parts turpentine). Allow two or three days between coats for drying. Rub the oil after applying it, and remove all excess with dry waste or rags.

9. Shellac with diluted denatured alcohol shellac, consisting of 2 parts liquid white shellac, ½ part orange shellac, and 1 to 2 parts denatured alcohol. The shellac should dry from 8 to 24 hours. Use fresh shellac only.

10. Sand very carefully with No. 000 sandpaper.

11. Apply at least two coats of floor wax, and rub to a polish about 15 minutes after each waxing. Instead of waxing, some finishers prefer to varnish over the shellac coat with a flat or dull varnish for the last process. Varnish should not be put over wax without removing the wax with gasoline.

SELECTED REFERENCES, CHAPTER VI

Chemical Stains

H. R. Jeffrey, *Wood-Finishing*, Chapter II, pp. 30-39.

A. A. Kelley, *The Expert Wood-Finisher*, "Fumed Oak," pp. 45-49.

G. M. Nyman, Industrial Arts Magazine, Vol. 12, No. 6, June, 1923, p. 232.

A. C. Newell, *Wood and Lumber*, "Chemical Analysis of Wood," pp. 73-78; "Tannins and Extracts from Wood," pp. 86-89.

W. K. Schmidt, *Problems of the Finishing-Room*, Chapters XX, XXI, XXII, XXIII, XXXV and CXIX; Formulas, pp. 367-68.

W. K. Schmidt, Furniture Manufacturer Magazine, "Fuming," January, 1923, p. 13, and June, 1925, p. 296.

A. W. Schorger, *The Chemistry of Cellulose and Wood*, p. 122.

F. N. Vanderwalker, *Wood-Finishing Plain and Decorative*, pp. 67-84.

Chapter VII

Colors and Their Application

Colors Used in Wood Staining. The colors which are most commonly used by the wood finisher are red, orange, green, brown, and black. Other colors in combination are frequently put together, often shading into neutral grays. Yellows and blues, while not used in the finishing room in their pure form, are needed for mixing with other colors.

Definitions of Terms. A statement of the meanings of *hue, chroma, tint, shade,* and other terms, as used by the discriminating colorist, may be of help to the wood finisher.

Hue is frequently used in the sense of *color,* as red, yellow, and so on. It is also employed in referring to a *variation* of a color as a result of mixing a small quantity of another color with it. Thus we say that the hues of blue spread out toward the violet blues on one side, and toward the green blues on the other. To the scientist, hue means a color of a definite wave length.

Chroma refers to the strength, brilliancy, or intensity of a color. We can say that chrome yellow is a brilliant color of high chroma; or that it is a strong color, while yellow ochre is a dull color of weak chroma. Colors lose in chroma or intensity as a result of being neutralized or grayed.

Shade refers to the darker effects produced by adding black to a color. In a broader sense the term shade is commonly used to include the tints of lighter steps of a color, as well as the darker effects. The shade of a color in its exact meaning refers to a spectral or brilliant color to which black has been added, thus lowering it in tone.

A *tint* of a color is a lighter effect produced by adding white to an oil color or water to a transparent stain. A tint is lighter and more delicate than the standard color, which is the spectral hue.

The *value* of a color refers to its position in a scale from dark to light. The tints and shades are therefore various values of the color itself. Black or white may be mixed with a color, and a change of value is the result; but there is no change in the hue or color itself.

Tone refers to the general effect, as "painted in dark tones" means that the effect is dark. Tone has reference to the degree of luminosity or power of reflecting light possessed by a color. Adding black or white to a normal color changes its tone.

Saturation of a color refers to its purity, or to the amount of white light which is contained in the color. White in the form of pigments, of course, has no hue and no saturation.

Warm colors are the fire colors represented by red, orange, and yellow. Red is sometimes called a hot color.

Cold colors are the ice colors of blue, and its neighbors in the spectrum, green and violet. A yellow-green may be called a warm green, and in the same sense a red-violet is a warm violet.

Colors of the Prismatic Solar Spectrum. White light or sunlight is composed of seven prismatic colors, since the time of Newton who pointed out this fact in the year 1666. When a beam of white sunlight is passed through a prism, refraction breaks it up into a band which shows the seven colors of the rainbow, namely: red, orange, yellow, green, blue, indigo, and violet. Some of these colors are not primary colors, however, for they can be produced by mixing other colors together.

The Three Primary Colors. For many years *red, yellow,* and *blue* have been called the primary colors because it was thought that they cannot be made by mixing pigment colors together. A statement of this fact is found in the writings of Aristotle who lived about 2300 years ago. The name primary colors still clings to red, yellow, and blue, although now these so-called primaries can be made by mixing colors adjacent to them on the color circle.

Walter Sargent says that red can be made by mixing violet and orange; that blue can be made by mixing green and violet; and that yellow can be produced by a mixture of orange and green. The three so-called primary colors which are produced by mixtures of adjacent colors on the color circle are what most people call tertiary colors. They are dull and low in brilliancy, and appear like bright colors that have been grayed. It is best for the pigment-color mixer to have brilliant reds, blues, and yellows to start with, and then to make the other colors, considering the three hues just named as base, fundamental, or primary colors.

Secondary Colors. Red, yellow, and blue pigments when mixed together in pairs produce new hues called secondary colors. Red and yellow make *orange;* yellow and blue produce *green;* and red and blue give *violet.* The above refers to mixing of pigments or dyes, and not to combining colored lights. Sargent tells us that blue and yellow lights blended together produce white; and that disks of the same colors when rotated produce gray; while pigments of a similar blue and yellow when mixed as stains or paints produce green.

The artist and mixer of paint or stain should keep these facts in mind and not be confused by the many color theories of the scientist who works with lights rather than with pigments. The artist or wood finisher who mixes pigments or dyes in making other colors considers red, yellow, and blue to be the primary colors; and orange, green, and violet are regarded as the secondary colors. Some writers and colorists use the term *purple* in place of violet; generally, the colors purple and violet are considered to be the same or nearly so.

Tertiary Colors. By mixing the secondary colors, orange, green, and violet, in pairs we have a new series of hues known as *olive, citrine,* and *russet,* called tertiary colors. Orange and green mixed in the right proportion produce citrine; green and violet make olive; and orange and violet combine into russet. In mixing colors for citrine, which is also called citron, four parts of orange and one part of green are required. Olive is made from four parts of green to one part of violet. Russet is obtained by taking four parts of orange and one part of violet.

Quaternary Colors. The quaternary colors are obtained by mixing together the tertiary colors in pairs. By combining pigments of citrine and russet we have *buff;* russet and olive produce *plum;* and citrine and olive make *sage.*

Complex Mixed Colors. Many other colors can be produced by mixing primary, secondary, and tertiary colors together in various proportions. The color which results from any mixture depends upon the chroma or brilliancy of the primary colors

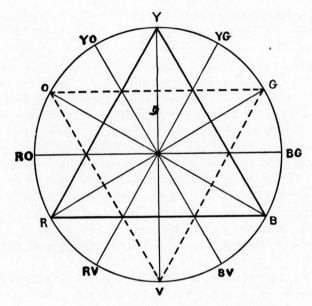

7—1. The 12-step color circle with triads.

used as the original pigments, and also upon whether black or white has been added. The strength of the color can sometimes be changed by dilution with various liquids, as by adding water to water colors or turpentine to oil stains.

Neutral Colors. *Black and white*, while not colors in the ordinary sense, are known as neutral colors. They can be used for contrasting effects with any of the other colors and make a color harmony. Black and white are often mixed with any of the colors to make tints and shades. When mixed together they make a gray. Any color can be neutralized or changed to a neutral gray by adding a sufficient amount of its complementary color.

The Color Circle. Many authorities on colors arrange twelve of the colors of the spectrum in a circle using red, orange, yellow, green, blue, and violet, with intermediate or half steps between. This plan enables one to select approximately color harmonies in triads as well as with opposites on the circle (Fig. 7-1).

Complementary Colors. Effects that can be produced by mingling or blending lights cannot be reproduced by mixing pigments. The complementary colors in the two cases are not exactly the same. The pigment-complement of any hue can be found by what is known as the after-image. One method of seeing the color of an after-image is as follows: (1) Select a piece of bright colored paper, as yellow; (2) Make a tube of dark paper, or use one hand as a tube to cut off the surrounding light, and look through one of these "telescopes" at the colored paper for some time, as half a minute or until the eye becomes tired; (3) While still looking through the tube, remove the paper or look at a white background. An after image of the complementary color will be seen for a few seconds as a rather faint but definite hue. If one looks at yellow paper through the tube until the eye is somewhat tired, as suggested, the after-image which appears on a white background is a violet or possibly a blue-violet color. Violet is opposite to yellow on the color circle and is called the complementary color of yellow.

The pigment-complement of a color is the color which mixed with it produces a neutral gray.

The approximate complement of any pigment color can be found by looking at the opposite ends of any diameter on the color circle, (Fig. 7-1); thus, green is complementary to red; violet is complementary to yellow; orange is complementary to blue; yellow-orange is the complement of blue-violet, and so on.

Contrasts. Effective contrasts can be secured by using black or white adjacent to a color, or by placing complementary colors side by side. A neutral gray can also be used with colors if a less striking or more subdued contrast is wanted. One or both of two complementary colors may be omitted, and the colors adjacent to either one on the color circle substituted for the broken-up hue, in order to produce more subtle or delicate contrasts. An illustration of broken-up colors can often be seen in the morning or evening sky, at sunrise or sunset, where the clouds vary from red-orange to orange and then to yellow-orange, and all are contrasted with blue which also may vary.

Color Triads. An equilateral triangle of the proper size, so that the three points of the angles just touch the circumference of a color circle, when the triangle is placed over the circle,

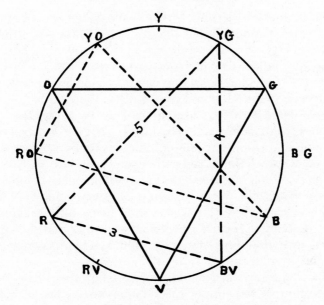

7—2. Color triads and near complements.

will divide the color ring into three equal parts. The points of the triangle will, in any position that it is placed, point to three colors that are approximately harmonious, because any two mixed together will produce the complement of the third color.

In Fig. 7-2, *O-V-G* represents a triad or three-color harmony with contrasting colors. The triangle *B-YO-RO*, which is shown in dotted lines, represents a color, blue, with its near-complements yellow-orange and red-orange. The use of a color with its near-complements is generally effective, producing softer and more delicate contrasts that are often of great beauty.

A very great number of interesting color combinations can be discovered by shifting the triangle in Fig. 7-2 about the color circle. If the equilateral triangle is placed with corners at *Y-B-R*, we have a combination of the three primary colors, which is the least pleasing of the harmony groups made by placing the triangle over the color circle.

Another pleasing combination, recommended by some artists, is made by the use of a triangle with three, four, and five steps on the sides, as shown at *R-BV-YG*, in Fig. 7-2. Triads containing one of the so-called primary colors can be used in such a combination without the unpleasant group of the three primary colors. In some cases two of the primary colors, such as blue and red, may be included in a triad. If the 3-4-5 triangle in Fig. 7-2 is revolved one step counterclockwise, a color triad with yellow, red-violet, and blue will be the result.

Color Harmony. It is very difficult to lay down fixed rules as to just what colors are pleasing when they are placed together. Each color has an unlimited number of variations changing toward the adjacent hue on each side of it on the color circle. Each hue has many values which may be produced by dark and light, or by mixture of black and white. The chroma or intensity of colors varies from full brilliancy to neutral gray. The texture of the material to which the color is applied gives different effects of light and dark as well as of tone and of reflection.

Color harmony, in general, can be secured: (1) by a careful selection of the proper hues, either analogous, or related, or in contrast; (2) by having one color dominant; (3) by having the colors selected and arranged for a tone balance; (4) by considering lights and darks of the hues or shades and tints; (5) by varying the chroma, or partially neutralizing one or both of the colors; and (6) by selecting hues suitable to the texture of the material or surface upon which they are to be applied.

Analogous and Contrasting Colors. There are two types of color harmonies, which are known as *analogous* and *contrasting* harmonies.

Analogous colors are closely related colors, or those that are adjacent to each other on the color circle. An example of a group of analogous colors is red-orange, orange, and yellow-orange, as shown on Fig. 7-2. This type of color harmony produces delicacy, softness, and attractiveness. It lacks contrast and boldness; but brings refined beauty, which under many conditions is very suitable and pleasing. Analogous colors are much used in decorative schemes for the home, and in women's costumes.

Contrasting colors may be made harmonious through a tone balance in several ways: (1) There may be a color-contrast harmony, through the use of a color and its complement. Such colors are found at the ends of any diameter on the color circle, as yellow and violet. The areas covered by the two contrasting colors are often quite different in producing a harmony by contrast. (2) One or both of the colors may be subdued or grayed in a contrasting color harmony. (3) The values of the colors in the contrasting pair may be varied enough to secure a pleasing tone balance. The values are changed by making the colors darker or lighter.

The Modern Theory of Color. The old theory that red, yellow, and blue are the primary colors is still the basis for mixing colors in many trades and industries, and is generally used in public schools. Modern scientists in experimenting with light ray colors have come to the conclusion that *light rays* separate into red, green, and violet-blue as the basic or primary

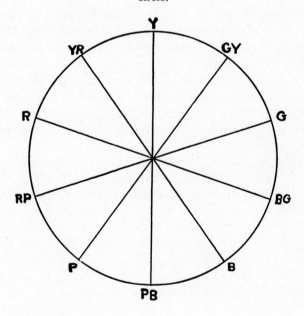

7—3. The modern ten point color circle. The complete list of contrasting colors can be made by observing the names of colors which are located at the opposite ends of the diameters of the circle.

colors. Students of color, such as A. H. Munsell, use a five point color circle, with intermediate half steps. This color circle is made up of red, yellow, green, blue, and purple, with the intermediate colors, yellow-red, green-yellow, blue-green, purple-blue, and red-purple (Fig. 7-3).

Modern research has shown that no mixtures of other light rays will produce red, green, and violet-blue, and for this reason these three colors are called primary colors. Other colors can be produced by mixing light rays from the three colors: dark red, green, and violet-blue.

It must be remembered that mixing the rays of colored lights and mixing pigments or dyes are two very different things. The spectral colors all come from white light, and they can be recombined into white light by the use of a second prism, which must be inverted and placed so as to gather the rays of light that have been dispersed into a spectrum by a similar prism, which originally broke up the white light into spectral colors. If pigments of the same spectral colors are mixed together, the result is not white, but gray. This shows plainly that we cannot mix pigment colors by the same methods that are used in combining light rays and secure similar results.

The contrasting colors which are at the ends of the diameters of the ten point color circle are very pleasing. With the five basic colors—red, yellow, green, blue, and purple—other colors can be secured by mixing. The color harmony is not quite the same as that obtained from the old theory of six colors with a twelve-point circle. According to this new theory the complementary color of red is blue-green; the complement of green is red-purple; and the complement of purple-blue is yellow.

Acceptable Color Combinations. The amateur colorist should not allow himself to become confused by the two theories and two methods of mixing colors. Both methods are used and both are offered in this book in order to meet the needs of persons who have learned one method and do not understand the other. While it is probably true that the new theory is more scientific and produces more pleasing complementary colors, the old system is still used widely, and cannot be overlooked in a discussion of color mixing.

LIST OF GOOD COLOR COMBINATIONS

1. Black and white.
2. Blue with gold, or orange, or maize.
3. Blue, with salmon, or red-orange.
4. Blue with black or white, or with orange added.
5. Blue with gold, crimson, and sometimes brown.
6. Red with red-orange, orange, or gold; black may be added.
7. Scarlet with violet, or black, or white.
8. Crimson with orange, or red-orange, or green.
9. Yellow with violet.
10. Green with gold, crimson, red, or orange.
11. Purple, red, and scarlet.
12. Gold with lilac, or blue-violet.
13. Lilac with scarlet, white, or black.
14. Gold with practically any color.
15. Black and white with any color.
16. Shades and tints of the same color are good together.

This list of colors which most authorities will say produce pleasing harmonies, is offered in the hope that it may be helpful to persons who are not experienced in selecting good combinations from one or the other of the color circles. Another reason why this list is valuable is that it introduces two so-called colors—black and white—which are often employed to produce certain effects that are obtainable in no other way.

Some of the color combinations are analogous or closely related colors. A few of the pairs, such as yellow and violet, are complementary colors according to the old color theory, and are shown at opposite ends of a twelve point color circle. The combinations in the list are in general based on the old theory of three primary colors and a twelve point color wheel. It should be noted, however, that slight changes in some of the hues will make the combinations correct according to the ten point color circle.

Hue is not the only characteristic of a specific color. It has already been pointed out in the section on Color Harmony that each color has a number of values which are known as tints and shades, and that brilliancy and partial neutrality must also be considered in arranging a pleasing color combination. In general, color combinations are most pleasing when one hue is dominant, and when shades, tints, and partial neutrality are all considered.

The wood finisher of the present day should have a list of pleasing color combinations, a very good eye, and taste if he is to be successful in the use of paint enamels or lacquer enamels because colors are often demanded in various color harmonies for finishing close grained woods that are now frequently used in making certain types of furniture. Let us suppose our colorist has an end table that he wishes to finish with a body color of blue. The "List of Good Color Combinations" will indicate several possible colors that can be used as trimmings. Such a list indicates that greater freedom can be used in some cases than would be apparent from a slavish following of the combinations indicated on either of the color circles. Many other satisfactory color combinations in pairs or triads might be added to the list just given. The list, while not complete, suggests harmonies that are accepted by the color critics in general.

Palette of Colors for Staining. The wood finisher can secure practically any color effect that he wishes by having a palette of the twelve hues shown on the color circle. The colors most used at the present time are browns, greens, reds, oranges, and blacks, in various combinations, sometimes in tints or shades, and again in tones that approach neutral grays. Such primary colors as brilliant yellow and blue are not usually put on wood in their full strength and hue; nevertheless, they are valuable in mixing with other colors. It is necessary to have the primary

7—4. Simple color wheel showing the relationship of colors.

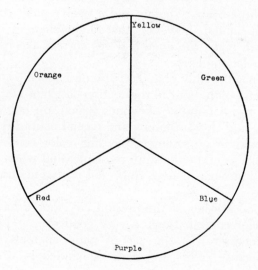

colors, red, yellow, and blue, in full chroma or brilliancy if any of the mixed colors are to be intense and brilliant. Ivory-black is commonly used to darken or make shades of the various colors.

The Practice of Color Mixing. In previous chapters the materials used for wood staining have been discussed. Now comes the problem of using stains in everyday furniture finishing practice. First the mixing or blending of colors must be considered. Wood stains used in production are nearly always made by blending. This is true whether soluble colors or pigment colors are used. Wood stains are obtainable ready mixed and matched to individual standards, but there are always problems in color correction and adjustment as well as those of developing new colors and new finishes. A competent finisher must therefore know something of the general principles of color blending and color matching. Only practice can develop color matching skill, but the basic theory of color mixing is relatively simple. This is graphically illustrated by the color circle which shows clearly and simply the relationship of colors (Fig. 7-4).

On this circle are the three primary colors—red, yellow, and blue—spaced 120 degrees apart. Between these are the secondary colors—orange, green, and purple. The secondary colors are made by mixing the adjacent primary colors. Thus a mixture of red and yellow produces orange. A mixture of yellow and blue makes green.

Colors which are directly opposite each other on this circle are complementary. If they are mixed they will neutralize each other and produce gray. This principle is constantly used in matching and adjusting stain colors. If a mixture is too red or warm, it can be brought back with green. If there is no green base color, yellow and blue (blue-black) may be used. To give additional warmth to a mixture that is too green or cold add more red.

Most wood stains are some shade of brown. Mixing the three primary colors—red, yellow, and blue—will produce shades of brown. By varying the components one gets browns of every tone—red browns, green browns, yellow browns, purple browns, and so forth. A good illustration of how this color theory is put into practice is in the use of the non-grain-raising stain base colors, using a red, a yellow, and a blue-black. (Blue-black is preferable to a clear sharp blue because it works better in producing the great majority of wood stain colors.) When this blue-black is put in the color circle, the region between red and blue becomes brownish purple and the region between yellow and blue-black becomes olive green.

To this basic group of primary colors—red, yellow, and blue-black—is added orange. This orange is roughly equivalent to a mixture of ten parts yellow and one part red. Adding this orange base color to the regular yellow will give it good light-fastness and strength. Since most red and brown tones contain both red and yellow, it is a good idea to start with orange and obtain the desired color by adding red and blue-black.

A light lemon-yellow base color is also added. It is used for producing a bright yellow undertone, or is tinted with red and blue-black for colors which are strong in yellow. The reason this light yellow is not used altogether (eliminating the medium yellow) is that it is weak in strength, and quite strongly acidic. This causes some package troubles. Therefore its use is limited to those colors not obtainable with orange, or those requiring a high content of medium yellow. As a rule it is best to use orange whenever possible to keep the amount of medium yellow in any mixture low, and to use light yellow only for strong yellow colors.

Ninety-nine percent of the colors (in NGR stains) for wood finish undertone staining are made with these base colors —red, the two yellows, blue-black, and orange. Occasionally, for special purposes, it is necessary to use a bright clear blue, a deep maroon red, a bright green, a rich brown color, and a few others.

In the pigment colors a wider group of individual color pigments is used for reasons of cost availability and performance. Thus, for most brown tones start with natural brown-toned mineral pigments, such as umber and sienna. Raw umber is greenish brown, whereas burnt umber is reddish brown. Raw sienna is yellowish brown, but burnt sienna is quite red. With these, for further tinting use red and yellow iron oxides and occasionally red chemical pigments such as lithol or roselake. Use chrome yellow for a bright yellow color. By using white

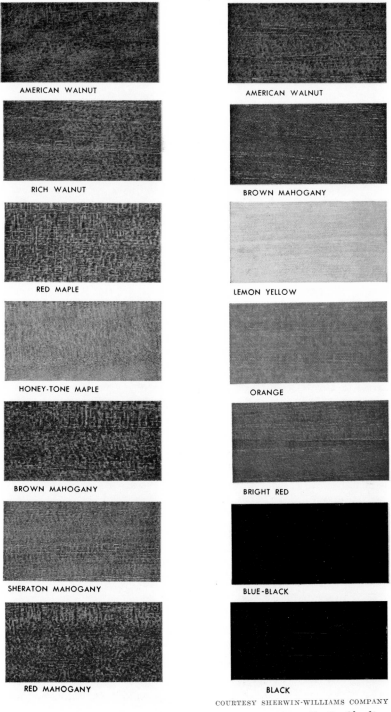

AMERICAN WALNUT	AMERICAN WALNUT
RICH WALNUT	BROWN MAHOGANY
RED MAPLE	LEMON YELLOW
HONEY-TONE MAPLE	ORANGE
BROWN MAHOGANY	BRIGHT RED
SHERATON MAHOGANY	BLUE-BLACK
RED MAHOGANY	BLACK

7—5. Samples of ready-mixed non-grain raising stains. 7—6. Shading lacquers are used for uniforming purposes. They are usually applied over the sealer coat but may be applied directly over stain or filler. 7—7. Wiping stains have the dual purpose of staining and filling in one operation. They are generally used on close-grained, soft woods.

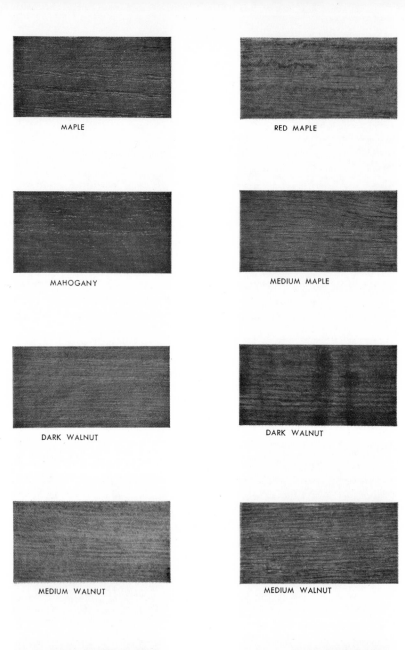

MAPLE

RED MAPLE

MAHOGANY

MEDIUM MAPLE

DARK WALNUT

DARK WALNUT

MEDIUM WALNUT

MEDIUM WALNUT

LIGHT WALNUT

7-6

MAHOGANY

7-7

9

it is possible to make a range of pigment stains or pigmented sealers in tones of bone, ivory, ecru, light tan, and so forth, which are variations of white. These may be used to produce the light background colors so popular in wood finishing.

Equalizing Applications. In most wood finishing systems there is a problem of matching up unlike colors in the natural wood. Sapwood areas or mineral streaks may cause variations from the normal color in the same wood, as will the use of different varieties of wood in the same piece. Case goods frequently have gumwood framing—posts, stretchers, and so forth—and mahogany, walnut, or other veneer drawer fronts, doors, and tops. If very dark strong stains are used, one overall application may bring these different woods to the same color or close to it. But if stains of medium shade and strength are used, a uniform overall application will produce widely contrasting colors over the different woods. You must use different treatment for the different areas. This is usually done by staining the lighter wood down to the average tone of the darker wood. It may require a separate stain mixture, or perhaps just a heavier application of the overall stain on the light wood. In practice this breaks down to the following procedures:

Sap Staining. The purpose here is to bring the lighter sapwood areas, such as those which frequently occur in walnut, down to the average natural wood tone. A special stain mixture is usually necessary. You can use a mixture of non-grain-raising stain, especially tinted for the job. Some finishers prefer to use water stains for sap staining. A good compromise is to use a water-alcohol stain made by thinning non-grain-raising stain with a mixture of equal parts alcohol and water. When using a straight non-grain-raising stain, as a sap stain, it must be spray-shaded in. When using water stain or a water alcohol mix, apply with a rag or sponge. In sap staining avoid the use of color ingredients which tend to bleed into subsequent coatings.

To develop the correct color of sap stain for any particular job, make a quick test for color as follows:

1. If the system involves a subsequent NGR body stain (followed by washcoat, filler, sealer, and so forth) apply the

trial mix on a test piece, let dry five or ten minutes, then wet with naphtha. The sap stained area should match the surrounding wood color *when wet.*

2. If the system involves a subsequent application of pigment sealer, the sap stained area should match the adjacent wood *when dry* (no naphtha wetting applied). In either case, always make a final test by recoating with the subsequent body stain plus sealer. If the sap stained areas do not match, make the necessary adjustment.

Trim staining. This is the same basic problem as sap staining, but is used when there is a white or light wood area which must first be stained to the average color of the veneer wood. You can often do this simply by first applying the body or undertone stain to the trim parts only, followed by an overall even application. Sometimes it is necessary to make a special trim stain mixture to tie the two woods together. It just depends upon the result that is desired, and can only be obtained by trial and error. The testing procedure is the same as for sap stain.

Equalizing or shading stain. This is another name for pigmented sealer. It is composed of pigment color dispersed in a lacquer sealer vehicle. (Lacquer enamels can also be used as equalizing stains.) The name is generally used only for those pigment sealers which are relatively high in pigmentation, and which are used in fairly opaque application, to hide color defects, such as mineral streaks in the wood. An even overall application of equalizing stain will produce a more even color than any solution stain applied in the same way, but at the same time may produce an opaque or "painted" appearance. Equalizing stains are useful when defects are too pronounced to conceal in any other way. Pigmented sealers are used for a great variety of present day light undertone finishes. To obtain good transparency use them sparingly and with quite a low pigment concentration.

Uniforming or wiping stains. This is another name for pigment stains. They are made by dispersing pigment colors in penetrating oil or varnish type vehicles. When they are evenly applied over woods of unlike colors, they produce an effect similar to that of the lacquer equalizing stains. In strong or dark colors they produce very good uniformity. The need for uniforming stains has lessened with the modern trend toward lighter wood finishes. The main difference between pigment uniforming stains and lacquer equalizing stains is that the uniforming stains can be wiped and when wiped they lie down in the surface pores of the wood and produce better transparency. They actually have some value in developing grain or figure in the small pore woods. When pigment-uniforming stains and pigment-equalizing lacquers are sprayed on without wiping, there is little difference in their performance.

Glazing. A process of highlighting is often accomplished by glazing. Glazes are pigments finely ground in oil which are brushed, wiped, and blended over the filler or sealer to give a highlighted, shaded, or antiqued effect. To give an antiqued effect, wipe the glaze clean from the flat surfaces and edges that are to appear worn, leaving it in the recessed areas. Tinting colors can also be used for glazing if they are reduced to brushing consistency with turpentine or mineral spirits.

Color Samples. The furniture finishing materials shown in Figs. 7-5, 6, and 7 are applied on soft, open-grained woods which bring out the true shade of the stain involved. The shade and depth of any color will vary with the method of application used and the type of wood upon which it is applied.

All of the finishing materials shown are transparent or semi-transparent coatings; therefore colors are additive, i.e., the resultant depth and appearance of the finish will be the color of the wood, plus the color of the stain, plus the color of the filler.

By applying several coats of ready-mixed stain, you may produce deeper tones with the same approximate color value. The shade and depth of the finishing material shown naturally appear much darker on a dark wood, such as walnut, than on a light wood, such as pine. Likewise a coat of stain in the selected color, plus a coat of the filler, will tend to produce a darker and stronger tone than either the stain or filler alone.

Close-grained woods such as maple, birch, and gum may be finished with ready-mixed stain or wiping stain, or one coat of each. The use of both produces a more uniform color with greater depth than if only one were used.

Open-grained woods, such as oak or mahogany, should be finished with stain and a filler. Only the filler is necessary in many cases to produce light shades on these woods. For instance, limed oak or natural filler would produce blonde or light finishes without any stain. In general, the color of the filler should be a little darker than the shade of the stain so that a contrast will be apparent between the pore and the flake of the wood.

After the stained and filled surfaces have had an application of lacquer sealer, it may be necessary to do some uniforming. Shading lacquers may be used for this. They are sprayed over the light sections of the piece of furniture until a shade is reached which will match the rest of the piece.

Ready-mixed stain concentrates may be added to stains to modify the color. For example, the addition of orange concentrate will deepen the orange tone. The addition of stain reducer will weaken the strength of the color.

To obtain the most satisfactory results there is no substitute for experimentation. Apply the stain or filler to a small portion of the wood first and make any necessary adjustments before proceeding with the entire staining and finishing operation.

Selected Samples of Furniture Finishes.[1] Through the combined efforts of paint manufacturers, furniture makers, and interior decorators, the numerous woods used in contemporary furniture are now finished in pleasing and attractive colors.

Figs. 7-8, and 9 show a number of selected finishes which have proved popular with the general public. Each wood shown is accompanied by a brief step-by-step procedure. These procedures are in no way complete, but are intended to show color only. The sealer and top coat operations have, for the greater part, been purposely omitted. All systems may be completed with a choice of any of the several, available sealers and top coats. For the convenience of wood finishers every fourth sample is treated in greater detail (numbers 4, 8, 12, 16, 20, and 24).

---

[1] Finishing systems reproduced by courtesy of the Sherwin-Williams Company.

FURNITURE FINISHING SYSTEMS

1. Limed Oak on Oak

(1) Brush on and wipe off the limed oak filler.
(2) Seal.

2. Desert Sand on Oak

(1) Spray with lacquer toner mixed as follows:
   150 parts white lacquer
    50 parts ferrite lacquer
     8 parts maroon lacquer
   Reduce the above mix with 10 parts of lacquer thinner.
(2) Brush on and wipe off harvest filler.

3. Driftwood on Oak

(1) Spray with gray lacquer reduced with 5 parts of thinner.
(2) Brush on and wipe off driftwood filler mixed as follows:
   200 parts limed oak filler
     3 parts raw umber first quality tinting color
   Reduce to brushing consistency with VM&P naphtha before using.

4. Silver Fox on Oak

(1) Spray with black lacquer reduced 1 part lacquer to 2 parts thinner.
(2) Sand lightly with 7/0 paper.
(3) Brush and wipe limed oak or white filler.
(4) Spray with lacquer sealer. Allow to dry 30 minutes to one hour.
(5) Sand with 6/0 paper.
(6) Spray with first coat of gloss lacquer. Let it dry 1 to 2 hours.
(7) Spray the second coat of gloss lacquer. Let it dry 1 to 2 hours.
(8) Spray the third coat of gloss lacquer. Allow it to dry overnight.
(9) Sand with #360 wet or dry paper, using a mixture of 50% paraffin oil
   and 50% mineral spirits for lubricant.
(10) Rub with 3F pumice stone and oil or lacquer rubbing compound.
(11) Wax.

5. Light Walnut on Walnut

(1) Spray with bleaching lacquer.
(2) Brush on and wipe off light walnut filler.

6. Early American Walnut on Walnut.

(1) Spray or brush on a stain mixed as follows:[2]
   1 gallon Sheraton mahogany stain
   4 ounces orange concentrate
(2) Spray on a wash coat of white shellac.
(3) Sand with 7/0 paper.
(4) Brush on and wipe off dark walnut filler.

7. Rich Walnut on Walnut

(1) Spray or brush on rich walnut stain.
(2) Spray on a wash coat of white shellac.
(3) Sand with 7/0 paper.
(4) Brush on and wipe off medium walnut filler.

8. American Walnut on Walnut

(1) Spray or brush on American walnut stain.
(2) Spray on a wash coat of white shellac.

---

[2]All stains whether ready-prepared or mixed are of the non-grain-raising type.

   (3) Sand with 7/0 paper.
   (4) Brush on and wipe off medium walnut filler.
   (5) Spray on lacquer sealer. Dry overnight.
   (6) Sand with 6/0 paper.
   (7) Shade if desired with shading lacquer. Let dry 10-15 minutes.
   (8) Spray on the first coat of water white lacquer. Let dry 1-2 hours.
   (9) Spray on second coat. Let dry 1-2 hours.
 (10) Spray on third coat. Let dry overnight.
 (11) Sand with #360 wet or dry paper using a mixture of 50% paraffin oil
       and 50% mineral spirits for lubricant.
 (12) Rub with 3F pumice stone and oil.
 (13) Rub to satin lustre with rotten stone and oil.
 (14) Wax.

9. Blond Mahogany on Mahogany

   (1) Spray with lacquer toner mixed as follows:

       200 parts white lacquer
         34 parts ferrite yellow lacquer
          2 parts gray lacquer
          1 part maroon lacquer

       Reduce the above mix with 4 parts of thinner.
   (2) Brush on and wipe off harvest filler.

10. Sheraton Mahogany on Mahogany

   (1) Spray or brush on Sheraton mahogany stain.
   (2) Spray on a wash coat of white shellac.
   (3) Sand with 7/0 paper.
   (4) Brush on and wipe off medium mahogany filler.

11. Red Mahogany on Mahogany

   (1) Spray or brush on red mahogany stain.
   (2) Spray on a wash coat of white shellac.
   (3) Sand with 7/0 paper.
   (4) Brush on and wipe off medium mahogany filler.

12. Brown Mahogany on Mahogany

   (1) Spray or brush on brown mahogany stain.
   (2) Spray on a wash coat of white shellac. Dry one hour.
   (3) Sand with 7/0 paper.
   (4) Brush on and wipe off medium mahogany filler.
   (5) Spray on lacquer sealer. Dry overnight.
   (6) Sand with 6/0 paper.
   (7) Shade if desired with shading lacquer. Let dry 10-15 minutes.
   (8) Spray on the first coat of water white lacquer. Let dry 1-2 hours.
   (9) Spray on second coat. Let dry 1-2 hours.
 (10) Spray on third coat. Let dry overnight.
 (11) Sand with #360 wet or dry paper using a mixture of 50% paraffin oil
       and 50% mineral spirits for lubricant.
 (12) Rub with 3F pumice stone and oil.
 (13) Rub to satin lustre with rotten stone and oil.
 (14) Wax.

13. Silver Gray on Maple

   (1) Spray lacquer toner mixed as follows:

       50 parts black lacquer
       20 parts white lacquer

       Reduce the above mix with 8 parts of thinner.
   (2) Allow it to dry and seal.

14. **Red Maple on Maple**
    (1) Spray or brush on red maple stain.
    (2) Allow it to dry and seal.

15. **Honey Tone on Maple**
    (1) Spray or brush on honey tone maple stain.
    (2) Allow it to dry and seal.

16. **Rich Maple on Maple**
    (1) Spray or brush on red maple stain.
    (2) Brush on and wipe off red maple wiping stain reduced equal parts with VM&P naphtha.
    (3) Spray on lacquer sealer. Let dry 30 minutes to one hour.
    (4) Sand with 6/0 paper.
    (5) Spray on first coat of gloss lacquer. Let it dry 1-2 hours.
    (6) Spray on second coat of gloss lacquer. Let dry 1-2 hours.
    (7) Spray on third coat of gloss lacquer. Allow it to dry overnight.
    (8) Sand with #360 wet or dry paper, using a mixture of 50% paraffin oil and 50% mineral spirits for lubricant.
    (9) Rub with 3F pumice stone and oil or lacquer rubbing compound.
    (10) Wax.

17. **Platinum on Birch**
    (1) Brush on and wipe off platinum oil stain.
    (2) Allow it to dry and seal.

18. **Wheat Color on Birch**
    (1) Brush on and wipe off wheat oil stain.
    (2) Allow it to dry and seal.

19. **Champagne on Birch**
    (1) Brush on and wipe off champagne oil stain.
    (2) Allow it to dry and seal.

20. **Rich Walnut on Red Gum**
    (1) Brush on and wipe off medium walnut wiping stain reduced equal parts with VM&P naphtha.
    (2) Allow it to dry.
    (3) Spray on lacquer sealer. Let dry 30 minutes to one hour.
    (4) Sand with 6/0 sand paper.
    (5) Spray on the first coat of gloss lacquer. Let it dry 1-2 hours.
    (6) Spray on the second coat of gloss lacquer. Let it dry 1-2 hours.
    (7) Spray on the third coat of gloss lacquer. Let it dry overnight.
    (8) Sand with #360 wet or dry paper, using a mixture of 50% paraffn oil and 50% mineral spirits for lubricant.
    (9) Rub with 3F pumice stone and oil or lacquer rubbing compound.
    (10) Wax.

21. **Bisque on Korina**
    (1) Spray or brush on stain mixed as follows:

      8 parts blue black concentrate
     12 parts orange concentrate
      5 parts red concentrate
    575 parts stain reducer

    (2) Brush on and wipe off 200 parts of limed oak filler mixed with 4 parts of raw umber. Reduce to brushing consistency with naphtha.

22. **Light Harvest on Korina**
    (1) Spray or brush on stain mixed as follows:

8 parts blue black concentrate
12 parts orange concentrate
5 parts red concentrate
575 parts of reducer

(2) Brush on and wipe off light harvest filler mixed as follows:
2 parts natural filler
1 part of harvest filler
Reduce to brushing consistency with naphtha.

23. Medium Harvest on Korina

(1) Spray or brush on stain mixed as follows:
8 parts blue black concentrate
12 parts orange concentrate
5 parts red concentrate
575 parts reducer

(2) Brush on and wipe off harvest filler.

24. Dark Walnut on Red Gum

(1) Brush on and wipe off dark walnut wiping stain reduced equal parts with naphtha.
(2) Allow it to dry and seal.
(3) Spray on lacquer sealer. Let dry 30 minutes to one hour.
(4) Sand with 6/0 paper.
(5) Spray on the first coat of gloss lacquer. Let it dry 1 to 2 hours.
(6) Spray on the second coat of gloss lacquer. Let it dry 1 to 2 hours.
(7) Spray on the third coat of gloss lacquer. Let it dry overnight.
(8) Sand with #360 wet or dry paper, using a mixture of 50% paraffin oil and 50% mineral spirits for lubricant.
(9) Rub with 3F pumice stone and oil or lacquer rubbing compound.
(10) Wax.

Finishing Plywood Panels.[3] The rapidly increasing popularity of plywood paneling as a means of beautifying the contemporary home makes it necessary to say something about the finishing methods used (Fig. 7-11 and 12). The public is gradually learning that plywood is made not only of fir and other softwoods, but also in a large number of hardwoods used for wall paneling, built-ins and so forth. Most paneled rooms are finished in what is frequently called the "light natural" effect. This is a finish which very closely retains the original tone and color of the wood. No stain, filler, or sealer is used even on open pored woods such as oak, walnut, and mahogany. The conventional finish consisting of a coat of shellac and two coats of varnish is to a great extent taboo, not only because it darkens the wood, but also because of the "built-up" effect it produces.

[3] The material on "Finishing Plywood Panels" is used by courtesy of Mr. Walther Hanser, Industrial Adhesives Division, United States Plywood Corporation.

7—11. This interior shows walls of walnut plywood and a table finished with birch weldwood.

7—12. Living room in walnut weldwood plywood. Panels are fastened to wall with special cement.

The homemaker, interior decorator, and architect all like the warmth and livability provided by wood paneling in the light natural effect. The beauty of most hardwood plywoods in their unfinished state is the main reason for the continued popularity of the natural finish. This finish is always in style and will remain attractive throughout the years. Part of its popularity is its ease of application and low cost. The shortage of skilled wood finishers makes it almost imperative that finishes for wood paneling be as simple and foolproof as possible. An unskilled workman will find it difficult to follow the complicated procedures of bleaching, staining, filling, and so forth, but he will have no trouble with the light natural effect, consisting of just two or three coats of an easily applied clear finish.

Although hardwood plywood is reasonably priced, an expensive finishing job would make the overall cost of the installation too high for most people. The light natural effect is the least expensive finish and, besides is simple enough that many homeowners do the job themselves with excellent results.

A special brushing lacquer was developed to meet this demand for a truly natural finish. Water-clear in color, it produces a finish shades lighter than normally obtained with varnish. This lacquer is especially formulated for brushing, as most wood paneling is finished after installation. It dries to the touch in about thirty minutes, completely in about four hours. As it picks up little or no dust on drying, only a light steel wooling is required after each coat. The wood is well protected without the built-up effect of varnish.

Next in popularity to the natural finish for wood paneling are the blond and pickled effects. These are especially effective in overcoming the slight yellow cast of woods such as American elm, tamo and sen. In the past, these finishes were obtained by wiping the surface with thinned paint or white lead, but, the result usually was a muddy or "painty" effect obscuring the grain of the wood. Now many architects are specifying a white resin sealer for blond and pickled effects, because it penetrates the grain of the wood and wipes clean without a smeary effect.

Softwoods such as knotty pine and cedar have a fairly uniform texture and can be finished in the same way as the hardwoods. Other softwoods, such as fir plywood and ponderosa pine, having alternate soft spring and hard summer growths, present certain finishing problems such as grain raise and face checking in paint and enamel work and so-called "wild grain" in stain finishing. Special resin sealers have been developed as an aid in finishing these woods.

A resin sealer, in effect, brings the soft spring growth approximately to the same density as the hard summer growth. It holds the grain of the wood in a tight grip that largely stops its movement, thus minimizing the possibility of grain raise and face checking in painted or enamel work. On stained effects a resin sealer assures more even absorption of stain resulting in a subdued and richer appearance.

Resin sealers are made in a clear and white pigmented version. The clear is used on softwoods prior to staining and in natural finishes with shellac and varnish as the finish coats. It sometimes is used prior to painting, especially where dark-colored paints are to be applied. White pigmented resin sealer is generally recommended for painted and enameled work, because it not only acts as a sealer but also provides an excellent undercoat for paint and enamel. Where required, it can be tinted with colors-in-oil to the approximate color of the finish coats. Pigmented resin sealers are also used for blond and pickled effects.

As in all finishing jobs, the importance of careful sanding should be stressed. Many inexperienced finishers feel that the average paneled room with 200 square feet or more of surface is too much of a sanding job. They either skip this part of the work, or do it poorly. However, the final result depends at least as much on the preparation of the wood surfaces as it does on the finishing materials, especially when blond, pickled, stained, or complicated finishes are required.

Nail holes left from the installation of the paneling have always been a problem. It is well to fill these holes after the first coat of clear finish is applied. To eliminate nailing and nail holes, much paneling is now completed with the use of prepared contact cement. A plastic wood putty of the correct shade or a pure linseed oil putty, tinted with colors-in-oil, a shade or so darker than the overall tone of the finished wood, can be used. It is very important to put the putty into the holes with a putty knife so that it does not get on the surface and make an oil ring. Any oil that does get on the face of the panel must be wiped off immediately. The putty must dry hard, usually 24 hours, after which it is lightly sanded and the subsequent coats of finish applied.

Another problem in the finishing of a paneled room is how to treat the trim when it is a different wood from that of the panels. Usually pine or birch is used for trim even when the paneling is a hardwood, such as oak, walnut, or mahogany. Ordinary stains usually are not satisfactory in staining the trim to match paneling of a darker wood, especially when a light natural effect is required. Clear resin sealer thinned about 20% with turpentine or mineral spirits and tinted with colors-in-oil makes an excellent stain for trim as shade and intensity of color can easily be regulated.

Procedure for Finishing Wall Paneling. A number of popular plywoods are used for wall paneling. To produce the light natural effect, the following procedure is suggested:

1. Apply one coat of clear resin sealer.
2. Allow four hours of drying time.
3. Fill all nail holes carefully with plastic wood or linseed oil putty of proper shade.
4. Apply the first coat of special brushing lacquer.
5. Allow it to dry and rub lightly with fine steel wool.
6. Apply the second coat of special brushing lacquer.
7. After this coat dries, rub it lightly with steel wool.
8. Rub with light colored wax.

To produce a blond or pickled effect, use white resin sealer instead of the clear sealer as used in clear finishes. After it dries for a few minutes, wipe with a dry cloth. When thoroughly dry, complete the finish with clear brushing lacquer as outlined above.

In closing this topic on panel finishing, it should be mentioned that quite a variety of plywood paneling now can be purchased pre-finished at the factory.

SELECTED REFERENCES, CHAPTER VII

Colors and Woodstains

Bustanoby, J. H., *Principles of Color and Color Mixing*. New York, Mc-Graw-Hill Book Company, 1947, 131 pages.

Denning, Matt., "How Color Helps Output of Active Machine Tools." *Industrial Finishing*, 18, pp. 12-17, April, 1942.

Grand Rapids Varnish Corporation, "Direct-to-Wood Stains, Classification of Materials," mimeographed article.

McGee, R. M., and Brown, A. G., *Instructional Units in Woodfinishing*, "To Mix and Match Colors," pp. 48-55, 1950.

National Safety News, "Color at Work," page 16, March, 1951.

Peck, E. D., "Color is a Science," *Organic Finishing*, 7, pp. 22-25, June, 1946.

The Sherwin-Williams Company, "Furniture Finishing Facts," 32 pages, 1954.

Smith, L. R., "Know Your Colors," *Organic Finishing*, 7, pp. 9-13, April, 1946.

Soderberg, G. A., "Color Rendering." *Industrial Arts and Vocational Education*, 38, page 36, March, 1949.

Ibid., *Finishing Materials and Methods*, "Color and its Application," Chapter XXIX, pp. 291-300, 1952.

Vanderwalker, F. N., *The Mixing of Colors and Paints*. Frederick J. Drake and Co., Inc., Chicago, Illinois, 1944.

Von Fisher, W. and Bobalek, E. G., *Organic Protective Coatings*, "New Pigments in Modern Color Design," Chapter VIII, pp. 167-209, 1953.

Chapter VIII

Coal-Tar Dyes and Their Use
as Wood Stains

Characteristics and Origin. Coal tar, once considered an almost worthless waste product, is a very black, opaque, thick mass, which is liquid at certain temperatures. It is formed through condensation from gas in pipes during the manufacture of coal gas, and is, therefore, a distillate from coal. The first coal-tar dyes were produced from aniline, which is one of the light tar oil derivatives from nitrobenzene. Many other coal-tar dyes are derived, not from aniline, but from medium and heavy tar oils, among these colors being many of the alizarine group.

In variety of tints and shades, and in brilliancy of hue, the coal-tar dyes are superior to all other dyestuffs. A French chemist is reported as having said that about 14,000 shades and tints of various hues can be made from coal tar. Less than one-tenth of this number is now made and actually used.

The fugitive characteristic of many of the early coal-tar dyes has long been overcome. Chemically, some of these artificial dyes are practically the same as corresponding natural dyes.

All Coal-Tar Dyes Are Not Aniline Dyes. Aniline is simply one of several derivatives from nitrobenzene, which is manufactured from light tar oil. Many other coal-tar dyes are produced from other derivatives.

Products of Coal-Tar Distillation. During the year 1845 Hofmann, a German chemist, discovered that the hydrocarbon, benzene, is present in coal tar. Research students, especially the Englishman, Perkin, discovered Mauveine or Mauve somewhat accidentally when working with aniline, a derivative of benzene; they also found out that a beautiful violet or mauve color of tinctorial power is produced by the oxidation of aniline. Benzene (C_6H_6) is simply one of many coal-tar derivatives, as is aniline which comes from nitrobenzene.

The various component parts of coal tar are separated by distillation at various temperatures. The most important groups are indicated as follows:

1. Temperature up to 110°C. produce first runnings.

2. Temperature from 110° up to 210° C. distil out light and middle oils.

From the above two groups at temperatures under 150°C. benzene (C_6H_6), toluene (C_7H_8), xylene (C_8H_{10}), and their many derivatives are obtained. The boiling point of benzene is 81°C. Toluene boils at 110°C., and xylene at about 130° to 141°C. Aniline comes from benzene through its derivative, nitrobenzene. This so-called naphtha, or light oil distillate, represents only about 3 per cent of the coal-tar weight, and the yield of benzene is about 1½ per cent of the original tar.

3. Temperatures between 210° and 240°C. produce the heavy oils, known as the carbolic oils. In this group are found cresol, and especially phenol, and naphthalene ($C_{10}H_8$).

4. Temperatures from 240° up to 270°C. distil heavy or creosote oils. Much naphthalene is produced in the lower temperatures of this group, but little is present near the 270°C. temperature. Many hydrocarbons are mixed with coal-tar creosote oil, some of them being phenol, naphthalene, and anthracene, the last named substance coming off at the highest temperatures, especially.

Coal-tar creosote is practically free from the light oils, which come off at the lowest temperatures, and "pitch" which remains as a residue at the temperature of 270°C. This creosote is similar in its properties to wood-tar creosote, and is used as a preservative. The creosote distillate represents about 10 per cent of the coal-tar weight, and may yield as much as about 8 per cent of naphthalene.

5. Temperatures between 270° and 400°C. produce anthracene or anthracene oil, also called "green oil." This distillate, considered to be the most valuable of all the coal-tar constituents, contains about 10 per cent of anthracene

($C_{14}H_{10}$) a liquid oil of high boiling point, and several solid hydrocarbons, such as paraffine, chrysen, carbazol, and phenanthrene. The oils and solid materials are separated after cooling; and, after certain purification processes, a 50 per cent anthracene compound is produced, which is sold to the manufacturers of alizarine colors. Important reds, oranges, blues, violets, and greens of the alizarine group are made from anthracene, which in its pure state is a white crystalline substance.

Anthracene oil often represents about 11½ per cent of the weight of the coal tar from which it is made.

6. Temperatures of 400°C. and above leave a residue or pitch which is a liquid but rather thick and viscous substance while hot. After the valuable anthracene is extracted, creosote or carbolic oils are often mixed with the hot pitch in order to produce a soft pitch or soft tar, some kinds of which are liquid at ordinary temperatures. Soft pitch commonly melts and is liquid at about 60°C., while hard pitch melts at about 120°C.

Pitch, which is a very high temperature distillate, frequently represents about 60 per cent of the coal tar by weight.

Methods of Classifying and Naming Synthetic Dyes. Two quite distinct classifications of dyes are now used. One is that made by the chemist, who classifies the dyes by their chemical structure, sometimes employing letters or numbers for further identification. This classification is a scientific system. The other method is a classification of dyes by their mode of application, or as the dyer or colorist groups them for use. The latter classification is practical and more intelligible to the ordinary user of dyes and stains.

The user can tell something of the color and class of dyestuff by learning a few things about how dyes are named by the chemists and manufacturers. Each dye is apt to have a trade name and a distinguishing letter to indicate the shade or tint; and also the manufacturer's or dealer's name may be shown. The chemist or manufacturing company discovering the color generally names it; sometimes giving any appropriate name, but often using a word showing the chemical class to which the given hue belongs, or suggesting an indication of the physical properties or method of application.

The particular quality of tone of a dye may be used in a name, as croceine scarlet or malachite green. Some dyes are named after prominent people as Bismarck brown, and Perkin's violet, or sometimes after places as Erie, London, Congo, and Kashmir. Many dyes have names that indicate the chemical group to which they belong, as azo rubine or methylene blue.

The amount of concentration of a dye is sometimes indicated by an X or the abbreviation *"conc."* or *"extra conc."* All of these marks show specially strong coloring matter. Degrees of dilution in strength are marked by Roman numerals, as Auramine I, II, III, the last named being the most diluted.

The letters S and SS are used to designate dyes of exceptional solubility; while "W" after the name indicates, usually, that the color is for wool.

Dyes are sometimes mixed by the manufacturers and given some name that indicates the color, strength, shade, or solubility. The names of such mixed dyes are likely to be still more confusing than those of single unmixed colors.

When the dye is given a Shultz number, it can be properly identified by the Shultz tables, and there need be no confusion.

Crudes and Intermediates for Dyes. The crudes or raw materials from which all coal-tar colors are made are derived from distillation. The chief crudes used today are: benzene, toluene, xylene, carbazol, naphthalene, and anthrocene—all made from coal tar. Pure benzene, toluene, and xylene are quite well known volatile and colorless liquids. Naphthalene, carbazol, and anthracene are colorless solids in crystalline form. From the above named crudes, and two or three other minor ones, are made about 325 substances called *intermediates* in the dye industry.

From the light tar oils benzene, toluene, and xylene are made; and from these crudes come intermediates, called nitrobenzene, resorcine, phenol, and benzaldehyde. From the medium heavy oils are distilled the crude naphthalene; and from this material are made such important intermediates as the naphthols, and naphthylamines, and the less valuable phthalic (thăl′ic) acid. The other important crude, anthracene, produces the intermediate anthraquinone, and from this material a very valuable series of alizarine dyes is manufactured.

The intermediate which is produced in the largest quantities at present is nitrobenzene, from which aniline is made. About one half of the aniline manufactured in the United States is used in making aniline dyes, while the other half is used in the rubber industry.

In making the "intermediates," the "crudes" are treated with such materials as nitric acid, sulphuric acid, chlorine, caustic soda, lime, and nascent hydrogen.

CHEMIST'S CLASSIFICATION OF COAL-TAR DYES

Chemical structure is the basis of the classification of dyes used by the chemist. Some dyes are made by combining intermediates; others are manufactured through processes of sulfonation, oxidation, or nitration. Many dyes, like the azo colors, are, however, the result of complex reactions.

The following are the most important of the chemical classes of dyes:

Azo Compounds. Azo dyes are found in several of the application classifications; some are neutral or acid, some are basic, while others may be direct; a number of them are mordant, and a few are spirit soluble. The azo compounds of rather simple structure are usually yellow or red in color, while those of more complex constitution may be in the dark colors, such as black, blue and violet.

The *acid* azo dyes represent a large group of colors, and include many ordinary wool yellows, oranges, scarlets, blacks, such as Matanil Yellow, Tartrazine, Azo Acid Blue, Naphthol Black, Azo Orange (II, IV, G. etc.), Ponceau, Azofuchsine, and others.

The *basic* azo group is quite small, but contains the Safranine azo colors (Janus Blue, etc.), Bismarck Brown, Chrysoidine, Tannin Orange, and New Phosphine.

Triphenylmethane Dyes. This is a rather large class, and includes many of the brilliant colors with their various nuances. To this class belong many colors that are well known and much used. This group includes basic, acid, and mordant dyes, but none of the other application classes.

Acid members of this class include acid violets, soluble and alkali blues, wool blues, Acid Magenta which is the same as

Acid Fuchsine, acid greens, patent blues, ketone blues, Neptune Green, Erioglaucine, and others.

Azine Dyes. This group contains 46 colors ranging from red, through the violets, over to and including some blues. Both acid colors and basic colors are found among the azines.

The *basic* members include spirit Indulines, Safranines, and Rhodulines. Perkin's Mauve or Mauveine, the first aniline color, belongs to this group.

The *acid* members among the azines include Nigrosines, Soluble Indulines, Rosindulines, Wool Fast Blue, and Wool Fast Violet; also a spirit soluble Nigrosine, and an acid water soluble Nigrosine with various brands of each on the market. The spirit soluble Nigrosine is used in black spirit varnishes and polishes, and also for a dye for coloring silk. It is a bluish black, and is used much like the spirit soluble Induline, except that the latter produces a more bluish violet tone. There is also an acid water soluble Induline that is quite fast to light. The Indulines are often mixed with other colors of similar application classes.

The acid water soluble Nigrosines are often used in connection with other acid dyes to secure darker colors. They are sometimes found in stains for wood and dyes for silk. They are, however, only moderately fast to light. Various brands of this color are sold, but they are all similar to Shultz's Nigrosine No. 700.

Spirit soluble Nigrosines, which are soluble in alcohol but not in water, are used in spirit stains for wood, and for darkening other colors. These Nigrosines are also used for staining leather, for printing calico and dyeing silk, and produce bluish black shades. They are often mixed with Chrysoidine R (spirit soluble), which is of a yellowish red color. The various brands of spirit soluble Nigrosines which are sold are similar to Shultz's No. 698.

Xanthene Colors. These colors form a group containing some of the most brilliant acid and basic dyes made, and are, in general, faster to light than the triphenyl methane colors, already mentioned.

Anthracene or Anthraquinone Dyes. This large group contains 67 acid and mordant dyes, and includes the alizarines and 82 vat dyes. These colors are, in general, remarkable for great fastness to light. The anthraquinone class does not include any basic colors.

The "acid" colors of the group are numerous and important, and include: Alizarine Direct Blue, Violet, and Green; Alizarine Sapphire, a reddish blue dye which is very fast to light; the German dyes, Alizarine Irisol D and R, bright bluish violet wool and silk dyes, which are very fast to light; Alizarine Emeraldol G (paste), a bluish green dye for wool and silk, moderately fast to light; Alizarine Astrol B and G, greenish blue, and very fast to light on wool and cotton; and the Alizarine Rubinols, some of which are of a bluish red color and fast to light, while others are pink and salmon in hue and are used on dress goods and carpets.

Nitroso and Nitro Dyes. The nitroso colors are few in number and contain only "acid" and "mordant" dyes.

The important acid water soluble dye in the Nitroso group is often called Naphthol Green B. It comes in powder or paste form, is very fast to light, and is used as a wool dye, the coloring matter being used in an acid bath containing an iron salt. Naphthol Green is also used in the manufacture of pigments. This color is a very useful yellowish green dye, recommended as a stain for wood finishing because of its light proof qualities.

The *Nitro* class is also small, containing several yellow acid dyes and a few mordant and pigment colors.

The most important "acid" member of this class is generally named Naphthol Yellow S, but is sometimes called Sulphur Yellow S, Acid Yellow, or Martius Yellow. It is used as a yellow color for silks and wool, and also is permitted as coloring matter in food in Australia and the United States. Victoria Yellow, and Picric Acid also belong to this group.

Oxazine Colors. This group contains about 44 dyes, and includes both basic and mordant colors but no acid dyestuffs. The colors are largely blue, Meldola's Blue or New Blue R being the most important.

Acridine Colors. The Acridine colors are about 15 in number, and consist of yellow and orange dyestuffs, all of which are basic dyes. They are only moderately fast to light, ranking, usually about 3 or 4 in the scale of 5 for fastness. Their chief uses are in dyeing leather and cotton, and in printing calico.

Thiazine Colors. This group consists of about 13 dyestuffs, mainly blue in color. It has representatives among the basic, acid, mordant, and sulphur dyes.

Basic colors. The most important dye among the Thiazines is the basic dye, Methylene Blue, which is high in fastness to light, ranking 2 in the scale of 5°, of which 1 is the most permanent of all. Methylene Blue is soluble in both water and alcohol. It is recommended as an excellent basic dye for wood staining on account of its fastness to light. It is also commonly used for dyeing cotton in half silk, jute, straw, and artificial flowers. On account of its excellent fastness to light, to washing and rubbing, to ironing, to water, and to acids, it is one of the most largely used of all the basic dyes.

Other important Thiazine basic colors are: Methylene Green, which ranks as the fastest of all of the basic green coloring matters, and Thionine Blue, also quite fast and soluble in both water and alcohol, although less easily soluble in the latter.

Acid color. Thiocarmine is the acid member of the Thiazine class, and is a good blue for wool and silk. It is not so fast to light as Patent Blue or Cyanol.

Thiazole Colors. This class includes a small group of six distinct colors, some of them having numerous names. There is one basic dye—Rhoduline Yellow T, or Thioflavine T—which is a moderately fast dye, grading 3 in the scale of 5°.

Quinoline Colors. The quinolines form a small group of 12 colors, only three of them being manufactured in the United States. These dyes are largely used in the manufacture of the color sensitive plates. The most important member of the group from a dyer's standpoint is Quinoline Yellow, which is a basic dye and insoluble in water, though sparingly soluble in alcohol. It is a yellow used to color paraffine, wax, and spirit varnishes.

From Quinoline Yellow, treated with fuming sulphuric acid, an acid dye soluble in water called Quinoline Yellow O is made.

Most of the other Quinoline colors are quite fugitive, and are unsuitable for use as stains for wood.

Indigoid Colors. This group contains 54 colors, including a number of valuable "vat" dyes. There are no basic or mordant colors listed in this class, and only one acid dye—Indigo Carmine—which is not much used, because it is not fast to light and has been replaced by Patent Blue.

Coal-tar Dyes Classified by Application

The average user of dyes does not understand the chemical structure of dyes which are made from the rather simple hydrocarbons, such as benzene (C_6H_6), toluene (C_7H_8), xylene (C_8H_{10}), naphthalene ($C_{10}H_8$), and anthracene ($C_{14}H_{10}$). If, however, dyes are classed together on a basis of methods of application to various fibers, and of affinity for and reaction on the fibers themselves, it is easier to grasp the significance of such a grouping.

It is of interest to the wood finisher to examine a list of the application classes which are known to the textile dyer. It should be remembered, however, that some colors can be placed in two or more classes, and applied by more than one method. This may be due to the peculiar chemical composition of the dyes which can be classified in more than one group, or to certain chemical or physical properties of the fibers of the materials. The application classification of dyes is as follows:

1. Acid dyes.
2. Basic dyes.
3. Salt, direct, or substantive dyes.
4. Mordant dyes.
5. Pigment dyes.
6. Developing colors.
7. Sulphur colors.
8. Vat dyes.

Acid Dyes. In general, acid dyes are very largely derived from azo compounds of toluene and benzene, both of which come from light tar oils. These dyes are said to be salts of color acids which are easily soluble in water. Most of the acid dyes require the presence in the bath of some acid which liberates the color-acid, and thus allows it to combine with bases which are found in the fibers being dyed, usually animal fibers, such as silk and wool. On these materials, acid dyes act as direct dyes, and need no mordant. Many acid dyes do not dye vegetable fibers, therefore they are not much used for dyeing cotton goods. It should be pointed out very clearly, however, that although pure cellulose does not usually take acid dyes, lignocellulose, such as is found in jute and wood, will combine directly with acid dyes.

The azo acid group is a large one, and contains many yellows, oranges, scarlets, blacks, etc. There is also a small class of yellow dyes, the most important member of which is Naphthol Yellow S, which is derived from nitro compounds.

Individual acid dyes vary considerably in fastness to light. In general, the azo dyes are quite permanent, while acid violets and greens, usually, are more fugitive. Some acid dyes are not entirely satisfactory on textiles, because they will not stand washing, especially if soap is used. On wood, however, these same dyes give no trouble, because the colors are fast to light, and are usually protected by varnish coats.

The acid colors do not usually show an acid reaction in themselves, but are sold in powders of alkaline salts of potassium or ammonium which are soluble in water. The neutral or alkaline powders of acid dyes are acidified in the solution, usually with sulphuric acid, for dyeing wool or silk. The acid reacts on the dyestuff in such a way as to set free the color acid, and also to change the composition of the fibers to be dyed. This leaves them in the proper condition to receive the dye.

Sometimes acetic or formic acid, or even ammonium acetate, is used as a substitute for sulphuric acid; in which case the dye is only slightly acid in reaction.

There is also a third class of acid dyes which will dye some fibers in a neutral bath. When acid dyes are used as wood stains, it is not usually necessary to add any acid whatever to the stain, because wood fibers generally react properly with such dyes and take the color easily. However, many acid coal-tar stains when used on wood "bite" more easily if one half pint of table vinegar be added to each gallon of stain.

Acid dye powders are soluble in water. They usually dissolve better in hot water, and are frequently prepared in this manner as less residue is left. A few acid dyes, such as Metanil Yellow, Orange II, Violamine RR, are somewhat soluble in alcohol.

Acid dyes are usually quite cheap, compared with other coloring materials, and the tones produced on most substances are pure and brilliant. In the latter respect, acid dyes are generally superior to both mordant and substantive dyes, but are not equal to basic dyes.

Wood stains for use on furniture are at present very largely made from acid coal-tar dyes (Table I).

TABLE I.

ACID DYES USED FOR WOOD STAINS. SOLUBLE IN WATER

Color	Shultz No.	Name of Color	Fastness to Light	Chemical Group	Maker
Red	227	Croceine Scarlet	2	Dis-Azo	DuPont
Red	42	Pontacyl Carmine 2G	2–3	Mono-Azo	DuPont
Red		Pontacyl Carmine 2B	2–1	Mono-Azo	DuPont
Red	163	Pontacyl Ruby G	2–1	Mono-Azo	DuPont
Red	161	Pontacyl Fast Red AS	4–3	Mono-Azo	DuPont
Red	82	Acid Scarlet 2R	3	Mono-Azo	Newport Chem. Wks.
Red	163	Azo Rubine R	2–1	Mono-Azo	Newport Chem. Wks.
Red	227	Croceine Scarlet MOO	2	Dis-Azo	Newport Chem. Wks.
Red	163	Azo-Rubine Ex	2–1	Mono-Azo	National Aniline and Chem. Co.
Red	169	Brilliant Scarlet 3R	2–3	Mono-Azo	National Aniline and Chem. Co.
Red	227	Croceine Scarlet MOO	2	Dis-Azo	National Aniline and Chem. Co.
Orange	145	Orange II	3–2	Mono-Azo	DuPont
Orange	145	Orange II conc.	3–2	Mono-Azo	DuPont
Orange	38	Orange G	2–3	Mono-Azo	DuPont
Orange	145	Orange A	3–2	Mono-Azo	Newport Chem. Wks.
Orange	145	Wool Orange A	3–2	Mono-Azo	National Aniline and Chem. Co.
Yellow	23	Tartrazine O	Moderate on Wool, Low on Silk	Azo	DuPont
Yellow	134	Metanil Yellow conc.	3	Mono-Azo	DuPont
Yellow	19	Pontacyl Yellow GG (same as fast light yellow)	2	Azo	DuPont
Yellow	19	Pontacyl Yellow 3G	2	Azo	DuPont
Yellow	23	Fast Wool Yellow G	Moderate on Wool, Low on Silk	Azo	Newport Chem. Wks.
Green Sea Green	566	Pontacyl Green SN extra	3	Triphenyl-methane	DuPont
Light Green	505	Pontacyl Light Green SF, yellowish	4	Triphenyl-methane	DuPont
Green	502	Acid Green B conc.	4–3	Triphenyl-methane	Newport Chem. Wks.
Green	503	Fast Milling Green B	3–4	Triphenyl-methane	Newport Chem. Wks.
Yellowish Green	4	Naphthol Green	1	Nitroso	Newport Chem. Wks.
Blue Greenish Blue	545	Pontacyl Brilliant Blue A	3	Triphenyl-methane	DuPont
Blue	545	Patent Blue A	3	Triphenyl-methane	Newport Chem. Wks.
Blackish Blue	217	Acid Blue Black, extra conc.	2–3	Dis-Azo	Newport Chem. Wks.
Violet	582	Violamine RR (Reddish violet)	2–3	Xanthene	DuPont
Bluish Violet	530	Acid Violet 5B conc.		Triphenyl-methane	Newport Chem. Wks.
Black Bluish Black	700	Nigrosine WSB powder	4–3	Azine	DuPont
Black	700	Nigrosine jet	4–3	Azine	Newport Chem. Wks.
Bluish shade	700	Nigrosine, blue shade	4–3	Azine	Newport Chem. Wks.
Black	700	Nigrosine 128 conc.	4–3	Azine	National Aniline and Chem. Co.

Basic Dyes. The characteristics and physical properties of basic dyes soon become known to the dyer, but the name itself may not mean much to him. To the chemist, however, the word basic is suggestive, because it indicates something of chemical structure and informs him as to the dye's reactions, with such reagents as acids and alkalies particularly (Table II). Basic colors are substances that have strong affinities for various acids and with them form salts that are more or less stable. Liberation from the salts can be secured by the use of the

TABLE II.

BASIC DYES
SOLUBLE IN WATER OR ALCOHOL
(Palette containing some of the best basic colors for staining wood)

Color	Shultz No.	Name of Color	Fastness to Light	Chemical Group	Maker
Red	573	Rhodamine B	3–4	Xanthene	DuPont
Red	679	Safranine T extra	3–5	Azine	DuPont
Red	679	Safranine Y	3–5	Azine	Newport Chem. Wks.
Red	512	Fuchsine or Magenta	4–5	Triphenyl-methane	Newport Chem. Wks.
Orange	33	Chrysoidine GE	4	Mono-Azo	DuPont
Orange	34	Chrysoidine R		Mono-Azo	Newport Chem. Wks. and DuPont
Yellow	493	Auramine O	4–5	Ketonimine related to Triphenyl-methane	Newport Chem. Wks. and DuPont
Yellow	618	Thioflavin T	3	Thiazole	Newport Chem. Wks.
Green	499	Brilllant Green Crystals	3–4	Triphenyl-methane	Newport Chem. Wks.
Green	495	Malachite Green Crystals	3–4	Triphenyl-methane	Newport Chem. Wks.
Green	495	Victoria Green SC	3–4	Triphenyl-methane	DuPont (same as Malachite Green)
Green	*924	Methylene Green	Very fast	Thiazine	Various manufacturers
Blue	659	Methylene Blue, extra conc.	2	Thiazine	Newport or DuPont
Blue	559	Victoria Blue BX	4–5	Triphenyl-methane	DuPont
Blue	558	Victoria Blue R	4–5	Triphenyl-methane	DuPont
Violet	515	Methyl Violet R conc.	4–5	Triphenyl-methane	DuPont or Newport Chem. Works
Brown	284	Bismarck Brown R Base	4–5	Dis-Azo	Newport Chem. Wks.
Brown	283	Bismarck Brown G or Y	4–5	Dis-Azo	Newport Chem. Wks.
Brown	283	Basic Brown G	4–5	Dis-Azo (Mahogany wood stain)	DuPont (same as Bismarck Brown)
Brown	284	Basic Brown BR	4	Dis-Azo (Mahogany wood stain)	DuPont (Bismarck Brown)
Brown	283	Bismarck Brown Y ex.	4–5	Dis-Azo (Mahogany wood stain)	Nat. Aniline and Chem. Co.
Brown		Nat. Bismarck Brown 53			Nat. Aniline and Chem. Co.
Black		Nigrosine			Various manufacturers

*No. 924 for Methylene Green is a "Color Index" number instead of a Shultz number.

volatile alkali, ammonia, or by reactions with fixed alkalines, such as soda and potash, which have strong basic action.

In chemistry, the word base refers to substances that are capable of uniting with acids, thus producing salts which are neutralized of acid properties.

The most important basic dyes are derived from triphenyl-methane; nevertheless, some valuable basic dyes come from various other chemical classes, such as the azos, xanthenes, azines, acridines, thiazines, and thiazoles. Less valuable basic dyes, from the dyer's point of view, are made from the oxazine and quinoline groups.

A large number of the early aniline and other coal-tar dyes belonged to the basic group of dyestuffs. In many cases, these basic dyes are very remarkable for brilliancy of color, compared with vegetable colors; but, quite often, they are more or less fugitive to light. Basic dyes sold on the market are usually in forms which are chemically known as chlorides, being salts of dye bases with hydrochloric acid, but other salts such as sulphates, oxalates, acetates, and nitrates, are occasionally found. Dyes in the form of a free base are known, however, in a few cases. Methyl Violet, Magenta, and some other colors made by the "melt" process are in a crystalline form; while most of the basic dyes manufactured by other methods are in the form of powders.

In a dye bath, basic salts seem to separate into an acid and a dye base. When dyeing animal fibers, such as wool or silk which seem to possess acid properties in themselves, the dye base combines with the fibers, and acid is left in the bath. When cotton is dyed with these dyes the dye base combines with the acid mordant. Cotton requires a previous preparation in a tannic acid bath, called a mordant.

Mordanting of vegetable fibers, such as cotton and linen, is accomplished by steeping the material to be dyed in a cold tannin bath for several hours, and fixing in a tartar emetic; or following this treatment by passing the goods being dyed through a solution of some metallic salt, such as antimony potassium tartrate. Insoluble tannates of antimony or some other metal are finally formed.

Wool and silk because of their acid reaction are dyed with basic dyes in a neutral bath without previous treatment.

Brighter colors in wool and silk fabrics are sometimes secured from basic dyes by adding about two per cent of soap to the dye bath.

Basic dyes are not as valuable to the dyer of textile fibers as formerly, because we now have other dyes of greater fastness that can be applied by easier methods. Cotton and linen fabrics which have been dyed with "salt" or "sulphur" colors are often improved by "topping" or redyeing with basic colors. This application of basic dyes increases the fastness to light of "salt" colors, and produces more brilliant tones over "sulphur" colors. No mordant is needed for "topping" fibers with basic dyes, because the previous dyeing serves as a mordanting where "salt" mordant or "sulphur" colors have been used.

For wool and silk, basic dyes have very largely been replaced by more permanent and easily applied but less brilliant acid dyes which are more numerous and produce more even tones.

For bark-tanned leather which contains much tannic acid, basic colors are recommended, because the leather absorbs these dyes easily, and evenness of tone and fastness to light are not so important.

Woodstains which are produced by dissolving basic dyes in water or alcohol are used by the wood finisher to a limited extent. The colors obtained by the application of basic dyes to wood are clear and brilliant; but, in many cases, beautiful tone effects are changed and faded by exposure to light. It has already been pointed out that a mordant is used with basic dyes when they are used on vegetable fibers. The wood finisher does not wish to spend his time using mordants on stains, therefore he prefers the more convenient and more permanent acid dyes.

Spirit stains are made from the most permanent of the basic dyes, and are used with reasonable satisfaction on articles that are not exposed to bright sunlight. Mordants are not commonly used with spirit stains. Such stains dry very quickly, and are very hard to apply.

Salt, Direct, or Substantive Dyes. The name "direct" colors is given to this particular class of dyestuffs because they really are direct dyes for cotton when used in a neutral or alkaline bath, and are applied without the use of mordants.

The "direct" colors are sometimes called substantive colors, and also occasionally are referred to by other names, such as Congo colors, diamine colors, and benzo colors. Most of the direct colors are alkaline salts of sulfonated tetrazo colors.

Salt or direct dyes may be used in a hot neutral or alkaline bath for dyeing silk or wool, and also in an "acid" solution. Direct dyes are, however, rarely used for dyeing animal fibers.

Direct colors are absorbed without being broken up, or having only the color acid taken out, as is the case with acid dyes. The salt or direct colors are ordinarily used in a bath of boiling water to which common table salt and soap have been added, and are adapted to coloring such fibers as cotton and linen. Some fibers, especially cotton, linen, and other vegetable fibers, will take direct dyes in a cold or lukewarm bath, but such dyeing will not stand hot soap and water.

More permanent colors can be produced with direct dyes by the use of a suitable after-treatment, such as warming in a weak solution of potassium bichromate which is acidified slightly with acetic acid or strong vinegar. This treatment may considerably change the color and is sometimes objectionable.

The salt or direct colors come from two of the chemical groups, namely: (1) the thiazols and (2) the azo colors.

The direct colors are soluble in water, and in general may be used much like acid dyes; they are useful, especially, on cotton and linen, while acid dyes in general will not color cotton or many vegetable fibers. Some of the direct colors are recommended for cotton, straw, wood chips, paper, linen, jute, and vegetable fibers in general. On wood they are not as convenient and satisfactory as acid dyes, and should generally contain one ounce of bichromate of potash to the gallon of stain.

In fastness to light the direct dyes are very satisfactory, especially, when given an after-treatment of bichromate of potash.

Direct dyes can often be mixed with acid dyes in making wood stains. Experts, however, recommend keeping the application classes separate for fear of a chemical reaction. It should also be noted that direct dyes are improved usually by having potassium bichromate in the dye solution or for use as an after-treatment, while acid dyes are commonly used with a small amount of acid, such as acetic acid, in the stain mixture. It has already been pointed out that such a mixture of an alkali and acid may change the color of a direct dye.

Mordant Dyes. Many of the old time vegetable dyes such as logwood, fustic, cutch, Persian berries, and the animal dye cochineal, are mordant dyes. It is also true that many of the best of the synthetic or coal-tar colors are mordant dyes. Treatment with metallic mordants in connection with the dye, but usually preceding it in application, is necessary with mordant dyes. The use of different mordants with a given color may produce varying shades of color, or even change the hue itself. Salts of chromium, such as chromates or bichromates, are now most commonly used; while formerly, tin, iron, and aluminum salts were generally used.

Mordant dyes are used on both cotton and woolen fabrics. A few mordant dyes produce color in a single bath containing a bichromate or chromate solution; but, usually, two or more operations are necessary, therefore exact reproduction of colors is difficult, and the many operations are expensive.

Several of the chemical groups of dyes contain mordant dyes, as indicated by the following list: nitroso, nitro, azo, triphenylmethane, xanthene, anthracene, oxazine, thiazine, and flavone—all including one or more mordant dyes.

On account of their difficulty in application, mordant dyes are not very commonly used as wood stains at the present time. The vegetable mordant dyes, which for many ages were generally thought to be the only satisfactory dyes, are gradually going out of use; and, judging by the demand for them on the market, they are not of much importance to the wood finisher today.

Pigment Dyes. Certain colors which are insoluble in water and in most solvents can be transferred to fibers by a method of chemical synthesis. Such colors are very fast to light and washing, and are not easily removed from the fibers. Aniline black can be made to dye cotton fiber by means of the oxidation of salts of aniline when bichromates or chromates are used in connection with certain so-called oxygen carriers, such as some of the salts of iron, vanadium, or copper. Other semioxidation colors are the Ursols, the Furols, and Paramine Brown.

Pigment dyes are derived from four of the chemical groups as follows: the azo, the nitro, the azine (which contains Aniline Black), and the oxazine classes.

In dyeing, the pigment colors are transferred to the fibers being dyed by a chemical synthesis and from colorless chemical compounds.

Developing Dyes. The developing colors resemble the pigment colors in that they are both insoluble and must be transferred and formed on the films of the material being dyed. The developing colors are not colorless dyestuffs, but react differently from ordinary dyes because a chemical reaction causes a coloring-matter to be developed and formed on the fibers.

Sulphur Dyes. These colors are also insoluble in pure water; but, if they are dissolved in an aqueous solution of sodium sulphide and heated, they will dye vegetable fibers, especially cotton, in a direct bath. These colors are little used on animal fibers. The resultant hues produced on fabrics are not bright, but appear as dull shades of green, brown, blue, and black.

These dyes contain sulphur in the molecules, but their structure is rather indefinite.

Sulphur dyes are considerably used, however, for dyeing cotton cloth, and also for yarns and hosiery.

An after-treatment with a salt of copper, zinc, or chromium is sometimes used to "fix" the sulphide colors.

Vat Dyes. The term vat dyes is used to designate certain dyestuffs that are themselves insoluble in water but which can be used in the form of their leuco compounds and then oxidized in the air, thus bringing out the colors. A leuco compound in chemistry is one that is colorless and is derived from a dye by reduction, having an unsatisfied affinity for nitrogen. By oxidation or the taking on of oxygen, leuco compounds regain color.

For many years indigo was the chief vat dye, but at the present time other indigoid vat dyes are used, such as the Ciba series, the Bromindigos, the Thioindigo series, and Brilliant Indigos. There are also anthracene and thiazine vat dyes.

Oil-Soluble Wood Stains. Oil-soluble dyes do not form a distinct class of colors either chemically or by application. Colors from any of the various coal tar groups that happen to be soluble in any one of the volatile oils are selected, especially the kinds that are most permanent on exposure to sunlight.

Some of the best oil-soluble dyes for use as stains on wood

TABLE III.

Oil-Soluble Dyes Used for Staining Wood.
(Soluble in Turpentine, Benzol, or Naphtha)

Color	Shultz No.	Name of Color	Fastness to Light	Chemical Group	Solvent	Maker
Red	76	Spirit Scarlet B extra	...	Mono-Azo	Alcohol and Oils	DuPont
Red	76	Oil Red O	...	Mono-Azo	Benzol, Naphtha	Nat. Aniline and Chem. Co.
Red	...	Oil Scarlet 6 G	...	Used as a furniture stain	Benzol or Naphtha	Nat. Aniline and Chem. Co.
Red	93	Sudan R	Good	Mono-Azo	Alcohol, Benzol, etc.	Newport Chem. Wks.
Red	232	Newport Oil Red No. 13044	2–3	Dis-Azo	Alcohol Benzol	Newport Chem. Wks.
Orange	36	Oil Orange No. 2311	...	Mono-Azo	Benzol or Naphtha	Nat. Aniline and Chem. Co.
Orange	36	Newport Oil Orange, extra conc.	...	Mono-Azo	Alcohol and Oils	Newport Chem. Wks.
Yellow	68	Oil Yellow No. 2681	...	Mono-Azo	Benzol or Naphtha	Nat. Aniline and Chem. Co.
Yellow	68	Oil Yellow	...	Mono-Azo	Alcohol and Oils	DuPont
Yellow	32	Newport Oil Yellow	...	....	Alcohol, Benzol, and other oils	Newport Chem. Wks.
Blue	559	Newport Victoria Blue	4–5	Triphenyl-methane	Alcohol, Benzol, and other oils	Newport Chem. Wks.
Black	990	Drop Black	...	Mineral Pigment	Turpentine	Various (This is not a coal-tar dye)
Black	...	National Oil Black Jet shade	...	....	Turpentine	Nat. Aniline and Chem. Co.
Black	...	National Oil Black Blue shade	...	....	Turpentine	Nat. Aniline and Chem. Co.
Brown	...	Oil Brown M	...	Mahogany brown Wood Stain	Alcohol, Benzol, or Naphtha	Nat. Aniline and Chem. Co.

are given in Table III. A few others are found in the following list:

Red—Bismarck Brown, Carmosine, and Oil Scarlet 6 G.
Orange—Oil Orange G, and Oil Orange Y (extra concentrated).
Yellow—Oil Yellow, Auramine Yellow, and Naphthalene Yellow.
Green—A mixture of yellow and blue.
Blue—Victoria Blue.

Brown—Oil Brown M, Loutre, and Seal Brown.
Brown Mahogany—Orange G or Y, and Naphthalene Black, or Oil Brown M.
Black—Oil Black, oil-soluble Nigrosine, and Naphthalene.

Oil-soluble colors are usually dissolved in turpentine, but benzene or benzol, naphtha, gasoline, and carbon tetrachloride, can also be used as solvents for nearly all such colors.

Classes of Dyes Used in Wood Finishing. Most of the books and magazine articles which have been written about dyes have been produced for the textile colorist or dyer, rather than for the person who wishes to use dyes for the purpose of staining wood. The dyes themselves were usually manufactured for dyeing cloth rather than for staining wood; consequently the characteristics of the various dyes are usually given with reference to their reaction on various kinds of cloth fibers.

Acid coal-tar dyes are used by the textile dyer to color fibers of silk and wool. Many of these acid dyes will not color cotton fibers, but they will easily stain the lignocellulose fibers which compose the chief mass of wood substance. Practically any of the acid coal-tar dyes which are ordinarily used for dyeing silk and wool can be considered as satisfactory stains for wood. Dyes for cloth must prove satisfactory in various tests such as fastness to light, fastness to washing, fastness to milling, and also to "stoving," to crocking, or rubbing.

In selecting an acid coal-tar dye for use as a wood stain the chief considerations are fastness to light and the price of the dyestuff. The best of the acid coal-tar dyes are the most light-proof colors that can be obtained and are now used extensively as wood stains.

Acid dyes can usually be mixed together to form new colors, even though the individual dyes may come from different chemical groups. Acid dyes should not be mixed with basic colors, even though the latter may be soluble in water, nor should either of these groups of stains be combined with spirit-soluble or oil-soluble dyes.

Acid dyes are not usually acid in reaction but are alkaline salts of sodium, potassium, or ammonium. Basic dyes are usually chlorides, but occasionally other salts such as sulphates, oxalates, acetates, or nitrates are found. If an acid dye in a solution of water is mixed with a basic dye in an aqueous solution, a chemical reaction may take place, and a new sub-

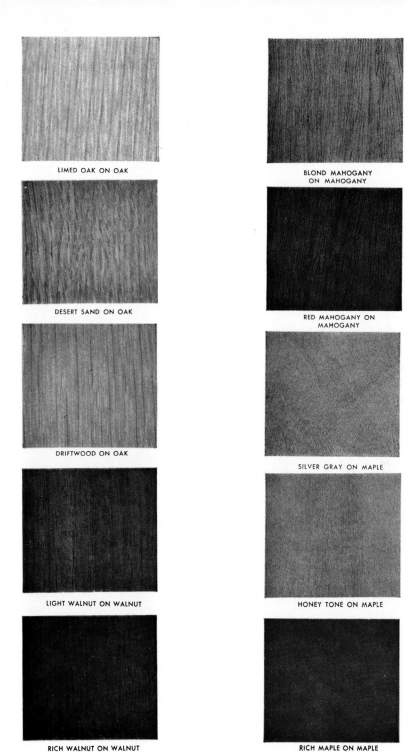

LIMED OAK ON OAK

BLOND MAHOGANY
ON MAHOGANY

DESERT SAND ON OAK

RED MAHOGANY ON
MAHOGANY

DRIFTWOOD ON OAK

SILVER GRAY ON MAPLE

LIGHT WALNUT ON WALNUT

HONEY TONE ON MAPLE

A

RICH WALNUT ON WALNUT

RICH MAPLE ON MAPLE

Selected finishes on typical furniture woods. Also see p. 128B.

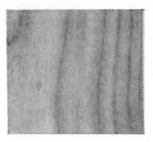

PLATINUM ON BIRCH

WHEAT ON BIRCH

RICH WALNUT ON GUM

BISQUE ON KORINA

LIGHT HARVEST ON KORINA

NATURAL

LIMED OAK

MAHOGANY

DARK WALNUT

MEDIUM WALNUT

HARVEST

Selected finishes on typical furniture woods, continued from page 128A.
Selected fast-drying paste fillers applied to open-grained woods.

stance which is soluble in water may be formed. In some cases a compound neutral dye may be produced.

Direct or salt dyes can be used in much the same manner as acid dyes for staining wood. In fact, direct colors can often be mixed with acid colors in preparing woodstains. The mixing of colors from the different application classes involves a greater risk, however, and is not recommended.

Basic dyes when used by the textile dyer are dissolved in water, are often used on cotton, and are "fixed" with a mordant. Basic dyes are generally soluble in alcohol, and are the colors used by a wood finisher when he wishes spirit-soluble colors. In general, basic colors are more fugitive than acid coal-tar dye colors, hence they are not as satisfactory for use in stains for wood.

Dyestuffs taken from the other application classes, while useful and practicable as textile dyes, are rarely used on wood because of the difficulty in application to such material. In other words, mordant dyes, pigment dyes, developing colors, sulphur colors, and vat dyes are not in common use by wood finishers, though they are valuable textile dyes.

Dyeing or Coloring Wood. Dyeing a piece of wood, in the true sense, consists in steeping it in a solution of dye, and giving it treatments similar to those used in dyeing textiles, straw, and the like, in which the color penetrates entirely through the wood mass and changes the hue of all the fibers. Rather large pieces of wood are sometimes stained or dyed to a uniform color throughout the interior instead of on the surface only. This can be done by removing the air in the cells, by placing the piece in a vacuum chamber, and then immersing it in a dye liquid under pressure of 80 to 120 atmospheres in a large tank. This procedure is useful for some purposes, but is not a common method of coloring or staining wood.

Staining or coloring wood is usually done by brush (or sometimes sponge) applications, by spraying with an air gun, or by dipping and wiping. This method of staining the surface, or dyeing, as it is sometimes called, changes the color only superficially, because the dye does not penetrate very deeply into the wood mass.

Plaits, strips, chips, small blocks, and sometimes matchsticks, are dyed by the first method of uniform penetration, but furniture and woodwork in general are treated by brushing, spraying, or dipping.

The dyes used for such staining are acid dyes, basic dyes, or substantive dyes that are quite fast to light and which are soluble in water. Basic dyes are soluble in either water or alcohol. Some dyes that are useless for dyeing textiles, because they are insoluble in water, are soluble in alcohol, and can be used as spirit stains for wood. Spirit-soluble dyes are also used in varnishes. There are also dyes that are insoluble in water but which are oil soluble, and can be dissolved in benzene or benzol, gasoline, kerosene, or carbon tetrachloride.

For the coloring of raffia, straw, wood chips, splints, and other similar materials frequently used in the manufacture of hats and baskets, basic coal-tar dyes of the most permanent kinds are much desired because of their brightness. There is usually enough tannic acid in most of the above materials, and also in jute and many kinds of wood, so that basic dyes can be used directly; that is, without the application of any other mordant than that already possessed by the fibers themselves.

Solubility of Dyestuffs and Wood-Staining Materials. Coloring matter intended for use in textile dyeing and wood staining is found on the market in one of three forms: (1) as a powder, (2) as a paste, and (3) as an extract. The powder form, very commonly used for textile dyes and wood stains, is the most difficult to dissolve. The different classes of dyestuffs, and the individual colors in the groups, vary greatly in their solubility.

Water-Soluble Colors. Dyestuffs of the usual solubility, when being prepared as wood stains, are generally dissolved in the proportion of about 3 to 3¼ ounces of powder to the gallon of soft water. Some of the dye powders of low solubility are used in wood stains in the proportion of one ounce, or even less, to a gallon of water. Dyes for wood are, however, very strong in color, and often as much as six ounces of color in powder form are mixed with one gallon of water in order to secure the proper strength.

Dealers in dyes for wood stains usually give instructions as to the amount of powder that should be used in the solvents, which are also named, as water, alcohol, benzol, turpentine, and others. It should be remembered, however, that straining a dye mixture through a cloth of fine mesh is generally advantageous, because this process removes specks and any undissolved powder that may settle to the bottom after the solution becomes cold.

The acid coal-tar dyes which are very often used in staining high-grade furniture are usually very soluble, which is also generally true of alcohol soluble powders. The oil-soluble colors are often harder to dissolve. Hard water when used in dyeing textiles is generally acidulated slightly with acetic acid, using only enough acid in the bath to give an acid reaction with litmus paper. It is, however, preferable in some cases to add a small amount of sulphuric acid to the water instead of acetic acid. This hint on the use of acid with acid dyes in dyeing textiles may prove advantageous to wood finishers in preparing acid water-soluble dyes for staining wood.

Water containing iron compounds should not be used in dye baths or stains without first making tests, because chemical reactions of this metal or its salts are liable to change the dye mixture itself in such a way that modified or duller colors may result. Salts of iron with alkali mordants were used as dyes by many ancient peoples, and are still of service in improved forms.

Most dyes, especially acid coal-tar dyes, are most satisfactorily dissolved by using boiling soft water. The mixing should be done in vessels of glass, earthenware, or copper, but never in containers of tin, if acid is to be added to the solution, or if the dye itself has an acid reaction, because the iron which forms the body of all tin plated sheet metal may change the dye itself.

Spirit Stains. Basic dyes are usually soluble in either water or alcohol. If water is used many basic dyes, such as Malachite Green and Methyl Violet, should be mixed with a small quantity of cold water slightly acidulated with acetic acid, and after stirring well, the thin paste formed can be added to boiling soft water. Some basic dyes should not be mixed or used at higher temperatures than about 180° F. When using the dye Auramine the temperature should not exceed 170° F., or the coloring matter may be decomposed or precipitated. A small amount of denatured alcohol is sometimes used in a basic dye solution to help in dissolving the dye.

Many basic dyes are not easily dissolved in water, and

for this reason the dye should be filtered through a flannel cloth, and any alkalinity of hard water should be neutralized with acetic acid to prevent the color base from precipitating. Spirit wood stains often consist of basic dye powders dissolved in strong denatured alcohol. Such a stain is very volatile, and dries so rapidly that it is difficult to apply with a brush.

Oil-Soluble Dyes. Other solvents besides water and alcohol are sometimes used in making dyes and stains. Ether, benzene, various acids, alum, tannin reagents, ferric chloride, sodium carbonate, and other chemicals will dissolve certain dyestuffs. Stains which are commonly called penetrating stains, or volatile oil stains, are made by dissolving in some oil solvent any of the coal-tar dyes that happen to be soluble in any of the nondrying oils of a very volatile nature. The solvent oils which are used most commonly are turpentine, benzol, xylol, solvent naphtha, gasoline, kerosene, and carbon tetrachloride. The dyes that are soluble in these volatile oils are not taken from any particular chemical group. All such dyes are, however, free from the sulphonic acid groups. The sulphonic acid groups contain the radical SO_2OH.

The amount of dry powder used in oil-soluble coal-tar stains varies greatly with the depth or strength of color desired. For light or weak colors, about four ounces of powder to each gallon of solvent may be used, while very dark or strong stains may contain as many as 32 ounces of dry powder to the gallon of stain.

SELECTED REFERENCES, CHAPTER VIII

Coal-Tar Dyes and Their Use as Wood Stains

"Analine," *Encyclopedia Britannica*, Volume I, page 959, 1937.

"Coal Tar Products Customs Regulations Are Overhauled," *Oil Paint and Drug Reporter*, page 165, March 22, 1954.

"Dyes Import Data Must Now be More Detailed," *Oil Paint and Drug Reporter*, Oct. 4, 1954.

"Dyes, Synthetic," *Encyclopedia Britannica*, Volume 7, pp. 797-807, 1937.

Kierstead, S. P., *Natural Dyes.* Bruce Humphries, Inc., 1950. 76 pages.

Klevens, H. B. and Platt, J. R., "Geometry and Spectra of Substituted Anilines," *Journal of the American Chemical Society*, 71, pp. 1714-1720, May, 1949.

Mattiello, Joseph J., *Protective and Decorative Coatings*, Volume 1, pp. 625-639, 1942.

Ibid., *Protective and Decorative Coatings*, Volume 3, page 210, 1943.

McNeil, D., "Coal Tar Research Association," *Journal of Chemistry and Industry*, pp. 1040-1043, March, 1953.

Pellew, C. E., *Dyes and Dyeing*, pp. 55-56. Robert M. McBride and Co., New York, 1928.

Perkin, Sir William H., "Coal-Tar Colors, Science Milestone," *Science Digest*, 37, pp. 88-91, April, 1955.

Pollak, R. B., "Solvents in the Paint Industry; Coal-Tar Hydrocarbons," *Paint Oil and Chemical Review*, 109, page 10, Feb. 21, 1946.

Rose, Arthur and Elizabeth, *The Condensed Chemical Dictionary*, pp. 178-179, Reinhold Publishing Corp., 1950.

Wampler, Rollin H., *Modern Organic Finishes*, page 36, 1946.

Chapter IX

Wood Fillers

The Purpose of Fillers. Wood fillers are used to level the surface of wood by filling the open pores or cavities in the cells. Fillers plug up the cell lumina, or openings, and prevent moisture from entering or leaving the wood; and, if composed of hard material, they help to form firm, compact, and more rigid surfaces that are less easily dented, scratched, or crushed in by pressure in small spots. Stained fillers are sometimes used to show contrasts, as in golden oak; or, very light effects

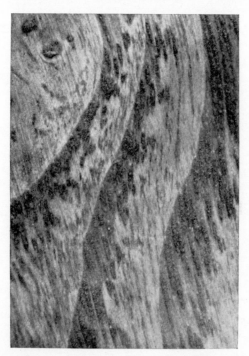

9—1. Pores of chestnut wood properly filled. Magnification about 5 diameters.

in the pores may be wanted, as in silver gray, in which finish the filler may be largely zinc white or a mixture of that substance with a silex paste. By plugging or filling the open cell cavities with non-absorbent material, a level surface is secured which will receive varnish coats and hold them on the surface, instead of allowing such finishes to sink unevenly into the wood (Fig. 9-1).

The type of filler to be used in a given case depends largely upon the porosity and character of the surface of the wood. In general, non-porous, diffuse-porous, and ring-porous woods require different treatment in filling.

A coarse filler is ordinarily needed only on woods that have large tracheal vessels which formerly served as the water courses for the upward moving sap of the growing tree. The other kinds of wood cells, except possibly the larger fiber tracheids which are found in some of the conifers, have small cell openings which can be sealed up with a liquid filler, because they do not require a coarse material such as are contained in paste fillers.

CLASSES OR TYPES OF FILLERS

There are three types of wood fillers:

1. An absolutely *transparent* filler, which is used as a sizing on woods that have such small cell openings that they are invisible to the eye. Such woods do not need to have the pores plugged or filled full of coarse material, and may be sized by oiling or shellacking.

2. A *liquid* filler, which is made of drying oils, varnish, turpentine, japan, and a coarse material such as silica or some substitute, such as cornstarch, China clay, whiting, carbonate of magnesia, or talc. Such a filler is intended for use on non-porous or diffuse-porous woods with small cell openings.

3. *Paste* filler, which is made from a silex or some other ground rock base, that furnishes coarse nonshrinkable transparent material for plugging cell openings and leveling the long narrow hollow places or depressions that are left by cutting through the tracheal vessels of ring-porous or coarse diffuse-porous woods. In addition to the silex, paste filler contains

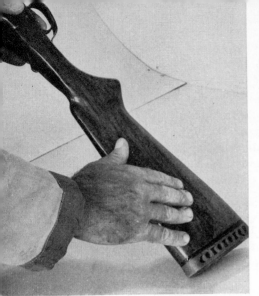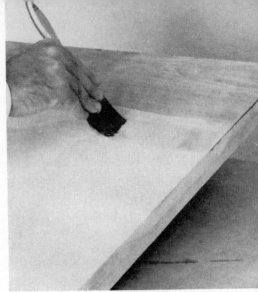

9—2. Filling and finishing a gun stock with boiled linseed oil.   9—3. Close-grained woods can be filled with a coat of wash shellac. A shellac wash is prepared by mixing one part shellac with 6-8 parts denatured alcohol.

drying oils and some thinner or solvent that makes it easier in application with a brush to the surface of wood.

Transparent Fillers. The time-honored process of filling wood was by applying many coats of some drying-oil, usually linseed oil, rubbing, and allowing each coat to dry before another was applied. This method of filling the pores and protecting the wood was quite effective on all except possibly the coarse open pored woods; but it was very slow, because such oils oxidize very slowly, and do not harden for a long time. Linseed oil practically always darkens wood, and is objectionable on some light-colored woods; but it enriches and brings out the grain and beauty of others, as is the case with walnut (Fig. 9-2).

Shellac as a transparent wood filler came into use later chronologically than linseed oil. It is commonly used for this purpose on woods that have pores too small to be seen with the naked eye. Some of the close-grained hardwoods, and most of the coniferous woods, come under this classification, and can be sized or given a surfacer of thin shellac. Two thin coats are better than one heavy application (Fig. 9-3).

Shellac is a spirit varnish which is very transparent and dries hard in about 8 hours, instead of taking many days, as does linseed oil. It keeps the wood in almost the natural color, darkening it but little, and does not obscure the grain.

With the increasing popularity of lacquer as a finish, the use of shellac as a transparent filler has been somewhat replaced by lacquer sanding sealer. Sanding sealers serve the dual purpose of filling the small pores of close-grained woods and of holding down stains and paste fillers.

The more popular sanding sealers contain about 21% solids. Because of their extremely fast-drying nature, they are best applied with a spray gun. They dry in 1-2 hours or less, leaving a somewhat rough surface. After a light, careful sanding, and removal of the fine, white dust, a first coat of lacquer can be applied.

Liquid Fillers. Certain surfacers on the market, called architectural fillers or liquid fillers, which are not much used in finishing furniture, are suitable to apply as a sizing material for a first coat on many of the rather soft, close grained woods that have inconspicuous cell openings. Less labor is required in the application of this type of filler, because it is painted on much like a coat of varnish, and is not rubbed off. Liquid filler obscures the grain to some extent because the silex or coarse material, although nearly transparent when mixed with linseed oil, is stuck to the surface by varnish, instead of being left only to fill the large open pores, as is the case with paste fillers. Liquid fillers are quite commonly used on the less expensive soft woods, when a cheap finish is wanted. They are satisfactory as a first coat on many kinds of wood, especially in finishing the woodwork of houses; but they are not suitable to use on oak, ash, or other woods with large, conspicuous, open pores.

An experienced wood finisher will usually make one gallon of liquid wood filler cover about 250 square feet of surface.

The ingredients found in liquid fillers vary greatly, especially in the amount of silica (or silex) and varnish contained. Some liquid fillers are nearly pure varnish with the addition of small amounts of body materials, such as silica or whiting (calcium carbonate), together with some drier and thinner. Other liquid fillers are much like a thin paste filler, with only a small amount of varnish added to the mixture.

A filler having much varnish in its composition may be made up as follows (next page):

1 quart varnish of good grade, as a rubbing varnish.
1 pint light brown japan.
¼ to ½ pint turpentine.
1½ pounds, light or floated silica (much less silica may be used).
Colors ground in oil may be added in small quantities.

The silica should be added last and mixed in gradually while stirring. Varnishes do not quickly assimilate a thinner, or mix with other substances; consequently, the above liquid filler should stand for one or two days, then should be stirred again and thinned until it will work freely with a stiff varnish brush. It will spread on the wood more smoothly if strained through cheesecloth and allowed to stand another day or two before being used. The base or coarse materials are apt to settle, therefore the mixture should be stirred often while being applied.

A liquid filler with less varnish in proportion to the other ingredients may be mixed as follows:

1 quart body varnish, such as a rubbing varnish.
1 quart brown japan.
2 pounds fine silex.
Thin slightly with turpentine, if necessary, to make it spread better with a stiff brush.

A liquid filler of the thinned paste type may be made up as follows:

2 lbs. prepared paste filler.
½ pint turpentine.
⅛ pint rubbing varnish.

The mixture should be put together in the order named, and may be thinned further with turpentine or benzine if it is to be used on close-grained, nonabsorptive woods. A small amount of any of the colors ground in oil may be added to tint the filler to the proper color. A thin paste filler which contains no varnish can be used for a cheap finish on coarse-grained woods, such as oak and ash.

Liquid fillers are applied to wood evenly lengthwise of the grain, as in varnishing; and without being rubbed off, if they contain much varnish, they should be allowed to dry. They should then be smoothed with No. 00 or No. 000 sandpaper before the next coat of finish is applied.

The prepared liquid fillers sold on the market are usually made from valuable formulas, and by experienced men who have good equipment; therefore, they are, in general, more satisfactory than mixtures prepared by the ordinary wood finisher. Nearly all small shops buy ready-mixed fillers, which are usually put up in cans of various sizes.

Paste Fillers

Body Materials in Fillers. Furniture finishers usually prefer paste fillers. Liquid fillers act as sizing, and stop the suction of the cavities of the wood cells, or greatly reduce it, at least; but, when used on ring porous woods, like oak, ash, or chestnut, such mixtures are too thin to fill completely the large open tracheal vessels located in the spring wood of each annual layer of growth. Some method of filling these open pores and leveling the surface must be used if a good finish is to be secured. Many coats of liquid surfacer can be applied with quite satisfactory results, provided all the high spots are cut down with fine sandpaper between applications of the finish. The open pores or cell cavities gradually fill up, even with an absolutely transparent or liquid filler. Such a procedure, which was the old-time method of finishing, is slow and expensive.

About 50 years ago paste fillers, some of them having a vegetable body, were in common use for finishing all porous woods. It had been discovered that it was better to fill the open cell cavities on the surface of woods having large tracheal vessels with a solid mass rather than with several coats of liquid surfacers. Various materials were tried—among them cornstarch and wheat flour from the vegetable world, as well as other supposedly more permanent materials, such as whiting (calcium carbonate), China Clay, or Kaolin, which is a hydrated aluminum silicate, Silver White, which is a name given to several white silicate earths, plaster of Paris (sulphate of lime), and probably other similar substances were also used occasionally. All of these materials proved to be more or less unsatisfactory, because they were subject to decay or disintegration, or were not transparent enough, or expanded or contracted in the pores, or did not harden properly with the binders, or were too absorbent of shellac or varnish, or failed to meet expectations for some mechanical or chemical reason.

Silex, a comparatively new material to be used for the body of wood fillers, appeared in the Wheeler filler about

1876; on account of its many superior qualities, it has nearly supplanted all other substances, especially in high-grade paste fillers. Silex is one of the forms of silica, made by crushing to various degrees of fineness a dull-colored quartz rock called flint. Silica, which is very similar to silex, is obtained from ordinary quartz instead of flint.

The particles of silex which are made by crushing rock are in numerous rough shapes, such as wedges and needles, rather than in spherical forms. Such minute fragments will pack together with a proper binder and make a mass that will not easily break up or pulverize and come out of the cell cavities. Another good feature of silex is that when mixed with oils it becomes almost perfectly transparent; and, unless it is packed in considerable masses or is colored with pigments, it does not obscure the grain to an appreciable extent. The resultant clearness or transparency of the finish depends to some extent upon the fineness to which the silex is ground, because its oil absorption also varies with the size of the particles. Silex, when unmixed with oil, is a white ground powder that is far from transparent.

Ingredients Used in Paste Fillers. Many formulas have been used for making wood fillers. Certain ingredients, however, are likely to be found in all of them that give good results, including:

1. A *body material*, or filler, often called a pigment, preferably silex, but which may be China clay, barytes, whiting, cornstarch, and the like. The purpose of the body material is to provide a hard mass that will plug the open ends of cells and fill in all cell cavities that form depressions below the general level of the surface to be finished. Silex is not usually considered to be a pigment.

2. A *vehicle*, usually boiled linseed oil (raw linseed oil also gives good results), the functions of which are to act as a binder to the body material and to size the wood.

3. A *japan drier*, generally a light brown japan, which acts as a drier, and helps as a binder for the mixture.

4. A *solvent* or thinner, preferably turpentine, but which may be aliphatic or aromatic petroleum-base naphthas, such as gasoline, mineral spirit, or xylol. The solvent practically all

evaporates, but it thins the mixture so that it can be applied to the surface with a brush.

5. *Coloring matter,* which usually consists of colors ground in oil, is added, in order to stain the filler or both the wood and the filler. The so-called natural or white fillers contain no coloring pigments.

Most of the paste fillers now sold on the market are made with silex as a pigment or body for the filling mass. These ready-mixed fillers are put up in compression-top cans, containing 1, 5, 10, or 25 pounds. Such containers will keep paste filler almost indefinitely, if the covers are driven tightly into place thereby sealing the can when the mixture is not used. Prepared fillers always must be remixed by stirring thoroughly, and usually require thinning with turpentine, naphtha, benzine, or even gasoline. Such fillers can be purchased under the following names: ebony; red, brown, light, and dark mahogany; natural or transparent; antique, Antwerp, dark, and golden oak; walnut; special white and others (Fig. 8-1, pages 128A and B).

An experienced workman can make one gallon of thinned paste filler, which contains six to eight pounds of ready-mixed filler with thinner, cover as much as 300 square feet of surface. The area that can be covered with a given amount of paste filler varies greatly with the kind of wood and the experience of the man.

A practical formula for making "natural" or colored paste filler is as follows:

(a) 2 quarts boiled linseed oil.
(b) 1 quart brown japan.
(c) ½ pint turpentine.
(d) Add silex gradually while mixing until a stiff mass is obtained.

Some formulas suggest ¼ to ⅙ by weight of China clay instead of all silex. A better blending of substances is secured by permitting the pasty dough to stand one or two days before thinning.

Thin the silex mixture with turpentine or benzine to the proper thickness for application with a stiff brush.

Color the filler with pigment colors ground in oil. If strong colors are required, it is often best to stain with oil-soluble coal-tar dyes rather than with pigment colors. If the mass of pigment color is equal to ⅙ to ¼ of the amount of silex, the filler would be weakened in adhesion and would not be as firm a mass in the cells; consequently aniline or other coal-tar colors are preferable in such cases. Colored paste fillers which are to go over stained or dark wood are generally made slightly darker in tone than the surfaces which are to be filled. This is done because the wood slowly darkens with age and later on will be as dark as the filler which is used.

Home made fillers containing brown japan in large quantities should generally be used within two weeks. If the mixture is too old, it becomes somewhat hard and does not work into the pores as well as it does when it is fresher and softer.

The solvents used in making paste fillers are very volatile; therefore, it is important that the mixture be kept in cans or buckets having closely fitted covers so that the containers are practically air tight.

Colored Pigments Used in Producing Special Paste Fillers. Painters' pigments ground in oil are generally used to give color to paste fillers. Dry colors, which are mineral pigments in the form of powders, are sometimes used, but they are more opaque and weak in chroma.

Manufacturers of fillers, however, furnish paste fillers colored to the standard tones or effects; and these can be obtained under such names as the following: natural or uncolored antique oak, golden oak, dark oak, mahogany, walnut, and the like. Special fillers for various kinds of wood can easily be mixed and colored.[1] See Table IV.

Quick-drying Fillers. With the speed-up in furniture production, the drying time for fillers has been greatly reduced. This was accomplished by replacing linseed oil by a synthetic resin vehicle of a type used by paint manufacturers. Fillers prepared with this vehicle dry in 30-60 minutes.

As a class, these fillers are difficult to use and are likely to cause greater trouble than the more conventional, slow-drying kind. Lacking the lubricant property of linseed oil, they have a tendency to produce a tacky, sticky surface. To improve wiping conditions and general removal of all surplus filler, a slow-drying thinner may be added. When this is done, it is well to follow the manufacturer's directions as given on

---

[1] Natural fillers still have a small amount of coloring matter added to them. A more appropriate name would be "neutral fillers."

TABLE IV.

Coloring Natural Paste Filler with Pigments Ground in Oil

Name of Wood or Color Effect	Colors to be Mixed with the Natural Paste Filler
Ash (Light brown)	Natural filler is often used, or colored with burnt umber. Various oak fillers can be used.
Birch (Reddish)	Paste filler is seldom used; tone with yellow ochre, burnt sienna, and burnt umber.
Cherry (Reddish brown)	Filling is generally omitted; use 50 per cent each of burnt sienna and yellow ochre; or Venetian red or burnt sienna.
Chestnut (Dark brown)	For light effects, natural filler is used. Burnt umber. Oak fillers are often used.
Ebony (Black)	Drop black.
Gray (White over gray stain)	Tinges of light gray with touches of ultramarine, yellow ochre, and yellow; or zinc oxide ground in oil with paste filler.
Green, Forest (Dark green over yellow-green stain)	One part chrome green to 20 parts natural filler, or chrome green and drop black (equal parts) and often a little brown, such as burnt umber.
Gun Metal Black	Fill with fine black graphite, japan drier, and benzine.
Mahogany, Adam brown (Very dark)	Vandyke brown and a touch of rose pink.
Mahogany (Light brown)	Tint with Vandyke brown.
Mahogany, Red	Burnt sienna, rose pink, and drop black; or burnt sienna, Vandyke brown, and yellow ochre; or, for a browner tone, burnt umber, Vandyke brown, and rose pink; or 60 per cent burnt sienna and 40 per cent maroon lake.
Mahogany, Sheraton (Very dark brown)	Vandyke brown 5 parts, burnt umber 4 parts, and rose pink 3 parts with natural silex paste.
Oak, Antique (Very dark)	Vandyke brown and drop black in oil; or Vandyke brown 3 parts, and Venetian red 1 part, to 20 pounds of filler.
Oak, Antwerp (Black)	Drop black in oil to make black filler. Use over shellac wash.
Oak, Bog (Dark green stain)	Vandyke brown two parts, drop black in oil one part.
Oak, Baronial (Stain is a warm dark brown)	Filler not generally used. Vandyke brown. Wax finish over shellac, or use flat varnish.
Oak, Dark	Eighty per cent of raw sienna, with 10 per cent each of burnt sienna and burnt umber.
Oak, Dutch brown (Dark reddish-brown stain)	Match stain with Vandyke brown with touch of burnt sienna. Use over a shellac wash which sizes the stain.
Oak, Early English (Very dark yellowish or greenish-brown stain)	Drop black in oil and Vandyke brown, equal parts, or nearly all black.
Oak, Flemish or Flanders (Black stain, very dark green, and very dark brown stains are used)	Some finishers use no filler. Drop black in oil, if filled; or black with part burnt umber for black or green Flemish. For brown Flemish, color filler with Vandyke brown.

TABLE IV.—Continued

Coloring Natural Paste Filler with Pigments Ground in Oil

Name of Wood or Color Effect	*Colors to be Mixed with the Natural Paste Filler*
Oak, Fumed (Orange brown, or brownish-yellow in various rather light shades)	No filler is used in standard finishes. If filler is desired for special effects, use a dark filler, or match the stain with burnt sienna, yellow ochre, and touches of brown, or even green or blue to neutralize slightly.
Oak, Golden (Yellowish stain with a dark filler)	Asphaltum with Vandyke brown, burnt umber, drop black, and yellow ochre. Sometimes a filler is made with two parts Venetian red and one part burnt umber.
Oak, Jacobean (Dark orange brown)	No filler is used. High lights wiped in stain.
Oak, Light (Natural color)	Use a little yellow ochre, or yellow ochre and raw sienna in the proportion of 50 per cent each.
Oak, Malachite (Very dark blue-green stain)	Drop black 5 to 6 parts to one each Vandyke brown and chrome green. Filler must be very dark green or all black.
Oak, Mission (Shades vary from gray to brown)	Pores often unfilled, especially with brown tones. Fillers of gray, green, and brown may be used. Fillers of zinc white and floor-wax can be used over a gray stain and a shellac wash. Brown filler is made of three parts burnt umber and one part Venetian red. Fillers should match color of stain.
Oak, Olive (Stain is dark olive green)	Filler is colored with drop black and applied over olive-green stain.
Oak, Novelty colors (Water-stains used first)	Use a white filler of zinc white with natural filler, or tint silex filler with green, gray, or brown, and use over a dark stain making pores show up lighter.
Oak, Silver and Kaiser (Stain is silver gray but has a tinge of yellow)	Fill over stain with zinc white and linseed oil, thinning oil with five to seven parts naphtha or turpentine; or use Wheeler's Special White Filler for white-pored effects. Silver-gray paste filler or natural filler may also be used.
Oak, Weathered	No filler is used for the standard effect. A filler of warm or neutral gray to match the stain color could be used if a flat varnish instead of shellac and wax finish is desired. Sometimes a black filler of drop black ground in oil with natural filler is used.
Redwood	Not usually filled. Burnt sienna and a touch of rose pink; or burnt umber, Vandyke brown, and burnt sienna.
Rosewood	Use a shellac wash under the filler. Tint filler to match color of wood with 3 parts Vandyke brown (preferably ground in japan) to 1 part rose pink in japan or oil.

TABLE IV.—Continued

COLORING NATURAL PASTE FILLER WITH PIGMENTS GROUND IN OIL

Name of Wood or Color Effect	Colors to be Mixed with the Natural Paste Filler
Walnut, American (Black walnut in natural color)	Fifty per cent Vandyke brown and 50 per cent burnt umber in oil to match walnut wood in color; or use burnt umber and a small amount of rose pink or Venetian red. For an evener tone, stain before filling with an acid water-stain, a Dakalite walnut stain, an oil-soluble dye, or a drying mixture of boiled linseed oil, turpentine, and japan drier tinged with Vandyke brown in oil.
Walnut, Antique (Pores to be white or with a gray tinge)	Use a white paint filler with 3 parts white lead in oil, one part zinc oxide in oil, thinned with a drying-solvent of 2 parts japan drier and 1 part each of turpentine and benzine. Wheeler's Special White filler may be substituted for the paint filler. Filler may be grayed slightly.
Walnut, Circassian (Transparent effect)	Apply a drying-oil composed of 1 to 2 parts boiled linseed oil, 1 to 2 parts turpentine, and 1 part japan drier. Fix the color with a shellac wash. Color filler with Vandyke brown, or burnt umber and reds to match wood, but of a slightly darker tint.

the container. A good all-around thinner is VM and P naphtha. When adding thinner, allow additional drying time. Failure to do this may cause a coat of lacquer to blush, giving the filler a grayish appearance.[2] Shorter drying schedules call for a fast grade of aromatic naphtha.

Brushes and "Picking Sticks" for Filler. Three kinds of brushes are useful to the workman in applying filler: (1) a 3″ or 4″ coach duster having rather fine stiff bristles makes an excellent brush for dusting and removing sand particles and broken wood fragments from wood surfaces that are to be filled. A house painter's duster having rather fine stiff bristles may be used. (2) Special brushes for applying filler can be obtained of brush manufacturers. Filler brushes should be quite stiff, so that the bristles will be sure to enter the lowest parts of the exposed cell cavities of the wood (Fig. 9-5). Brushes should be of good size and have plenty of bristles in order to hold considerable filler. An old half-worn or short-bristled flat paint brush may be used for large work. Oval or

---

[2] Soderberg, G. A., *Finishing Materials and Methods,* page 109.

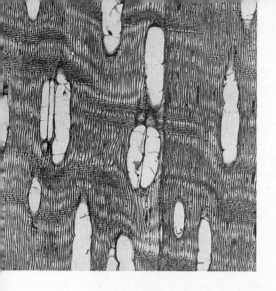

COURTESY FOREST PRODUCTS LABORATORY
9—5. Open pores show the need of dusting before filling. This radial section of black walnut shows the open pores and the need of dusting with a stiff brush to clean out the fragments of woody tissue before applying wood filler. Magnification 50 diameters.

round brushes are preferable for small work, because they hold more filler where narrow brushes are needed. (3) Picking brushes are often needed for rubbing out the excess filler from uneven surfaces, such as carvings and moldings. Special very stiff and rather coarse-bristled brushes, with the handle on the back like a shoe-blacking brush, are made for this purpose, and can be bought on the market under the name of picking brushes. They should not be used where the filler can be rubbed off in the usual manner.

Picking sticks, about ¼″ to ⅜″ in diameter, and 6″ or 8″ long, may be made of maple dowel rods, or from close-grained hickory or some other similar wood. Frequently they are whittled and sanded with one wedge-shaped end for scraping the filler out of corners and other places where it can not be rubbed off. The other end generally tapers to a rather sharp point. Chisel-like scrapers of various sizes and shapes can be made at the ends of these picking sticks. Bone, horn, and old toothbrush handles are favored by some finishers as material for homemade picking sticks. A narrow strip of cotton cloth is frequently held tightly over the wedge-shaped end of the picking stick when removing the filler. If the filler becomes too hard, it may be necessary to dampen the cloth with turpentine when scraping out the corners where the mixture has dried too long.

Brushing and Dusting Wood Before Filling. Experienced wood finishers make a practice of brushing wood surfaces with a stiff brush lengthwise of the grain just before filling. Such a brushing, if done thoroughly, removes many loosened or

146

9—6. Unfilled pores of oak wood. This photograph shows the pores or tracheal vessels of oak wood without any filler. Fuzz also shows plainly on the surface. Magnification about 5 diameters.

broken fragments of cell walls that otherwise might come off after filling and leave specks or small defects. The cell cavities on the surface are also cleaned out of small fragments of sand and dust neither of which mixes well with a filler. The wood finisher generally says that brushing and dusting open up the pores of the wood and prepare the surface to receive a filler (Fig. 9-6). If the finishing room is equipped with compressed air, many loose particles and dust can be removed with the air hose.

Sanding Water Stained Surfaces Before Filling. A cleaner, less muddy effect can be secured over water stained surfaces if they are given a wash coat of shellac and sanded after the shellac is thoroughly dry. Use dry sandpaper, 3/0 or 4/0, held in the hand or over a felt pad, as water is not good for rubbing shellacked surfaces. The sanding must be done very carefully, or streaks and corners will be sanded too much, and the even tone of the stain will be spoiled. The wash coat of shellac should consist of seven to ten parts of alcohol to one part of liquid shellac. If the shellac has four pounds of gum to the gallon of denatured alcohol, a wash coat should consist of eight parts of denatured alcohol to one part of liquid shellac. The shellac wash stiffens any fibers that were raised above the general level of the surface by the staining process, and a light sanding removes all these fragments flush with the surface. Wood filler can be rubbed crosswise from such a surface leaving it clean and clear in appearance.

Why Wash Coating Before Filling? When a finish with a fairly light or bright undertone color and a dark or strong pore color is desired, it is common practice, prior to filling, to apply a coat of wash shellac or lacquer sanding sealer.

The term "washcoating" as used in furniture finishing means the application of a very thin coat of sealer after staining and before filling. Its primary purpose is to prevent staining action by the filler. It also produces a smoother, harder surface, which facilitates wiping and cleaning of filled surfaces.

A washcoat must leave a very thin film; otherwise it would seal off or bridge the large pores and prevent proper filling. Two types of washcoats are generally used: The first and oldest is shellac, usually reduced in the proportion of 1 part 4 lb. cut shellac to 7 or 8 parts of denatured alcohol. A shellac washcoat dries within one hour. It sands to a smooth finish and takes filler nicely.

Many finishers now use lacquer wash coats. So-called lacquer sanding sealers may be bought ready to spray, or they may be thinned to washcoat consistency with lacquer thinner. Sanding sealers dry to a hard coat and are ready for sanding in 30-60 minutes.

Process of Filling. Filling wood with paste filler is not a difficult operation, but it requires knowledge of materials, and proper equipment, in addition to skill that comes from experience and good methods of work. Preliminary processes of finishing may precede the application of filler. Sometimes the wood is stained and allowed to dry, and the filler is applied over the stain. The filler may "lift" or raise the stain when this method is used. In order to prevent this change of shade, a wash consisting of a very thin coat of shellac is frequently put over the stain to hold it in place and prevent the "lifting" of the color.

If shellac of the standard or ordinary mixture is used, instead of a wash as suggested, the pores of the wood will be coated and filled with such a thick smooth covering that the wood filler will not stay in the pores on account of poor anchorage for the filler pigment or body material. Paste filler can be applied successfully over a wash coat of shellac without raising the stain or changing the shade or tone of the color.

Sometimes an oil stain is applied and not rubbed; and, after about 20 minutes, a filler is brushed crosswise over the wood, absorbing some of the excess stain. At other times filler that is either stained or "natural" is applied to unstained and unshellacked wood surfaces as a first coat of finish. If a stained filler is used, the wood may be stained and filled in one operation. The stain in this case does not usually penetrate deeply into the wood, and the general tone is light because less color is absorbed by the wood from the filler than is used with most other methods of staining. Greater penetration of the stain can be secured, however, by substituting about 15 or 20 per cent of benzol for that much benzine in the solvent or thinner.

Paste filler must be thinned to the proper consistency with turpentine, benzine, or naphtha before use. Should it be too thin it will not fill the pores of a coarse-grained wood which has large open cells, because it would contain too little pigment. On the other hand, if the filler is too thick, it will not enter the cell openings properly, especially when applied to woods composed largely of tracheids, or having tracheal vessels that are relatively small in size.

Ordinarily, paste filler should be about as thick as paint or thick cream when it is applied. The finisher should remember, however, to use a thick filler on woods with large open pores and a rather thin filler on woods with small pores. Woods with very small pores, such as are found in the conifers, do not need a paste filler and are usually given a coat of transparent or liquid filler.

Linseed oil, preferably boiled, is sometimes painted over wood just before paste filler is applied, to prevent too great absorption of oil from the filler by the wood, thus reducing the binding qualities of the vehicle in the pores. If the filler has a proper amount of oil mixed with it, the preliminary oil-

9—7. With a fairly stiff brush, fill the pores thoroughly. Brush with the grain first, next brush crosswise.

ing is unnecessary. Oiling always darkens wood and is pleasing in some cases, as with black walnut; it usually is displeasing with very light woods, such as pine and maple, and even with oak. Paste fillers that are to be used over surfaces that have had a shellac wash do not require as much oil in their composition as those that are to be spread on unsized wood.

Paste filler should be painted on the wood with a large, short-bristled, stiff brush, which should be kept moderately wet or full of the liquid (Fig. 9-7). The mixture in the can should be stirred often to keep the silex or body material from settling. The important thing in the application of filler is to force the pastelike mass down into the pores, and drive air bubbles out, thereby preventing specks or pinholes. This can be accomplished by working the filler into the pores by spreading it lengthwise of the grain, and by going over it crosswise with a rather wet brush.

Some finishers apply filler lengthwise of the grain only, while others say it should be brushed on crosswise. The important things are: to be sure (1) that the pasty mixture goes into the pores as deeply as possible; and (2) that the cell cavities are completely filled. Paste filler does not set quickly, consequently there is no danger of spoiling a finish by working the surface over and over with a brush.

Dulling or setting of paste filler for furniture usually requires about 20 minutes with most of the good ready-mixed commercial silex fillers of the present day. An excess of oil, the use of raw instead of boiled oil, and lack of proper driers—all cause the filler to set slowly. The quick drying thinners cause it to set more rapidly. If the filler dries too rapidly, add a little more linseed oil; but one should remember that too much oil makes a sticky mass that may pull out of the pores because it is tough and not in a condition to wipe off properly, and also that an excess of oil in the filler may injure the varnish coats over it. A finisher should add japan drier up to about ½ pint to the gallon of filler, if there is too little binder and the mixture pulls out of the pores in rubbing. On the other hand, a filler which is too stiff, lacking in benzine or turpentine, will not brush into the pores properly, and is very apt to pull out of the cell cavities during the wiping process.

Two very important rules should be remembered, namely: *first*, paste fillers contain ingredients that readily settle to the bottom of the can or pail, and, therefore, it is very important that the mixture should be stirred thoroughly very often, at least once in every three to five minutes; *second*, the finisher must rub the filler at just the right time, because if it is rubbed too soon the filling mass will pull out of the pores, and if the finisher waits too long the excess of material above the surface that ought to be removed has dried too hard, and will not come off unless it is softened with turpentine or benzine.

Rubbing Paste Filler. Rubbing off the filler in such a manner as to leave well-filled pores and a level surface is the real test of a wood finisher's skill. After painting on the filler the condition of the surface must be watched, and the excess of the dulled mixture should be rubbed off crosswise of the grain at the proper time. If the filler is rubbed too soon, before the thinner has evaporated, the thickening body mixture of silex and pigment will pull out of the pores because it has not had time to stiffen and form firm anchorages, and a poorly filled uneven surface will be the result (Fig. 9-8). If the finisher waits too long, the filler will not come off the surface easily; and some of it may pull out of the pores, as it is too stiff, instead of being cut off just at the surface. The filler that has settled down into the ruptured cell cavities should not be disturbed, while all excess which is above the surface of the wood must be rubbed or scraped off. Filler should be rubbed soon after

9—8. Chestnut wood poorly filled. The filler has come out of some of
the tracheal vessels or pores. This is a common fault when filling is done
by inexperienced persons. Refilling is the remedy. Magnification about
5 diameters.

it has dulled and no longer looks wet, for prompt action at
that time is necessary to secure good results. The finisher
should not fill too large an area before he begins the rubbing
process.

Various materials can be used for rubbing off the filler
from wood surfaces. The newly filled floors of buildings are
frequently rubbed with soft shavings, saw dust, or excelsior,
because these substances cost little or nothing and are available. Shops and furniture factories generally use better material, such as hairlike sea moss or sea grass which is commonly used in upholstering, jute or flax, or hemp tow, rags,
burlap, or even cotton waste which is objectionable if it leaves
lint on the surface. Almost anything will answer the purpose
which is not too stiff and is somewhat absorbent, that will
scrape or rub off the excess filler from the surface without
digging it out of the pores.

Crosswise rubbing of paste filler is the proper method,

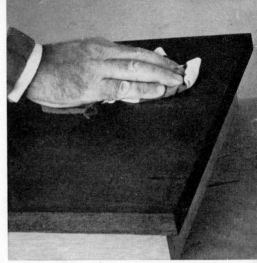

9—9. After a filled surface takes on a dull appearance, the excess filler is removed by wiping across the grain with burlap, shavings, seamoss or some other coarse material. 9—10. After removing most of the excess filler, wipe the surface with a soft rag.

since rubbing lengthwise of the grain tears the filler out of the pores to a greater extent (Fig. 9-9). The finisher should obtain a handful or pad of jute tow, sea grass, or rags, and rub one surface after another crosswise with considerable pressure, taking more material as soon as that in the hand becomes too wet or full of filler. A cleaner surface can be obtained by making a few light strokes with cotton cloth or rags lengthwise of the grain in finishing the process, thus removing the crosslines of filler left by the first hard rubbing (Figs. 9-10 and 11).

Two or more coats of filler are sometimes required to fill the pores completely. If the first coat is too thin, a second application is added. Since upright or slanting surfaces do not hold the filler in the pores as well as horizontal surfaces, the mixture which is to be used on vertical surfaces should be quite thick, or it may run out of the pores. Examination will show whether the pores are full of the filling material.

A second coat can best be applied as soon as the first one has become set or dull. After a filler has been rubbed, it is wise for an inexperienced workman to examine portions of various surfaces of a filled article using a pocket magnifier of from 12 to 18 enlargements. A hand glass of even lower magnification will help. If the filling is not well done, the

153

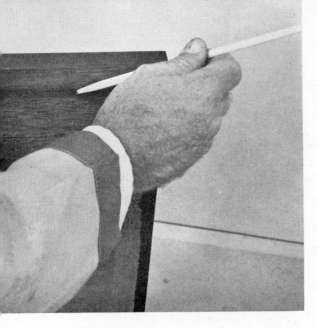

9—11. Remove excess filler from inside corners with a flat shaped picking stick. Use a special picking brush (or old toothbrush) to clean up carvings and moldings.

glass will show it instantly (Fig. 9-12). Additional coats of filler can be applied, if the pores are not full, after rubbing off the excess from the first application. It is thought best by many finishers to paint another coat of rather thin filler over the rubbed surface as soon as possible, at least before the mass in the pores is thoroughly dry and hard. This second coat of filler can be rubbed when it has set just as was the previous application; and, usually, a satisfactory level surface properly filled is the result. Sometimes a second or third coat is given to a filled surface that has dried hard.

9—12. Black walnut highly magnified showing wood filler in the pores. The dark streaks are made by a very dark walnut paste wood filler in the tracheal vessels or pores. The filler has largely come out of the tracheal vessel running lengthwise of the picture and a little to one side of the middle. This condition is indicated by brilliant spots of light.

154

Drying Paste Filler. The rapidity of drying of paste filler depends upon atmospheric conditions, such as warmth and dryness, and also upon the amount and the kind of oil used, the quantity of driers, and the volatility of the solvents. Raw linseed oil in the mixture and damp cool air check or slow up the drying of filler in wood. Under ordinary shop conditions most of the standard paste fillers sold on the market should have at least 48 hours to dry before shellac or any other finish is applied over them. Sanding can generally be done after 24 hours. Oxidation of linseed oil, especially raw oil, is a slow process; and, as there is linseed oil in paste fillers, plenty of time must be allowed for the drying of the filler or various finishing troubles may follow later on after the article is varnished.

Spraying Fillers. In most commercial shops the filling of pores of open-grained woods is done by means of a spray gun. The saving of time is considerable. With the proper equipment, one man can spray-fill as many pieces as four men can do in brush-filling.

To do the job of spray-filling properly, a pressure tank with agitators is needed. The agitators prevent the settling of the heavy pigments . The spray gun used has a special tip, needle, and air cap. A heavy, wet coat is applied at 30-50 lbs. air pressure. Correct pressure is important, since excess pressure may cause the filler to dry too quickly, causing what is known as "pinholing." In pinholing, a thin layer of filler breaches the pores, but does not fill them properly. During the drying process, the air escapes, breaking the film, and in so doing leaves a number of small holes. Special machines are used to pad the filler into the pores, and remove any excess filler. To do the job properly, a small amount of hand filling and clean-up are often necessary.

Sandpapering a Filled Surface. Filling always leaves a slightly rough surface, which should be sanded very lightly with No. 00 and No. 000 sandpaper. Small fragments of filler may be left on the surface after rubbing; the filled surfaces in the cell cavities may be slightly rough or not quite level, as revealed by a magnifier; and in addition to these, the fuzz on the surface of the wood may have been very slightly raised by the oil in the filler or the solvents that were used to make

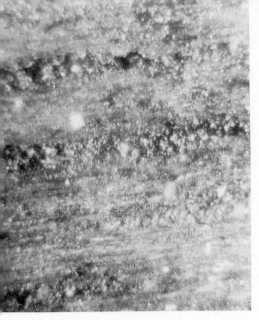

9—13. Filled surface of walnut wood as seen through a high power microscope. Some of the filler has been pulled out of the pores. The entire surface shows great roughness, caused by improper cleaning of the filler and fuzz. The remedy for such a condition is sandpapering.

it spread to better advantage (Fig. 9-13). Fine sandpaper should be used, and it should be handled with great care to prevent cutting through at corners and other exposed places.

The inexperienced finisher should be warned to sand lengthwise of the grain with light strokes, or his work may be damaged. The sandpaper should not be placed over a hard block and used in that manner, for streaks and spots may be cut through the filler and perhaps a stain coat that was applied previously. Soft felt blocks should be used, or the paper may be held over the hand for much of the sanding. Fine water-proof garnet finishing paper, over a felt pad well moistened with water, can be used to advantage over filled surfaces (Fig. 9-14).

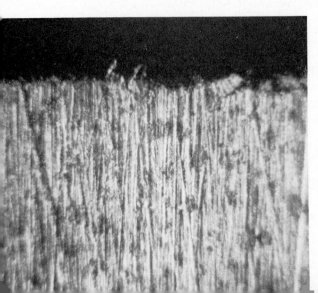

9—14. Sandpaper scratches on the end grain of walnut that has been filled and shellacked. Very highly magnified. The surface has been very badly scratched with No. 2/0 sandpaper. Remedy—use finer sandpaper. The rough surface at the top of the picture is usual on a smoothly-planed but unsanded surface. Remedy—sandpaper all surfaces and round off all arrises.

The appearance is often improved by wiping a filled surface with a cloth moistened with benzine as a final operation after the sanding has been completed. Small particles of sand and fragments of wood together with any muddiness from excess portions of filler, are removed leaving an effect of greater transparency as a result of the wiping operation.

TABLE V.

KINDS OF FILLER USED ON VARIETIES OF WOOD

Pores invisible to the eye. Paste filler not needed. Use liquid filler or shellac.	Pores small but generally visible. Paste filler sometimes used. Liquid filler or shellac generally used.	Pores large. Paste filler usually used. Liquid filler unsatisfactory.
Basswood	Basswood (sometimes) Beech Birch Boxwood	Ash Beech
Cedar, red and white Cucumber Cypress	Cherry	Butternut
	Cypress (after water-stain) Cottonwood	Chestnut Cocobola Coffee Tree Wood
Ebony Fir (including Douglas)		Elm
	Gumwood	Hackberry
Hemlock Holly Larch or Tamarack Magnolia		Hickory Locust Mahogany
	Maple, hard and soft	Mahogany, Philippine Oak Osage Orange Rosewood
Pine, white and yellow Poplar or Whitewood	Sycamore	Sassafras Satinwood Sycamore
Spruce Tupelo Willow	Redwood	Vermillion Walnut, black Walnut, Circassian

Common Filler Troubles.[3] Some of the troubles most frequently encountered in the application of fillers are the following:

Graying. When graying of filler occurs, the filler takes on a milky, gray cast. This may be caused by:

1. A lack of sufficient drying time.

---

[3] Deniston, G. L., *The Science of Modern Woodfinishing*, Ch. 8, pp. 123-124.

2. The use of a wrong thinner to reduce the filler to proper brushing or spraying consistency.
3. The addition of raw linseed oil.
4. The addition of too much boiled linseed oil.
5. Too little oil, resulting in insufficient wetting of the pigment particles.
6. Improper formulation by the manufacturer.
7. Incorrect choice of the sealer used.

Bleeding. This trouble is often related to poor drying. When a surface is sealed before the solvents in the filler have had a chance to dry properly, the sealer penetrates the filler and mixes with the filler solvents. As the surface dries, any soluble coloring matter comes out with the escaping solvents, causing spots around the pores. To avoid bleeding, apply light rather than heavy sealer coats.

Popping or Puffing. The solvents in some lacquer sealers have a tendency to dissolve any undried oils. This results in an increase in the volume of the filler, creating a rough "washboard" effect. As the solvents escape, the surface levels off due to the subsequent shrinkage of the filler. This shrinkage is what causes the trouble.

Muddy color. This is often due to fillers which contain unsuitable pigments and the presence of undried oils. Also, careless and improper removal of filler may leave this muddy appearance.

Pinholing. When filler is sprayed on with excessive pressure or when the filler is not brushed thoroughly into the pores, pinholing may result. Although the pores may be breached with a thin film of filler, these films break upon drying. Small holes in the surface are the result.

To secure good filling results, follow these suggestions:

1. Select a filler that has maximum safety built into it.
2. Apply and remove filler properly.
3. Allow for sufficient drying time.
4. Avoid excessively heavy sealer coats.

Certain Woods Require a Paste Filler. A complete enumeration of all woods that require paste filler would be hard to prepare, but a list of typical species may be of assistance. As a general rule, woods that have open pores or cell cavities that are plainly visible to the naked eye should be filled with a paste filler. A wood that has been colored with an oil stain containing linseed oil does not need a paste filler as much as one stained with a water stain. For this reason woods having fine cell openings, such as birch, are frequently filled after a water stain; and, generally, they are not filled after application of linseed oil stain, because the drying oil mixed with the color sizes the wood and plugs the cell openings to some extent. The volatile oil stains made from a solvent and an oil-soluble coal-tar dye do not size wood much more than water stain.

The list of woods in Table V, based largely on the size of the cell cavities, is suggestive in deciding whether a given kind of wood should be filled with a paste filler, but it must be remembered that special types of finishes for unusual effects may be the determining factor.

In some cases Table V shows the name of a wood in two columns. This indicates that at least two methods of finishing these woods are commonly used, and that both methods are considered to be good under certain conditions.

Paste Fillers Are Best on Floors. The finishing of floors is not considered in Table V, for the reason that liquid fillers are not satisfactory on any kind of wood used for floors. More suitable finishes for floors can be obtained by treating all kinds of flooring, both hardwoods and softwoods, with a paste filler in order to give a good foundation of very hard, non-absorptive, long wearing material as an undercoat for varnish. All woods are porous, because cavities or openings exist in all kinds of cells in the various woods. The microscope shows the closest grained nonporous woods to be full of cells, and the end grain of such a wood, under a glass, appears like a sieve. The finest particles of a properly ground silex are small enough to lodge to some extent in the cells of even the closest grained wood and plug up or fill the cell openings.

SELECTED REFERENCES, CHAPTER IX

Woodfiller

Adams, R. C., "Quick-Dry Fillers," *Industrial Finishing*, 24, pp. 88-98, Aug., 1948.

"An Ancient Industry Goes Modern," William Zinsser and Co., New York, 1948.

Deniston, G. L., *The Science of Modern Woodfinishing*, "Fillers and Filling," Chapters VIII, IX, pp. 105-146, 1949.

Fuller, W. R., "Finishes for Furniture," *Industrial Finishing*, 24, pp. 88-98, April, 1948.

Gibbia, S. W., *Wood Finishing and Refinishing*, "Filling the Pores of Wood," Chapter IV, pp. 55-66, 1954.

McGee, R. A. and Brown, A. G., *Instructional Units in Woodfinishing*, "To Prepare and Apply Paste Woodfiller," Chapter II, pp. 16-21, 1950.

Soderberg, G. A., *Finishing Materials and Methods*, "Woodfiller," Chapter XVI, pp. 108-112, 1952.

Wampler, Rollin H., *Modern Organic Finishes*, "Stains and Woodfiller," Chapter III, pp. 35-49, 1946.

Wampler, Rollin H., "Shellac in Wood Finishing," *Industrial Finishing*, 24, pp. 86-94, Oct., 1948.

Wampler, Rollin H., "Thirty Minute Fillers," *Industrial Finishing*, 23, pp. 48-52, Aug., 1947.

Chapter X

Spirit Varnishes

Spirit Varnishes Defined. Shellac, dammar, mastic, and sandarac varnishes are quick-drying, well-known finishes which are often called spirit varnishes. The term spirit varnish has a slightly different meaning in England and France from that which is common in the United States. Abroad, the term spirit varnish refers to a mixture made from one or more gums or resins that may be dissolved in alcohol, turpentine, acetone, or similar volatile solvents, but which contains no drying oils such as linseed oil or tung oil. In some foreign countries, it is customary to classify alcoholic spirit varnishes and turpentine spirit varnishes in one group. In the United States, two groups are sometimes made, gums or resins dissolved in alcohol being called spirit varnishes while those cut with turpentine are called volatile oil varnishes. Other American authorities use the foreign classification. In this book, the two groups are classed together, and the term spirit varnish refers to solutions of gums, or resins and volatile liquids. Some resins such as dammar, mastic, and elemi are largely soluble in both alcohol and turpentine.

Soluble in turpentine or benzol	Partly soluble in turpentine or benzol
Dammar	Sandarac (26% to 33%)
Mastic	Manila gum, hard (27% to 36%)
Rosin	Manila gum, soft (36% to 42%)
Elemi	

Soluble or nearly soluble in alcohol	Partly soluble in alcohol
Sandarac	Dammar (71%)
Shellac	Mastic (64%)
Rosin	Brazilian copal (62%)
Elemi	Manila gum, hard (44%)
Manila gum, soft	
Benzoin	

161

Resins Used in Spirit Varnishes. Various resins, frequently in mixtures, are used in spirit varnishes. The solvents which are most commonly selected are turpentine or alcohol, although many of the resins will dissolve, either wholly or in part, in benzol or ether. It should be remembered, however, that some resins are largely or entirely soluble in turpentine and only partly soluble in alcohol. In other cases the reverse is true. The lists on page 161 indicate the solvents that can be used with several of the resins.

Three Useful Soft Gum Varnishes

Dammar Varnish. The best known of the clear or transparent varnishes sold in limited amount on the American market is called dammar varnish. This resin, classed as a soft resin, comes from Indonesia, is harder than rosin, but is much softer than are the copals in general. Dammar resin is frequently dissolved in turpentine in which substance it is almost completely soluble; while, if alcohol is the solvent, there is about 29 per cent residue remaining which is soluble. Other solvents which are sometimes used in dammar varnishes are carbon tetrachloride, benzine, heavy naphtha 48°, and heavy benzol.

Dammar varnish when spread upon a surface does not show the brilliancy of a shellac finish, nor does it have the durability of good fixed-oil varnishes which include linseed oil or some other drying oil in their composition. In such finishes, the turpentine, alcohol, or other volatile solvent dries out leaving a thin film consisting of the gum or gums spread over the surface.

Like other spirit varnishes, dammar varnish dries rapidly, because the solvents used evaporate quickly leaving a rather glossy and moderately hard film. Dammar varnish is used on light or white surfaces at times in place of a fixed-oil varnish, which would usually slightly darken the tone on account of the presence of drying oils. The film or coat left by applying dammar varnish is not very durable because the resin becomes weak in cohesion and gradually rubs off. This varnish should be applied quickly—much as shellac is flowed over a surface— because it dries quite rapidly after being spread with a brush.

Dammar varnish, with its greater transparency as compared with oil varnishes or even shellac, is used occasionally to preserve the natural color of wood or other materials. When burnt wood designs or decorations in pyrography are popular, dammar varnish is often used for finishing boxes, plates, wastebaskets, and other small articles of basswood or holly in order to keep the unburned portions of the designs as light in tone as possible. Dammar varnish has been used rather largely by paint manufacturers to impart a gloss to paints, and is sometimes mixed with zinc white in the preparation of white enamels because it contains no linseed oil which is apt to turn yellow with long exposure to light.

Dammar resin is produced by various living pinaceous trees of the genus *Dammara*, which grow in Indonesia chiefly, and to a minor extent in Australia and New Zealand. The best dammar resin comes in five grades from the island of Java, and is known as *Batavia*. Other dammar resins sold on the market are shipped from Padang, Sumatra, Borneo, and Singapore.

Dammar varnish is made up in varying proportions of resin and solvent, the following being suggestive:

Dammar gum, Batavia Grade A, government standard, or Singapore dammar gum, 4½ to 5 parts.
Turpentine, 6 parts.

Transparent Picture Varnish:

Dammar (pale gum), 12½ parts.
Camphor gum, 1 part.
Turpentine, 25 parts.

A tougher more elastic dammar varnish:

Dammar (Singapore, or Grade A, Batavia), 2 parts (by weight).
Sandarac, 1 part.
Mastic, ⅕ part.
Turpentine, 4 parts.

The following is a United States Navy Department (52V2a, 1914) specification for dammar varnish:

Composition I.—To consist exclusively of a solution of pure dammar resin in petroleum spirits (turpentine substitute) and to be absolutely free from all foreign matter. To contain not less than 55 per cent nor more than 60 per cent by volume of petroleum spirits.

Mastic Varnish. The most important European resin, with the exception of colophony (col'o-pho-ny) or colophonium, which are other names for common rosin, is *mastic*, which comes largely from Chios, one of the Greek islands located in the Aegean sea. Similar resins are found in some parts of Greece, Africa, and Syria. Mastic resin is the product of exudation from the lentix tree (*Pistacia lentiscus*), also called the Pistacia, a Mediterranean evergreen tree. The resin is thrown out in response to wounds, which are vertical incisions in the bark, and is collected in the form of spherical or slightly flattened tears or grains. After being exuded from a wound the liquid resin gradually becomes dry and hard. In Turkey it is sometimes used as a chewing gum, though it has a slightly bitter taste. Its odor is, however, rather agreeable and pleasing.

Mastic gum soon softens when placed in the mouth and crushed between the teeth; while sandarac, a somewhat similar resin, is crushed into powder. A lentix tree in good condition yields as much as eight to ten pounds of mastic resin per year, if properly cared for during the gum-producing season. The tree, which is sometimes called the lentiscus, is hardly more than a shrub, usually growing to the height of only ten or twelve feet.

Mastic resin, when it appears on the market, is of a pale yellowish or slightly greenish color. It is a very soft resin, fusing at a temperature slightly below the boiling point of water (95° C.). The gum, however, begins to soften at a temperature of about 85° C.

The active ingredient in mastic resin is known as mastic acid ($C_{40}H_{64}O_4$).

Mastic resin is used to a limited extent in the manufacture of a number of transparent or colorless varnishes, being completely soluble in turpentine, ether, and benzol, and largely soluble in acetone. In alcohol, about 36 per cent of insoluble matter is left as a residue. Petrol ether has only a slight solvent action on the gum.

Artists are the chief users of various kinds of mastic varnish. It is often mixed in small quantities with turpentine and boiled linseed oil and used as a vehicle in mixing with artists' oil paints, thus giving more luster to paintings than would be produced by using either linseed oil or turpentine or a mixture of both.

One form of mastic varnish, known as *"megilp,"* contains boiled linseed oil in its composition and is rather thick or gelatinous. "Megilp" is used by artists in connection with oil paintings.

A portion of mastic resin is sometimes mixed with dammar and other gums in order to make the resultant varnish more elastic and tough.

Sandarac. Another resin that is completely soluble in alcohol is sandarac, which comes from a tree that is somewhat similar to the cypress or juniper and which is indigenous to North Africa, especially Algeria and Morocco. The Moors collect the sandarac resin which is exuded to some extent naturally from the trees. Incisions are made in the bark, from which the tree throws out sandarac resin, much as the longleaf and loblolly pines of the southern part of the United States exude crude turpentine gum, the raw material from which turpentine and rosin are manufactured.

Sandarac is a rather hard member of the group of soft resins, and has a specific gravity of 1.073, which is high for a resin. On account of its hardness, toughness, elasticity, and great luster, it is sometimes mixed with shellac gum in the production of alcohol-soluble varnishes. It was at one time often chosen as an ingredient of compounds, called lacquers, used to cover brass and other metals to prevent tarnishing. Sandarac resin is also selected as an ingredient of various alcoholic spirit varnishes, known as bookbinders' varnishes, label varnishes, and photographic-negative varnishes.

The best quality of sandarac resin comes to the market in the form of small, rather elongated, bitter tears or globules, which are of a pale yellowish color and have a slightly bitter taste, and a faint odor. The resin will not soften in the mouth in an attempt at chewing and can, by that means, be distinguished from mastic gum.

Sandarac resin fuses at a temperature of about 145° C. Other solvents for sandarac besides alcohol are ether and acetone. It is also partly soluble in chloroform (44 per cent), turpentine (26.4 per cent), and benzine (32.6 per cent).

SHELLAC VARNISH—PREPARATION, APPLICATION

Lac Gum. Shellac, the best known and by far the most important of all the spirit varnishes, is made from a rather hard resin called *lac*, which is shipped throughout the world principally from Calcutta, India. The resin itself is heavy for a material of this kind, and has a specific gravity varying from 1.113 to 1.214. The lac gum or shellac of commerce is almost completely soluble in either wood or grain alcohol, leaving 3.6 per cent of residue which is known as shellac wax. Shellac gum is, however, almost insoluble in dilute mineral acids, ether, linseed oil, and turpentine (90.9 per cent), although this last solvent, especially Venice turpentine is sometimes added to liquid shellac for special reasons. It is interesting to know that shellac gum is soluble in ammonia and alkaline solutions. The alkalies generally used for a mixture of this kind, which is known as a water shellac, are borax and alkaline carbonates.

The market quotations show various grades of shellac gum, the best and highest priced being known as D.C., V.S.O., and Diamond I. Other cheaper grades are superfine orange, fine, T.N. ("Truly Native"), garnet lac, button lac, and bleached (ground); the poorer grades being given last.

10—1. Cutting lac-encrusted branches from tree.   10—2. Close-up view of lac-encrusted branches.

COURTESY WILLIAM ZINSSER & CO., INC.

Shellac gum, a resin commonly called *lac* or *"lakh"* (meaning 100,000), is produced by certain scale insects on various species of trees which are found especially in northern India, and Assam which was formerly part of eastern Bengal. Lac resin at present is produced in Bengal, Siam, China, Ceylon, Burma, and the Malayan Archipelago; but Calcutta, India, remains the great market place and shipping port for this important industry.

The insect which excretes the lac is commonly called the *Coccus lacca,* but is also known as *Tachardia lacca,* and *Carteria lacca.* The insects incrust most commonly the twigs of various fig trees which are sometimes spoken of as the Ficus (Fig. 10-1 and 2). In various places they are found on 88 species and varieties of trees, including the mimosa, the acacia, the dalbergia tree which produces the rosewood of commerce, and also on India rubber and banyan trees. The deep red insects, about $\frac{1}{12}''$ long while young, attach themselves to live twigs where they can puncture the bark with their beaks and suck up the sap from the growing stems. Important changes take place in each insect which exudes, through the pores of its body a resinous material which finally incrusts it. The exudations from innumerable insects ultimately cover the twigs with a thick layer, much as ice forms on branches of trees in winter in this country. The female insects, which are far more numerous than the males, form most of the incrustation of gum about themselves, and there they remain practically immovable.

In one of these cells, later on, each female insect lays about 1000 eggs. Sometimes the lac may cover the twigs to a thickness of from $\frac{1}{4}''$ to $\frac{1}{2}''$ The insects are not active and have little vitality, but they are so numerous at times while feeding gregariously with their bodies closely packed together, that they give a red color to the branches of the trees.

Trees can be inoculated from infested stems so as to produce crops either in late spring or late autumn. It should be noted, however, that individual trees are trimmed but once a year, generally in June or February.

Stick lac is the name given to the incrusted twigs of even length after they have been gathered. The stems, which are thickly covered with the exuded and coalesced scales of lac,

COURTESY WILLIAM ZINSSER & CO., INC.

10—3. Scraping lac from branches by native Indian workers. Notice
bundles of lac sticks in lower right-hand corner.

are gathered about the time that the feeding or sucking of
sap stops and before the young insects hatch out; and in this
condition they can be shipped or used to inoculate other
trees. The spring crop is said to be used to a large extent for
propagating purposes, and is not of as much importance for
gathering for the market as is the autumn or winter crop. The
color of stick lac on the twigs varies from a dark red to a
rather pale orange yellow. When they are used to infest new
trees, the young insects come out of the cells, which form
around the bodies of the mother insects, and move about until
they find a place to attach themselves, and thus a new crop
is started. When lac dye was valuable it was important to
gather the stick lac before the departure of the young; for,
after that time, the red fluid found in the cell of gum about
the female insect's body disappears.

The stick lac or gum-covered twigs that are broken into
sticks of even lengths, and the particles which fall to the
ground in fragments under the trees, are gathered at some

place where the resin is first scraped from the branches and then crushed (Fig. 10-3). Frequently this is done in a mill similar to that used for breaking up grain. By sifting and sorting, the fragments of wood and the bodies of the insects are removed; and the crude lac, then called seed lac, is washed in hot water (Fig. 10-4). A purple or reddish dye, which was quite valuable before the recent discoveries in aniline and other coal-tar colors, is removed by washing and is known as lac dye. This dye, at one time more valuable than shellac itself, was supposed to be the same as cochineal, but chemists finally discovered that it contains a different acid. The cleaning process is completed by sifting and winnowing the seed lac (Fig. 10-5).

In manufacturing shellac the dried seed lac is mixed with orpiment (arsenic sulphide) to the extent of 0.05 to 0.25 per cent, and also with varying small amounts of rosin, an adulterant that is much cheaper than shellac gum and does not seem to be harmful up to 3 to 5 per cent, but which is very ad-

10—4. The process of washing lac to remove lac dye, insect remains, and other impurities.

COURTESY WILLIAM ZINSSER & CO., INC.

COURTESY
WILLIAM ZINSSER & CO., INC.
10—5. Sifting and winnowing seedlac, a further cleaning process.

vantageous to the workmen because it makes the melting of the seed lac much easier. The mixture is then placed in long thin cotton bags, which are about the size of a baseball bat, except that sometimes they are nearly 20 feet long. When the bags are heated over a charcoal fire and twisted in opposite

10—6. Native method of shellac manufacture. The seedlac is first put into cloth bags, shaped like a 2″ water hose. By holding the filled bags before a charcoal fire, the lac melts and is forced out by twisting the bag.

COURTESY WILLIAM ZINSSER & CO., INC.

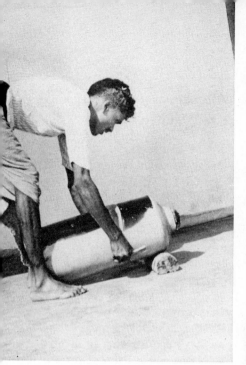
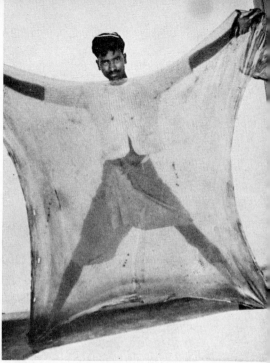

COURTESY WILLIAM ZINSSER & CO., INC.

10—7. Molten lac is placed on a hot earthenware jar. It is next stretched into sheets by smoothing it with a palm leaf. 10—8. Stretching the lac into sheets. These sheets are next broken up into small shellac flakes. It is in this form that it is shipped to paint manufacturers all over the world.

directions by two men, the melted resin oozes out through the meshes of the cloth and is scraped off and spread out over a large porcelain cylinder containing cold water (Figs. 10-6 and 7). After cooling, the sheets of shellac are removed from the cylinder and stretched into thinner sheets several feet square in size (Fig. 10-8).

While the resin is being squeezed from the bags some of it drops to the ground, and makes little flakes known as *button lac*. The buttons are usually of a dark ruby color, and when sold on the market they frequently have from 10 to 20 per cent of rosin mixed with the shellac gum, thus cheapening it.

Garnet lac is another grade which is sold in sheets, and is said to have had the shellac wax largely removed. This grade on the market, however, generally has from 10 to 20 per cent of rosin mixed with it to reduce the cost and to lower its fusion temperature. Garnet lac is often made from the residue which will not squeeze out of the bags. The shellac gum is removed

171

from the impurities by the use of alcohol or sodium carbonate solution; and after filtering, the solvent is liberated, or acid is used to destroy the alkali.

Stick lac in its crude form is not pure shellac gum, and contains about 66 per cent of lac resin, six per cent shellac wax, six per cent gluten, and eleven per cent coloring matter. Shellac wax is not soluble in alcohol and, if present in liquid shellac, is the cause of its turbid appearance.

Alcoholic Solutions of Shellac Gum. Wood finishers purchase shellac varnish ready for use. It is prepared in factories where the shellac gum, also called shellac resin, is dissolved, usually in denatured grain (ethyl) alcohol, or in wood (methyl) alcohol.

Formerly, wood alcohol shellac was commonly used because it sold at a much lower price than shellac gum dissolved in grain alcohol, which was expensive because of a high government tax. Wood alcohol shellac is not much used at present because of its poisonous qualities, its strong disagreeable odor, and the difficulty in application. It sets so rapidly that brushing it on smoothly is almost impossible, especially when it is attempted by inexperienced workmen. This kind of shellac is not used in French polishing because it will not work smoothly under the rubbing pad. Bleached shellac is not entirely soluble in wood alcohol.

Strong or highproof denatured alcohol, such as the United States Revenue Bureau's formula No. 1, which consists of 100 gallons of 190° proof ethyl (grain) alcohol and five gallons of approved methyl (wood) alcohol, is necessary for dissolving shellac gum. The ordinary 160° proof ethyl alcohol, which is the grade frequently sold on the market, is not strong enough to dissolve shellac gum satisfactorily. Highproof denatured alcohol, which is poisoned with five per cent of wood alcohol in the United States, is consequently the solvent commonly used in dissolving shellac gum.

Denatured-alcohol shellac sets more slowly than that made with wood alcohol, and for this reason it spreads better with a brush. This mixture hardens sooner than that cut with wood alcohol and does not have its pungent smell which is so irritating to most people. Grain alcohol has a great affinity for water and easily absorbs it in damp weather. Very small quantities of water mixed with alcohol will cause a milky or turbid appearance; for this reason the alcohol used should be at least 190° proof, which is the same as 95 per cent pure. Great care must be taken to keep water out of shellac, because even a few drops which have fallen into the mixture will cause precipitation of some of the gum, and any measurable quantity will change the liquid into a slimy coagulated mass that is useless. *If a brush is wet with water* when it is put into the liquid shellac, it will cause the same trouble, ruining the mixture and making the brush unusable.

The proportion of shellac resin to the alcohol solvent varies somewhat. A thick shellac varnish which is sometimes called standard may be made by using the following:

5 pounds bleached shellac resin or gum to the gallon of 190° proof denatured alcohol; or

4 pounds orange shellac resin to the gallon of 190° proof denatured alcohol.

These proportions make a very thick shellac varnish, and it will be necessary to warm and agitate the mixture considerably before such a large proportion of resin will dissolve. Some extra heavy shellacs are made in the proportion of 6¾ pounds to the gallon of solvent. The cutting of shellac resin is a slow and difficult process, and is best left to experienced men who have proper equipment in factories.

Good grades of shellac varnish sold on the market are supposed to have four pounds of gum to the gallon of denatured alcohol. The cheaper grades of liquid shellac are apt to be made of some of the poorer adulterated gums and contain less than four pounds or frequently only three pounds of shellac resin to the gallon.

Most of the thick shellac varnishes should be thinned before use. A mixture of two pounds of orange shellac or two and one-half pounds of bleached shellac is usually heavy enough for application on wood.

Effects of Metal Cans and Dust on Shellac Varnish. It is unfortunate that liquid shellac as prepared by the manufacturers does not keep well in metal cans. After a few months, shellac which is kept in metal cans gradually darkens. This discoloration in the case of white shellac becomes serious after two or three years, and can always be noticed in the contents of a tin can that has been opened but not used promptly. The dark color can sometimes be removed by the addition of a very few white crystals of oxalic acid to the shellac mixture. The use of oxalic acid in shellac varnish is a very questionable practice, however; because, if there is an excess over that which is necessary to remove the discoloration in the shellac, the acid may bleach the stain under the shellac, or lighten the tone of the wood itself. Some manufacturers put up their product in glass bottles in order to avoid all discoloration that comes from contact with metal. Experts recommend that prepared shellac varnish be kept away from strong light, and in a reasonably warm room during cold weather, in order to prevent settling of the resin.

If a can or bottle of shellac is not kept tightly corked serious trouble will soon follow, because the alcohol will evaporate very rapidly, and after a time the thickened residue cannot be thinned in such a way that the solution will spread properly under a brush. The most serious trouble that comes from leaving a shellac can open, comes from dust which soon settles into the mixture. Every speck of dust that goes into an open can of either shellac or varnish means a speck in a finish after it is applied to a surface, and this speck can never be removed. Shellac varnish that has stood open in a room for any great length of time is always ruined for wood finishing.

Orange and White Shellac. The natural color of most grades of lac gum that have not been bleached is some shade of orange, the depth of tone varying with the grade. The best grades of orange shellac are not as apt to be adulterated with resin as the bleached. If more than a rather small per cent of rosin is present in shellac varnish, it will prevent the film from drying on a surface as hard as it should, leaving the finish tacky for a number of hours.

Orange shellac when dissolved in alcohol makes a better varnish than white shellac, because a film made with it is stronger and more elastic; and, in addition to these good qualities, the gum and prepared mixtures keep better. Alcoholic solutions of orange shellac do not depreciate in quality through rather long periods of storage, and are far more stable than is the case with white shellac solutions, which gradually deteriorate and become darker in color. Orange shellac is objectionable for many purposes on account of its color.

Bleached or white shellac is made from the various orange or colored shellacs by several processes. The coloring matter consisting of red lac dye can be removed by the use of various weak alkaline solvents. Sometimes the orange shellac resin is boiled in a weak solution of carbonate of potash, melted under water, and pulled till it is white. Another process is to dissolve the gum in some alkali and pass a stream of chlorine gas into the mixture to bleach the shellac, which is then melted under water and pulled when soft. Treatment with hypochlorite of soda or potash, and then neutralizing with sulphuric acid, followed by filtering and washing in an elaborate process, is a commercial method.

Bleached shellac is sold on the market in a coarse granular or ground form in order to make it more soluble in alcohol. Sometimes it is obtainable in large hanks which keep to better advantage. The bleaching process reduces its solubility, leaves it in a condition so that it is very apt to deteriorate with age, and renders a spirit varnish made with it less elastic than that made from the untreated orange resin. Bleached shellac dissolves in alcohol much more readily soon after it is manufactured. The gum gradually deteriorates with age or storage, and its solubility in alcohol is greatly reduced.

White shellac varnish when spread on a surface produces an effect of great brilliancy and unequalled transparency. It dries very hard, however, but on account of its lack of elasticity it is apt to crack if it is bent or exposed to unusual conditions.

Use of Shellac. Spirit varnishes made from shellac gum in solution are used for many purposes, such as the woodwork of a house, including the floors and trimmings, the making of toys, furniture, and musical instruments, for sizing or stiffening straw hats, for many kinds of insulating in electrical instrument manufacture, for some kinds of waterproofing, for the making of leather dressings, and sometimes in the place of oil varnish for an undercoat on willow, rattan, and paper fiber goods.

It is often the most desirable material known to use as a first coating over close-grained or nonporous woods, and to size stained and filled work so that varnish or wax may be used successfully later on. Shellac varnish is superior to other varnishes in nonpermeable qualities, because it almost hermetically seals up the pores of wood, closes up resin ducts, thereby preventing exudation from knots and pockets, and prevents the "bleeding" of stain into the final coats of varnish. Manufacturers of spar varnish, however, object to the use of shellac undercoats, because shellac does not weather as well as these "long-oil" varnishes. Practical wood finishers agree that it is unwise to use shellac under spar varnish on all woodwork that is exposed to outdoor conditions.

Spirit varnish made from orange shellac gum and alcohol is used commonly by pattern makers, and to some extent by other woodworkers. When a shellac varnish is applied to dark-hued woods, it is quite common to use a mixture of orange and white shellac. Too much orange shellac in such a mixture is apt to give an orange tint that spoils the natural hue of some woods or changes the color effect of the stain. For this reason white shellac is preferable for most finishes, especially for light tones.

Spreading shellac is one of the very most difficult operations the wood finisher is called upon to perform. The alcohol in the mixture evaporates so rapidly from a shellac film that it is almost impossible to avoid laps, streaks, and untouched spots unless one has had considerable skill and experience.

As a transparent filler or surfacer on woods without open pores, there is no other finishing material equal to denatured alcohol white shellac. When applied as a first coat to size wood, it is wise to dilute liquid shellac of ordinary strength, such as a mixture of four pounds of gum to the gallon of alcohol, by using about one-half alcohol and one-half liquid shellac. Two coats of thin shellac, with a slight sanding between the applications, will make a much better finish than one heavy coat; chiefly because it is much easier to spread thin shellac evenly, and also on account of the greater probability of covering every portion of the surface by going over it twice with a brush.

Shellac must be applied to wood with great speed by the use of a wet brush and spreading lengthwise of the grain. The operator should stand in a position from which he can see just what he is doing, thus avoiding laps, streaks, and uncovered places. Frequently, it is possible to place the object between the finisher and the light by shifting it into such a position that the freshly covered surface will show a bright gloss where it has been shellacked. Every portion of the surface should be covered with the brush while the coat is being put on, for after about one-half minute no touching up can be done satisfactorily. Attempts to retouch tacky shellac often cause trouble, as rough places will result which generally harm the finish more than uncovered spots do because these small areas will be covered over by later coats of finish and usually do not show unless an effort is made to repair them after the film has partially set.

Drying and Sanding Shellacked Surfaces. Shellac dries hard, usually in about eight hours, ready for sanding with fine sandpaper. While two coats of shellac can probably be put on during one day, it is best that a full day should elapse between applications. Great care and fine sandpaper must be used when smoothing and cutting off the gloss of shellac films, especially when thin mixtures have been applied. If both the shellac coat and the stain are cut through by careless sanding, it is very difficult to make a repair that will not show. A thoughtless finisher with sandpaper in his hands can do more damage in a few minutes than an expert can repair in many hours.

Shellac Washes. Washcoats of shellac are frequently used under paste filler in order to size the wood and keep the stain from raising with the filler when it is rubbed. Washcoats are made of thin shellac in the proportion of one part of standard liquid shellac to seven or eight parts of alcohol. Mixtures as thin as one to ten are usually satisfactory under paste filler. The proportion of one to seven is considered best when using a four-pound gum compound for the liquid shellac portion.

Methods of Making Shellac Spread More Easily. Camphor gum is sometimes dissolved in liquid shellac in the proportion of one ounce of camphor to a gallon of shellac in order to make the mixture spread more easily under the brush. Small quantities of camphor gum are frequently put in spirit varnishes made of shellac, sandarac, and mastic cut in alcohol. A weak solution of glycerine and alcohol may be added to shellac varnish. Its action is similar to that of camphor gum because it retards the setting.

Venice turpentine may be added to shellac in the proportion by weight of:

1 part Venice turpentine,
10 parts shellac gum.

For the ordinary liquid shellac, this means that about five ounces of Venice turpentine may be added to each gallon of prepared shellac varnish. Venice turpentine also makes shellac spread considerably easier under the brush because it lengthens the time between the application and the setting of the film.

Effects of Moisture on Shellac. Damp weather may cause trouble when spreading shellac on account of the affinity of alcohol for water. If the film has a greenish hue or is not transparent showing a turbid, cloudy appearance, the finisher should stop work until conditions are suitable. During rainy weather the shop windows should be closed. If the room is too cold, shellac will not spread well. Thin shellac varnish will, however, spread better in damp weather than will a thicker mixture. The effect of humid air on shellac can usually be seen if a finisher attempts to spread bleached or white shellac varnish over a dark colored wood, such as walnut, during damp weather. The shellac film is apt to turn white or yellowish white because the rapid evaporation of the alcohol changes the temperature of the surface enough to cause moisture to condense and leave light streaks where the brush has applied the shellac. As soon as the water in the film dries out, the proper color is almost always restored. If white shellac is mixed with a small amount of orange shellac, or slightly colored with a spirit dye, the discoloration from moisture is greatly reduced or is less obvious.

Good and Bad Qualities of Shellac. A film of shellac is an excellent finish in several respects: it forms an unexcelled binder between filler and varnish coats; it does not show white when scratched; it seals the pores of fine-grained work satisfactorily; it is very transparent; it does not often cloud or darken wood appreciably; and it makes a hard surface which is a good undercoat for other finishes. It is the best surfacer known for preventing pitch from exuding from knots; but it may disintegrate after becoming damp, and become powdery and rough; therefore it is not suitable for outdoor finishes.

All of the lac gums except garnet lac contain various amounts of shellac wax, which is practically insoluble in alcohol. In manufacturing bleached or white shellac, an attempt is made to remove the wax; and, as a result, only three to four per cent of this insoluble matter remains. If any shellac wax is left in a shellac varnish, it may cause trouble after a coating of such an unpurified shellac has been spread over a surface. The wax can be separated out to a considerable extent by filtering the liquid shellac; the wax being removed in the alcohol, as it is usually insoluble. Moisture contained in bleached shellac gum itself may also cause a milky appearance, sometimes showing this effect later on, especially on French polished or rubbed shellac surfaces.

Shellac, on account of its acid nature, is affected by various alkalies. Ammonia which is found in the air, especially when present in unusual quantities, soon reacts with a shellac film and decomposes it. A coat of shellac can frequently be removed by washing it with a strong solution of soap and water.

Shellac softens at a very low temperature and melts at a very moderate heat, this fact being shown by its manufacture. The heat of a charcoal fire causes the crude lac gum to melt and ooze through the meshes of a cloth bag. A thin film or coating of shellac varnish shows the same sensitiveness to heat; consequently, articles of furniture that are finished with shellac, even though covered with an oil varnish, should not be placed near a fire nor left outdoors in intense sunlight. Films of shellac are apt to blister if they are heated much above ordinary room temperature.

Rubbing Shellacked Surfaces. Every coat of shellac should be rubbed in some way before the next layer of finish is applied, the chief reasons for which are: (1) a more level surface is obtained by this operation, especially if sandpaper is used; and (2) a dull, rougher surface is produced which causes better adherence of the next coat of finish that may be applied. Shellac varnish will stick to an unrubbed undercoat of shellac, however. Undercoats of shellac may be rubbed with very fine sandpaper, preferably using No. 3/0 or No. 4/0 in order that the finish may not be scratched and to prevent cutting through the coats of shellac and stain thus producing light spots or streaks. The sandpaper may be held in the hand for sanding the edges, especially, or it may be bent over a very soft-faced felt or rubber block when used on large surfaces.

If the novice is careless or uses too much pressure on the sandpaper, he is very apt to do serious damage in a very short time. Beginners should be warned that spots and streaks cut through stained and shellacked surfaces can not be repaired without much labor. Sometimes it will be necessary to remove the entire finish, and the whole surface which has been damaged by sanding must be refinished. Curved surfaces are sanded to the best advantage by the use of thin and flexible sandpaper. Fine steel wool is also useful for rubbing between coats on irregular or curved surfaces. Very light pressure should be used, because there is great danger of cutting through the coats of shellac and stain, even when rubbing with the very finest grades of steel wool, such as No. 2/0, which is about as fine as No. 3/0 sandpaper, or even with the No. 3/0 grade which is still finer.

Rubbing with a standard mineral rubbing oil and pumice stone on a felt pad is the best way to smooth the final coat of shellac if several coats are used. While water and pumice stone may be used properly in rubbing varnish no water should be used in rubbing shellac.

PROCEDURE

Procedure for Producing a Shellac Finish.

1. Prepare a mixture of 60% 4-lb. cut white shellac and 40% pure denatured alcohol.
2. With a 2″ brush apply the first coat of shellac.
3. Sand lightly when dry with 7/0 or 8/0 finishing paper.
4. Apply 3 additional coats of shellac; sand lightly between each coat.
5. Remove the shine on the last coat with No. 2/0 or 3/0 steel wool.
6. Apply two successive coats of wax; polish each with a soft cloth.

If a highly polished rubbed finish is desired, proceed as follows:

1. Prepare a mixture of 50% linseed oil and 50% turpentine.
2. After four coats have been applied, rub the final coat with No. 8/0 finishing paper or No. 3/0 steel wool, using the above mixture as a lubricant.

3. Rub next with FFF pumice stone, using the above lubricant. Rub with a felt-covered block.
4. After cleaning all surfaces with a cloth, lightly dampened with alcohol, apply two successive coats of wax. Polish with a soft cloth.

Shellac Substitutes. The high prices of good grades of shellac gum and alcohol have suggested a number of shellac substitutes. Nearly all of these substitutes have been found to be much inferior to high grade shellac varnishes; consequently they have almost disappeared from the market. Not a single such substitute has been generally accepted to be as satisfactory as shellac, though a few are still sold on account of their low prices.

Substitute shellacs are usually made by replacing part of the shellac gum with some other cheaper resin such as rosin, manila gum, manila dust, or an artificial kauri gum, usually called French kauri. Common rosin, which is cheaper than most of the other resins, is practically completely soluble in alcohol, and is substituted for shellac resin in various proportions up to about 50 per cent. For a cheap substitute, such a mixture of shellac gum and rosin of the W-W, or water white, grade is cut in denatured alcohol in the proportion of two and one-half to three pounds of resin mixture to the gallon of solvent. Some of the poorer shellac substitutes that have been offered on the market contain no shellac resin at all. They have sometimes been made from a mixture of rosin and manila dust, cut or dissolved in a solvent largely of wood alcohol, which can be replaced in part by 25 to 33⅓ per cent of naphtha and acetone.

Shellac substitutes dry very rapidly because of the solvents used and, in general, do not spread as well under the brush as genuine shellac varnish.

Selection and Care of Shellac Brushes. The solvents used in dissolving shellac resin all evaporate very rapidly; therefore it is best to use a large brush when applying shellac varnish because of the rapid setting and drying of the film after it is spread on a surface. Much more rapid work can be done on a large surface by the use of a brush at least 4″ in width. For shellacking furniture and small articles the brushes should be from 2″ to 3″ in width. A large brush enables a finisher to dip up more shellac at a time, and he is less apt to try to work with a nearly dry brush, which is a serious fault because it causes streaks, laps, and uncovered spots, instead of an evenly covered surface. Touching up or rebrushing cannot be done skillfully enough so that it does not show; therefore, great care must be used in the application of shellac varnish to prevent the setting of the film from one brush stroke before the next is spread adjacent to it at its outer edge.

Brushes having the bristles set or vulcanized in rubber are the most satisfactory for use with shellac. It is possible to apply shellac varnish with brushes set in glue, but such brushes do not last as long nor give as satisfactory service as fitch rubber-set brushes with rubber ferrules. Brushes having the bristles set in shellac cannot be used at all in spreading shellac varnish, because the bristles will all come out of the ferrules in a short time. For applying shellac, it is best to select brushes having rather fine, soft bristles because they will leave a more even surface with fewer brush marks.

Shellac cannot be brushed into the grain and then smoothed out lengthwise of the fibers of wood in the manner of applying wood filler or even varnish. It must be applied quickly with a well loaded brush, using quick strokes and light pressure, because this method of spreading shellac varnish reduces the number of air bubbles. Shellac varnish is apt to pile up and be rough or too thick at the laps; consequently, it is best to select a rather large, soft brush, and to apply the finish lengthwise of the grain only, using quick, light strokes. Fast careful work prevents laps, which are the result of slow work, and the rapid evaporation of the alcohol solvent.

Brushes used in applying shellac varnish should be cleaned very often in either wood alcohol or denatured alcohol; if this is not done, fragments of partly-dried shellac will work out of the bristles around the ferrule and the film on the surface where the finish has been spread will show specks. If the brush cannot be satisfactorily cleaned in alcohol, a paint and varnish remover may be used as a cleaning agent. Brushes which have had the partly dried and hardened fragments of shellac removed by washing in paint and varnish remover should be dried and then softened in alcohol in order to remove traces of the cleaning fluid from the bristles before putting the brushes back into shellac again.

Shellac brushes should never be washed or soaked in either water or turpentine. Water will cause serious trouble as has already been mentioned in this chapter. Some finishers make a practice of washing all brushes in soap and water after they have been thoroughly cleaned. If this is done, the brushes must be allowed to dry thoroughly before returning them to the shellac container.

Brushes used in shellac varnish should be cleaned daily, and kept suspended in a tank of alcohol or very thin shellac varnish when not in use. If allowed to dry over night after being cleaned, they always become somewhat stiff. This stiffness usually disappears, however, if the brush is soaked in alcohol for a few minutes before it is used in shellac varnish again.

French Polishing. Before the discovery of methods of making oil or oleoresinous varnishes, French polishing was often used in finishing articles of furniture when a surface with a high polish or brilliant, glossy effect was desired. In those days there was no commonly known method of applying a varnish to a surface with a brush. It is possible that some of the famous violin makers did have secret methods of making varnishes from amber and other high grade resins, and that these finishes were used to a limited extent long before our modern oil varnishes were known. The oldtime finisher had few choices in his materials, and usually was compelled to choose an oil finish, a wax finish, or a French polish.

French polishing has almost disappeared from among modern finishing methods, largely because of the slowness of procedure which is necessary, and the large amount of labor which is always involved. In addition to these serious objections, French polishing requires much skill, and is really a job for an expert. Occasionally, a student or amateur wood finisher in the home or shop has some article or furniture, such as a red cedar chest, or a table made of some foreign wood, which he wishes to finish in natural colors with a brilliant, lustrous effect. Such work can be done at odd times, and the cost of the labor involved is not considered.

Several procedures are possible in French polishing. The

method is not often attempted on open pored work, such as oak or chestnut. In case such woods are to be finished with French polish, it is best to stain and fill the surfaces before any polishing with a rubbing pad is attempted.

A filler in its natural color will darken any wood to a certain extent on account of the linseed oil which is an ingredient of the filler itself. French polishing is more commonly attempted on close grained woods such as red cedar, or diffuse porous woods having small tracheal vessels or, in other words, rather inconspicuous pores, such as those of mahogany or walnut.

Various mixtures of thin shellac are recommended for French polishing. Sometimes the following is used:

> 6 ounces orange or white shellac gum,
> 1 quart denatured alcohol—190° proof, formula No. 1,
> ½ ounce Venice turpentine.

The mixture should be stirred or churned for a number of hours before use. The Venice turpentine is supposed to add durability and toughness to the film and make the solution easier to apply with the rubber. Shellac gum is not commonly kept among the supplies in a present day shop; therefore the old formula may be stated in a more convenient form as follows:

> 1 pint prepared denatured alcohol shellac varnish,
> 3 pints denatured alcohol—190° proof,
> ¾ ounce Venice turpentine.

Sometimes, raw linseed oil is substituted for the Venice turpentine. These substances are used for their lubricating qualities. Linseed oil is only partly soluble in alcohol and is very largely removed by the spiriting off process at the end of the polishing operation. Bleached linseed oil is preferable if one wishes to keep the wood in its natural color.

Another shellac mixture for French polishing that is preferred by some finishers is as follows:

> 4 ounces prepared denatured alcohol orange or white shellac varnish,
> 1 quart alcohol (denatured)—190° proof,
> 1 ounce benzoin gum,
> 1 ounce poppy oil.

If the mixture is to be used on woods which have pronounced hues, color that is made from spirit soluble coal-tar dyes should be added, using Bismarck Brown for mahogany, and Bismarck Brown with more or less spirit soluble black or even a touch of Methyl Violet to give less deadness to the tone whenever dark brown is desired. Bismarck Brown, which is much more red than brown in tone, can be grayed as desired by the addition of a complementary color, such as Victoria Green, Malachite Green, or any of the spirit soluble greens. The wood finisher should always be very careful about coloring shellac, using as little stain as possible, because most of the coloring matter will remain above the surface and obscure the grain of the wood to a certain extent.

French polish is applied with a rubbing pad rather than with a brush. Many experienced finishers prefer a cone shaped pad, made by winding strips of clean muslin into a conical form of about 3″ or 3½″ in length, and 1″ to 1¼″ in diameter at the base. The covering for the rubbing pad is made of linen, or rather of fine lintless cotton cloth, about the size of a man's handkerchief. The cone should be well wetted with the shellac mixture and covered by the cloth. A good way to wrap the cone in the cover cloth is to place it near the middle, fold over the end of the cloth back to the point of the pad, and then fold and gather the excess cloth about the back of the cone but at one side of it.

In applying the polish some finishers dust a small amount of fine pumice stone over the surface to be finished, and this material is then rubbed into the pores as a filler. The pad is always used with circular motions, gradually covering the entire surface. On close grained woods no pumice stone is used as a filler, the shellac itself being rubbed on the surfaces and into the pores. Mixtures for French polishing which contain oil can frequently be rubbed over the surfaces without coating the surface of the pad with raw linseed oil. The rubbing pad requires the addition of more shellac from time to time as the surface of the wood absorbs the polish. Many coats of the thin shellac varnish are necessary for the successful French polish. The finished surfaces should always be allowed to dry from a half hour to two hours between coats. Each coat of polish needs to be slightly smoothed or cut off with very fine sandpaper, No. 6/0 to No. 8/0 sizes. It is usually more satisfactory to use thinner shellac for the last coats than for the under-

10—9. Materials needed to do French polishing.

coats. All that is necessary is to thin the polishing mixture with more denatured alcohol.

The final "spiriting-off" process removes any small roughness or ridges that may be left in the polishing processes. A rubbing pad that has only a little shellac in it should be used. The surface of the pad is moistened with pure 190° alcohol, and the polishing is continued with circular strokes over the entire surface. Somewhat smoother results can often be secured by making the circular motions with the pad in the direction opposite to that used during the earlier applications of the polish. The finisher should be very careful not to use too much alcohol on his pad, or much of the polish that has been applied previously may be removed. The "spiriting-off" process removes any excess lubricating oil and leaves the surface with a very clear, beautiful finish having an exceptionally high luster.

Procedure for French Polishing.

1. After all surfaces have been sanded as smooth as possible, raise the grain of the wood with a rag lightly dampened with water.
2. Resand all surfaces with fine sandpaper.
3. Prepare a mixture of shellac according to the following formula:

  1 pint prepared denatured alcohol shellac varnish,
  3 pints denatured alcohol, 190° proof,
  ¾ ounce of Venice turpentine or raw linseed oil.

186

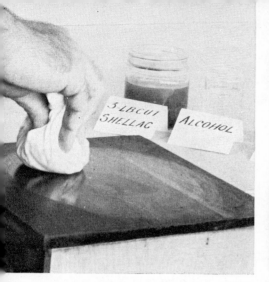

10—10. With a cone-shaped polishing rag, apply the shellac in a circular motion. A good polishing rag is made by winding strips of muslin into a conical shape and covering with a piece of soft linen. 10—11. A small amount of pumice stone sprinkled on the surface fills any hairline cracks. It is rubbed in with the shellac rubbing pad.

Have on hand any other needed materials (Fig. 10-9).

4. With a cone-shaped pad, made of muslin covered with a soft linen cloth, apply the shellac in a light, circular motion. Work from the middle to the sides (Fig. 10-10).

5. When the first coat has dried for 20-30 minutes, apply the second coat. Sprinkle a small amount of pumice on the surface to fill up any hair line cracks (Fig. 10-11).

6. After another drying period, proceed with the next shellac application. Put a little more alcohol in the shellac and place a few drops of oil on the rubbing pad.

10—12. After applying several coats of shellac and allowing for sufficient drying time, remove any excess oil with a clean rag lightly dampened with denatured alcohol.

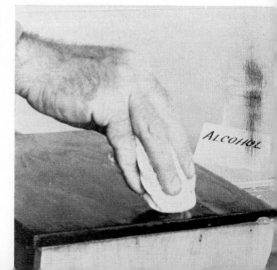

7. After three coats have been applied, allow all surfaces to dry overnight.
8. Apply from seven to eight coats of shellac, thinning the shellac with alcohol after each coat. Also increase the drying time.
9. After the last coat has dried thoroughly, remove any excess oil with a clean rag, lightly dampened with alcohol. This operation is usually referred to as "spiriting-off" (Fig. 10-12).

French Polishing on the Lathe. Polishing with shellac on a lathe is a modified form of French polishing that is often used in school shops. For polishing in the lathe, a "rag" or piece of cloth is substituted for the rubbing-pad which is used on flat surfaces. Cotton waste is recommended by some teachers, but it is apt to catch and wind up on spindle turnings and is not satisfactory for that reason. A rather stout, smooth cloth that is lintless and torn to a size 2″ or 3″ wide by 12″ to 16″ long makes a good "rag," that can be held against a spindle on the lathe with one hand at each end of the cloth, thus securing the proper pressure and avoiding the danger of catching and winding up. The mixture of shellac is similar to that already suggested for French polishing. The following formula has been found satisfactory:

1 ounce white shellac varnish,
4 to 5 ounces denatured alcohol,
$\frac{1}{10}$ ounce linseed oil (raw oil preferred).

A number of coats of thin shellac are needed in order to fill the pores of wood properly and build up enough thickness of film to give a good gloss to the wood when the mixture is applied with a "rubbing rag." Some finishers use a slightly thicker shellac mixture for the first few coats, and a thinner or weaker polishing shellac similar to the formula suggested for the last few coats. From six to ten coats of thin shellac are required in order to furnish a satisfactory finish. In polishing with a shellac rag, the lathe should be run at about its slowest speed, and the cloth, moistened in the middle, should be stretched between the two hands and the shellac applied in this way. The finisher should keep the rubbing rag moving constantly to spread the polish and keep it from piling up in ridges or rings. More of the thin shellac must be placed on the cloth from time to time as the polish is drawn off from the rubbing rag to the wood. The last operation should be a polishing or "spiriting-off" with 190° proof alcohol alone, on an old polishing-cloth that has some shellac in it from previous use. The cloth should not be soaked with alcohol for the finishing process, or much of the previously-applied film of shellac may be removed. Careful work with a polishing rag, dampened with alcohol and kept in motion along the piece being polished while the lathe is in motion, will smooth a surface and give it a beautiful gloss. In addition to smoothing the surface, the clear alcohol removes most of the linseed oil which was mixed with the shellac for the purpose of lubrication. The removal of the oil improves the luster and imparts to the smooth film of shellac a more brilliant gloss.

Rubbing varnish which has been thinned with from three to five parts of turpentine can be used with a rubbing rag on the lathe just as thin shellac is used. The coats of varnish take much longer to dry than is the case with each film of shellac. Each of the thin films of varnish adds more body to the finish than does a coat of shellac, and should have about 24 hours for drying, while the shellac finish requires only from one half hour to an hour for hardening between applications.

Procedure for French Polishing on the Lathe.

1. Prepare a small amount of shellac, consisting of one part of

10—13. Fasten the spindle to be finished securely between the live and dead center of the lathe. 10—14. Apply a small amount of shellac to the polishing rag. Add a few drops of linseed oil as additional lubricant. Oil avoids "piling up" of the shellac.

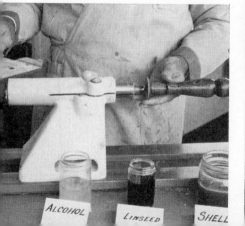

10—15. With the lathe turning very slowly, apply the shellac to the spindle. Move the rag back and forth constantly. 10—16. In another method, the rag is held in one hand, while applying a little linseed oil with the finger tips of the other hand.

white shellac and three parts of denatured alcohol. Add a few drops of raw linseed oil.

2. Fasten the wooden spindle to be polished securely between the live and the dead center of the lathe (Fig. 10-13).
3. Start the lathe, running it at a very slow speed.
4. Apply a small amount of shellac to the middle of the polishing rag (Fig. 10-14). Add one or two drops of linseed oil.
5. Hold the rag at both ends and apply the shellac to the spindle, moving the rag back and forth constantly (Figs. 10-15 and 16).
6. Apply more shellac as it penetrates the wood. Use a little oil for lubricant.
7. Allow this first application to dry for one or two hours, then repeat the above procedure.
8. Apply from six to eight coats of shellac, allowing sufficient drying time between coats.
9. After the last coat has been applied, "spirit-off" with a cloth lightly dampened with denatured alcohol (Fig. 10-17).

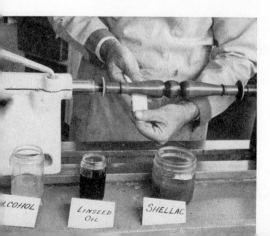

10—17. After the final application has been put on and is thoroughly dry, spirit off with a soft, clean rag, lightly dampened with denatured alcohol.

190

SELECTED REFERENCES, CHAPTER X

Spirit Varnishes

American Bleached Shellac Association, "How to Use Shellac for Best Results," 1941.

"Common Varnish Troubles and Their Causes," *Power Engineering*, pp. 99-100, Jan., 1952.

Fisher, E. M., *What You Should Know About Paint*, pp. 80-81, 1953.

Gibbia, S. W., *Wood Finishing and Refinishing*, "Shellac and How to Use It," pp. 67-81, 1954.

Mattiello, Joseph J., *Protective and Decorative Coatings*, Volume 1, "Ester Gum," Chapter X, pp. 292-301, 1941.

Ibid., "Rosin," Chapter VII, pp. 175-212, 1941.

Ibid., "Shellac and Other Lacs," Chapter IX, pp. 259-291, 1941.

Ibid., "Natural Resins for the Paint and Varnish Industry," Chapter VIII, pp. 213-258, 1941.

McGee, R. A. and Brown, A. G., *Instructional Units in Woodfinishing*, "To Prepare and Apply Shellac," Chapter III, pp. 22-28, 1950.

"Shellac," Shellac Information Bureau, 64 Pine Street, New York City, New York.

Soderberg, G. A., *Finishing Materials and Methods*, "Shellac, Varnish," Chapter IV, pp. 33-41, 1952.

U. S. Department of Commerce, *Paint Manual with Particular Reference to Federal Specifications*, page 55, 1945.

Wampler, R. H., *Modern Organic Finishes*, pp. 23, 259; 1946.

Chapter XI

Natural Fossil-Gum Varnishes (1)

Brief History of Varnishes and Varnish Making. The old saying, "There is nothing new under the sun" seems to be true about varnishes. The history of varnish reaches back almost to the very dawn of the history of human beings.

From time immemorial varnish has been used to *beautify* and preserve. The close connection between the two words —varnish and beauty—is shown by the derivation of the word varnish itself. History tells us that in the North African city of Cyrene, which was the capital of a Greek colony, there lived during the middle of the third century B. C. a very beautiful woman, Berenice, the attractive and faithful wife of Ptolemy Euregetes, King of Egypt. Soon after her marriage to the king this golden-haired woman made a vow that she would sacrifice on the altar of the goddess, Venus, her golden or amber colored hair if the king, her husband, should come back safely from a war in Asia. The story is mixed with mythology which tells us that the shining hair covered with jewels was wafted from the altar to heaven and formed a constellation in the Milky Way which we still know as *Coma Berenices*, or Berenice's Hair.

The Greeks, who were a seafaring race, had imported a beautiful resin which we now call amber, probably from France or Denmark or from the shores of some other distant northern sea. This attractive material was like the color of Berenice's hair, and it was then given the name of Berenice. For many centuries after the time of the famous Queen of Cyrene, the Greeks and Romans prized and valued amber, which was the resin that was used in making varnish, and continued to call it Berenice. The word was also written in Greek in a slightly different form—*Pheronice*—and sometimes pronounced with a sound like our V for the *Ph*. In Latin the

word was at first written in the form, *Verenice,* and later
changed to *Vernix,* which is said to be the root word of the
word varnish in the English language.

The inventor of liquid varnish is unknown. Its use, however, reaches far back into antiquity. From time to time samples of very old varnish have been discovered; for example,
when some of the tombs of Egypt were opened, mummy
cases, evidently 2500 or more years old, were found, finished
with a pale yellow varnish that was scarcely checked by age
and the elements.

Although the coats of varnish on the mummy cases and
other wooden articles have lasted well, the finishing materials
were very poorly applied, indicating that there were no
brushes at that period of the world's history. The workmen
evidently spread or smeared the liquid varnish over the surface with some tool having a flat surface—possibly a spatula or
trowel. It is known that spatulas were used in later centuries
for spreading thick varnish, and it is probable that this same
method was used for many centuries.

The composition of these old varnishes is unknown. They
are thought to have been compounds of some of the resins then
known in North Africa and an oil, probably oil of cedar, which
is quite similar to our turpentine. It is known that very ancient
peoples had flax, and that they knew how to prepare some
of the vegetable oils, particularly olive oil. It is, therefore,
quite possible that the Egyptian varnishes may have been
drying oil varnishes rather than volatile oil varnishes which
were made from an evaporating oil, such as oil of cedar.

Varnishes have evidently been used throughout all the
ages—from practically prehistoric times in Egypt down to the
present day. Mention of varnish is made in the manuscripts
of many of the world's great writers. Pliny, who lived during
the first century, A. D., in writing about Apelles (1.XXXV, C.
18), the court painter of Alexander the Great during the fourth
century B. C., wrote: ". . . that he spread the varnish over his
completed work so thin that it brought out the brilliancy of
the colors by reflection and protected it from dust and dirt."

The most important and valuable of the treatises on varnish
coming from the middle ages is found in the writings of
Theophilus Presbyter who was a Swiss or German monk. This

man was probably also the same person as Tutilo, or Tuotilo, who lived in the monastery of St. Gall. This monk tells how to make varnish out of fornis or glassa (amber) and linseed oil by use of a heating and mixing process. His formula called for one part of powdered amber with two parts by weight of linseed oil—the two substances to be properly heated together.

Varnish like the above was especially used to cover paintings. It was not spread with a brush, but was smeared over the surface of paintings with the fingers, and over boards, probably, with a spatula.

The various formulas for varnish making used during the middle ages contained linseed oil and a resin, such as amber or sandarac, which were mixed while hot. Some of the formulas after about 1520 suggested dilution of the varnish with naphtha, spirits of wine, or linseed oil. Burnt rock alum was often recommended for an ingredient to be mixed with the boiling linseed oil and resin.

While some slight changes were made from century to century, there was little improvement in varnish making for about 800 years—from the time of Theophilus in the tenth or eleventh century until near the end of the eighteenth century. It also seems quite probable that the oil and amber formula for varnish making was handed down to Theophilus from the mummy case varnishers of Egypt who knew how to make similar varnishes at least as early at 500 B. C.

Purpose of Varnish. It is very evident that man must have had some very definite purpose in mind which prompted him to use varnish on precious articles in the past and to continue to use it throughout all ages since the dawn of civilization. The reasons for the use of varnish as a finishing material are many, some of which are obvious to the casual observer, while others are discoverable only through the use of the material itself. The two chief purposes that the wood finisher has in mind for using varnish are the preservation of the material and the unfolding or development of beauty.

Preservation is secured in various ways—such as through the addition of hardness to the surface; through protection from wear and abrasion; through the exclusion of moisture to a large extent, thereby preventing swelling, warping, and raising of the grain; through the extension of the life of the article because of the shutting out of rot fungi and moisture which are the agencies of decay; and through protection of the surface itself in such a manner that cleaning can be done with water without damage to the material which is covered by the film of varnish.

Beauty is often made more manifest, and is amplified or revealed, by the use of varnish in a number of ways—such as through making more permanent the freshness, the newness, and the attractiveness of the grain if the article be of wood; through prevention of the fading of alluring natural colors or of stains which are somewhat fugitive; through warding off or delaying the dulling or graying changes from weathering, or the chemical action of gases or liquids; through the leveling effect of filling up pores or small openings; and through putting a polish on the surface itself, or through the production of a pleasing gloss or luster that adds attractiveness to the general appearance of the article.

Classification of Varnishes. The method of drying divides all varnishes into three distinct classes: (1) *spirit varnishes,* which dry through evaporation and contain various volatile solvents, such as alcohol and turpentine; (2) *oil varnishes,* which contain drying oils that dry or harden slowly through oxidation, the most important drying oils being linseed oil and tung oil or China wood oil; and (3) synthetic resin varnishes. (See Chapter XIII and XIV). The spirit varnishes can be divided into two classes, one of which contains an alcoholic solvent, and the other a rapidly drying volatile oil such as turpentine. Oil varnishes, which are often called oleoresinous or fixed oil varnishes, contain a volatile oil, which evaporates quickly, in addition to the fixed or oxidizing oil which remains in the film and gradually takes on more oxygen.

The resins selected for use in oil varnishes are generally chosen from the hard or semihard group, with the exception of rosin (colophony), and these resins are not easily soluble cold; consequently in the manufacture of varnish, all hard gums are heated until they are melted, and, in this condition, they are soluble in hot drying oils, forming a mixture that can be thinned with volatile oils before becoming cold.

The chief difference between spirit varnishes and oil varnishes is in their methods of drying, spirit varnishes drying by evaporation alone, and oil varnishes drying partly by evaporation, partly by oxidation, and other slow chemical changes.

Two other types of varnish which are somewhat different from spirit varnishes and oil varnishes are sometimes given in classifying varnishes; these are known as japans and enamels.

Japan varnishes, also called painters' japan *driers*, are sometimes considered as a third type of varnish. Japan driers are intended for mixing with drying oils, varnishes, and paints and for use as grinding liquids.

The purpose of the japan drier is not the same as that of varnish. Varnishes are ordinarily used as coatings or films, but japans are not meant for such purposes. Liquid japan drier is used simply as an ingredient in other mixtures in order to increase the rapidity of the oxidation of the drying oils. Japans are manufactured much like oil varnishes, and contain a gum, usually rosin because of its cheapness, a drying oil such as linseed oil, or preferably tung oil, or both, and solvents of volatile oils such as turpentine and heavy naphtha 48°, benzine, and kerosene 46°. An excess of drier, or at least more than is used in varnishes ordinarily, is added to the mixture. The driers are the same as those contained in oil varnishes; namely, litharge, red lead, manganese dioxide, manganese borate, manganese resinate, and lead and cobalt acetate. The oils, gums, and driers are given heat treatments somewhat similar to those used in manufacturing oil-varnishes.

The black baking japans are not driers, but are similar to enamels. They are much like varnishes but usually contain little or no varnish gum. Sometimes rosin is used; in which case it is substituted in part for some of the black gums, such as "parolite," a petroleum asphalt, or gilsonite, a very black, brittle gum that lends a high luster to baking japans. The oil used in these black baking varnishes is principally linseed oil, although cheaper oils such as soya bean and menhaden oil are sometimes used in the cheap grades. The thinners used are kerosene, benzine, and solvent naphtha.

The term *drier*, when used with discrimination, refers to cookings of China wood or linseed oil and drying salts, which are heated together at temperatures of about 500° F. (260 C.). True driers do not contain gums, such as rosin, while japans are made with rosin or some other gum as a base.

The term *enamel* is applied to various mixtures which are used in several industries that have little connection with each other. Wood finishers' enamels are of many kinds with varying compositions. They are very often pigmented varnishes or varnish paints, but sometimes they are similar to air drying japans usually with coloring matter in addition. The wood finisher thinks of enamels as being in the borderland between paints and varnishes.

Composition of Oil Varnishes. The essential ingredients in the composition of an oil varnish can be divided into four classes as follows:

(1) The *resin*, of either fossil or synthetic origin, hardens, thereby giving the film its luster, brilliancy, and hardness, and increasing its durability. The function of the resin is to give "body" or thickness to the film; it also adds beauty and utility.

(2) The *drying* or *oxidizing oils* are solvents for resins in a melted condition, and remain in the film, giving it elasticity and acting as a binder for the gums thus making the varnish more durable. Such oils affect the luster of films containing them to some extent and add waterproof qualities. The drying oils are often called the vehicle of the varnish.

(3) The *solvent* is a volatile oil such as turpentine, varnolene, or some other similar mineral oil that can be used to make the varnish more fluid and thin enough so that it can be spread with a brush.

(4) *Metallic driers*, such as dioxide of manganese, red lead, or some of the other salts of lead which will increase the rapidity of the oxidation of the drying oils.

Secrets of Varnish Making. During many centuries the details of varnish making were considered to be trade secrets, but with the rapid progress of science the old secrets have largely disappeared as such. Instead of being a process of alchemy, varnish making is now directed by a scientifically trained chemist whose knowledge is theoretical as well as empirical.

The manufacture of varnish has become a very highly technical process that requires considerable equipment, skill, and technical knowledge. The resins used in oil varnishes melt at various temperatures usually between 105° C. (221° F.) the melting point of rosin, up to 260° C. (500° F.), which is the temperature for melting hard congo gum. The heat treatments which are given to the resins and oils in the kettles change the qualities of varnishes to a great extent.

Most of the resins which are the best ingredients for oil varnishes are not soluble in the oils or solvents that are incorporated into varnishes until they have had a proper heat treatment and are reduced in weight from 15 to 25 per cent by evaporation. The amount of loss of weight that is necessary is in direct proportion to the hardness of the gum, and to age or degree of fossilization. The drying oils are generally poured into the molten resin while it is still hot enough to be fluid and after the kettle has been removed from the fire. The oil is also heated and mixed with driers and is usually hot when mixed slowly into the molten resin.

The oil and resin do not easily mix; consequently, the mixture must be reheated and stirred, and kept at a temperature around 287.7° C. (550° F.) until it is properly cooked, which requires from an hour or two to six or eight hours. Undercooked varnishes will not receive the proper amount of turpentine and other thinners nor spread in a thick film which oxidizes or dries slowly. Overcooked varnishes take up too much turpentine, are too thin, and dry too quickly. Overcooking makes the varnish darker in color and less durable, because films made from a varnish with much turpentine in its composition are thin. Undercooked varnishes are apt to have the resins poorly combined with the drying oils, and are difficult to thin to a proper brushing consistency.

During the heat treatments or cooking of varnishes, the resins are melted and kept hot for a long period of time, during which great changes take place. It is known that at the high heat used by the varnish maker the gums are decomposed, and vapors are driven off which contain some of the original ingredients of the resins themselves. The weight is often reduced as much as one fifth, leaving a residue which is materially changed chemically and physically. The vegetable drying oils are also changed by high heat, being oxidized in part, and probably polymerized or so modified that the molecular weights of some of the component parts of the oils are different. It is evident that heat treatments at different temperatures, or even variations from short and prolonged cooking at the same temperatures, produce varnish materials that vary in composition and characteristics, and that these variations cause just as great differences in films of the varnishes that are made from them. These changes in the raw materials, such as gums and oils, are so great during heat treatments that a chemical analysis of a varnish after it is made does not reveal much, and the raw materials themselves cannot usually be identified.

Resins Used in Oil Varnishes. Nature has produced a large number of resins that can be used in oil varnishes. To these valuable gums, some of which have become fossilized through contact with the ground during long ages, man has added others which he has produced synthetically. Some of the hardest and best of the fossil resins, such as amber, Benguela copal, and the Zanzibar animi, have practically disappeared from varnish making because it is almost impossible to secure sufficient quantities and the cost is great.

Rosin and Resinates. The cheapest of all the resins that can be used in oil varnishes is called rosin. It is made from the crude gum or oleoresin which is obtained by scarifying or "chipping" the sapwood of various species of pine trees, particularly the Southern longleaf yellow pine (*Pinus palustris*) which grows in the southern portion of the United States of America. Rosin probably might be called a byproduct of the manufacture of gum turpentine because it is a less volatile residue which is separated from the oil by distillation and remains in the still while the turpentine and water, on account of their lower vaporization point, pass out and are collected through condensation.

The composition of French rosin which is manufactured from crude gum from the maritime or cluster pine (*Pinus maritima* or *pinaster*), a tree of the coast districts of southwestern France, is somewhat different from that made from any of the pines which produce turpentine in the United States. Rosin has been studied very carefully by chemists during the past fifty years; but it is such a complex substance, and varies so much in composition, when made from gum taken from different species of trees, that it is still a great problem for research. American rosin is said to contain a large proportion of free abietic acid, which has certain isomers called pinic acid and sylvic acid. The French rosins are reported to contain, not abietic acid, but another similar acid which chemists call pimaric acid. While different rosins are not exactly alike chemically, they are said to contain resenes which are produced from terpenes by oxidation and other chemical reactions, such as polymerization. (Polymerization means a change in molecular weights while the various elements retain the same percentage relatively in the molecule.)

Rosin, or colophony as it is often called, is very brittle, breaking with a glassy fracture. It is highly acid in reaction unless treated with heat and pulverized quick lime (CaO), or 5 to 6 per cent of slaked lime ($Ca(OH)_2$) and cooked at 250° C. (482° F.) to 270° C. (518° F.) until there is a loss of weight of about 13 per cent. This mixture of treated rosin is much harder, and is called a resinate of lime or calcium resinate ($Ca(C_{20}H_{29}O_2)_2$). Other resinates are made from rosin by heat treatment with litharge, making a lead resinate ($Pb(C_{20}H_{29}O_2)_2$); with manganese dioxide, producing a manganese resinate ($Mn(C_{20}H_{29}O_2)_2$); with cobalt oxide, which forms a cobalt resinate ($Co(C_{20}H_{29}O_2)_2$); or with zinc oxide, which creates a zinc resinate ($Zn(C_{20}H_{29}O_2)_2$). The chief function of changing rosin to a resinate through heat and lime or through the addition of metallic oxides is to reduce the acidity of the rosin and to harden the mixture in order to make it wear more satisfactorily in a varnish film.

It should also be stated that lead and manganese resinates are well-known driers of great power, and that zinc resinate is a good hardener of oils as well as of rosin though it possesses no useful drying properties. Treatment with too much lime or oxides makes the resinate too hard and insoluble. Prolonged heat treatments decrease the acidity and increase the hardness of resinates. Ordinary rosin melts usually above 130° C. (266° F.), but the hardening effect during the heat treatments and the acid change in the formation of the resinate in some way combine to raise the fusing point of the new material about 50° C.

Specially prepared rosins for use in varnishes are now obtainable or can be made by many different methods. Rosin gum in preparation is very often melted at a temperature varying from 205° C. (401° F.) to 260° C. (500° F.), then slaked lime is added. Many of the best resinates are given other treatments, sometimes with lead acetate and concentrated lye in a solution of water which is poured into the melted rosin at about 205° C. (401° F.). The rosin mixture is then reheated to about 260° C. (500° F.) before the slaked lime is added. After this another heating to about 300° C. (572° F.) is given for a very short time.

Rosin has generally been considered the very poorest possible gum for use in a varnish, because films made with it are brittle, do not wear very well, and turn white in contact with water. The good fossil resins are the best material obtainable, but they are expensive and sometimes difficult to obtain. During the search for a cheaper resin it was discovered that rosin properly heat treated and changed to a resinate, in combination with tung oil which has superior qualities, can be used at least in part as a substitute for fossil gums and still produce very useful varnishes.

Rosin is used extensively in cheap varnishes, and in a small part at least in high grade varnishes. It is said that the acid of rosin is active in combining with small particles of manganese or lead from the driers thus making a clear, homogeneous fluid containing few specks. In this respect rosin is valuable in small quantities even in good grades of varnish manufactured from fossil gums. Rosin varnishes flow very evenly and help other varnishes to make more level and attractive surfaces. Large quantities of rosin in varnishes are, however, always used because the gum is cheaper and not on account of its good qualities. Rosin varnishes have a good appearance when new, but they are short lived. They soften easily in heat because rosin itself melts easily and becomes tacky at low temperatures—even in the hot sun or in contact with clothing in hot weather. Rosin is often used in very small quantities in melting high grade fossil resins because it causes these hard gums to melt more easily and become more fluid.

Rosin varnishes often produce a brilliant surface soon after they are applied, but they break down chemically and lose their luster. After a time they are apt to crack slightly through loss of elasticity, especially if the varnish happens to be a short oil varnish. The size of the cracks gradually increases with time, giving the crackled effect of alligator leather or of a crackle lacquer finish. In the case of the crackle varnish finish, the small pieces soon lose their adhesion to the surfaces, and chip off, making an entire refinishing job necessary after the old varnish has been entirely removed.

Ester Gum. A valuable resin has been produced synthetically by combining common rosin with glycerine through heat treatments. Rosin generally has an acid number of about 165 according to chemists. It has been discovered that the rosin acid or acids can be combined in part at least with glycerl, the basic radical of glycerine, and a somewhat different material is produced, called an ester, which is something like an organic salt. An ester is known as an alkyl salt of an acid; in other words, it is the product of the reaction of some alcohol with an acid. In the rosin esters the reaction comes from an acid, probably abietic acid ($HC_{20}H_{29}O_2$), with glycerine, which is called a glycyl alcohol or glycerl. The reaction takes place, however, at high temperatures after the rosin has melted. This new rosin or ester gum, which is thus formed, has a much less acid reaction than the original rosin. The acid number of ester gums varies from 6 to 50.

Ester gum is often manufactured by using 100 pounds of rosin and about 1¼ gallons of glycerine. The cooking should last from 2½ to 4 hours, at a temperature of about 275° C. (527° F.). The shorter heat treatment reduces the acid number of ester gum to about 45 or 50, while the longer period changes it to about 11 to 16, though with more glycerine it can be lowered to about 6. Ester gums having low acid numbers must not be heated above 282° C. (about 540° F.), or they will jelly with wood oil if used with it afterwards. Ester gums with higher acid numbers up to about 50 will admit of heat up to 296.1° C. (565° F.).

The melting point of low acid ester gums, having an acid number of about 11 or slightly lower, is 160° C. (320° F.), while gums having higher acid numbers of about 16 melt a few degrees lower—157.2° C. (315° F.).

Ester gum is nearly neutral in its reaction; and, when combined properly with tung oil, it produces a far better varnish than can be made from hardened rosins.

Ester gums are used in varnishes for outside use very extensively because such varnishes weather very well, being much superior to hardened rosin preparations. For waterproof varnishes, ester gums having very low acid numbers, such as 6 to 16, are required; and tung oil is used almost always, even in the cheapest of such spar varnishes. Many spar varnishes made from ester gum will stand submersion in water for long periods of time—several weeks—without turning white, and are said to be absolutely waterproof. Such varnishes should be cooked at temperatures of from 275° C. (527° F.) to 295° C. (563° F.) in order to be properly waterproof. Ester gum varnishes are much superior to varnishes made from high limed rosin, because the latter are brittle and hard and are not waterproof.

Ester gum varnishes when properly made produce a very good luster, though they may "flat" if prepared at too low cooking temperatures. The low acid number of ester gums helps in giving varnishes made from them a very neutral reaction which causes them to be excellent for use with pigments of lead and zinc. Ester gums are often found in mixing varnishes for various uses, though cheaper rosin varnishes are also employed for this purpose.

The appearance of ester gum varnishes is attractive after they are spread because they flow evenly and easily under a brush and make very level surfaces.

DRYING OILS IN VARNISHES

Linseed oil was the only important drying oil extensively used in varnishes until recently. Within a few years another drying oil, which has been well known in China for ages, has found an important place in varnish manufacturing. Each of these oils is at present recognized as having important functions in varnishes. Each has certain characteristics that are valuable though differing from each other, and it is very common for both to be used in the same varnish. The Chinese oil is called tung oil, or Chinawood oil. It is more expensive than linseed oil; therefore it is not considered an adulterant.

Drying oils are oils that change chemically, decomposing largely through oxidation when exposed to the air in thin films which gradually harden. The process of taking on oxygen, or oxidation, is rather slow, the rapidity varying with the different drying oils. The best known of the drying oils are soya bean (or soy bean), linseed oil, and tung oil. Soy bean oil does not dry rapidly owing to its low iodine value (130) unless stepped up by solvent extraction processes, which reject the slow-drying glycerides.

Linseed Oil. For several hundred years the drying oil which constituted the important vehicle used with resins in making oil varnishes has been linseed oil. In fact, only minor changes and improvements in varnish making were made during several centuries, until good fossil resins became scarce, turpentine greatly increased in price, and the good qualities of Chinawood oil for varnish manufacturing were recognized. Linseed oil is obtained from the seeds of the flax plant, which is extensively cultivated in Argentina, Canada, India, Russia and the United States.[1]

The proper form of linseed oil for use in manufacturing varnish is not raw linseed oil. Untreated raw linseed oil when heated with varnish gums to a temperature much above 176.6° C. (350° F.) is apt to "break," or become cloudy with a mucilaginous substance; consequently, treated oils are always selected for heating with resins in making varnishes.

Prepared or treated oils for varnish making are heated to various temperatures, and generally have driers added. There are many methods of treating oils with heat and driers, the method selected in any case depending upon the purpose for which the oil is to be used. The very palest oils are best treated in an aluminum kettle, because a copper kettle may color the heated mixture to a greenish tinge, and an iron kettle may darken the oil or impart a brownish hue to it. The best stirring rods for pale oils are made of brass or aluminum.

Sometimes a good linseed oil is bleached and given better drying qualities through heat treatment at about 287.7° C. (550° F.) for two hours. There is about two per cent loss in volume by such a treatment. Varnish oils are, however, usually given still more rapid drying qualities by the addition of various driers, such as manganese dioxide, manganese borate, calcined magnesia, litharge, red lead, lead acetate, and probably other metallic driers.

---

[1] Mattiello, Joseph J., Protective and Decorative Coatings, Volume I, Chapter I, pp. 58-59.

There is no standard temperature for the heating of linseed oils, nor is there a specified standard length of time for the treatment. A few illustrations will give a general idea of the procedure. A pale varnish oil with a manganese drier is sometimes made by heating V.M. (varnish-makers) linseed oil to 315.5° C. (600° F.) for about half an hour, then allowing it to cool and settle. The oil is finally reheated with a drier, such as manganese dioxide (MnO_2). About one pound of the nut-size manganese dioxide should be used to each two gallons of oil, though more may be added if a stronger drier is desired. The heat treatment for the above conditions should last for about eight to ten hours at a temperature of 160° C. (320° F.).

A darker oil of powerful drying properties may be made by heating V.M. linseed oil to 115.5° C. (240° F.), then slowly adding a mixture of equal parts of litharge (PbO) and red lead (Pb_3O_4), gradually raising the heat to about 215° C. (419° F.), or even 30° or 40° F. higher, if it is necessary in dissolving the driers. The driers may be used in the proportion of 16 pounds each of litharge and red lead to 100 gallons of linseed oil. The above proportions represent about four per cent of driers in the total weight. Linseed oil will receive considerably more drying salts than the amount mentioned before becoming saturated.

Prepared linseed oils for varnish making are somewhat similar in a general way to some of the boiled oils that are sold on the market. The manufacturer of varnishes would not consider any of the so-called boiled oils as exactly suitable or properly prepared for incorporating into varnishes, and usually treats his own oils with reference to some definite use, as for a particular formula. There are several methods of refining the raw oil to start with, and the various metallic driers which differ in their activity and reactions add somewhat different characteristics to the oil. Linseed oil also seems to be changed somewhat chemically, and probably physically, through heat treatments, especially at or above 260° C. (500° F.). Some of the boiled oils in common use have had proper driers added, but they have not received the necessary heat treatments for use in varnishes.

Linseed oil weighs about 7¾ pounds to the gallon at a temperature of 15.5° C. (60° F.). Its viscosity is about 4.00 or slightly less when compared with water, and its specific gravity varies from .931 to .933.

Tung Oil or China Wood Oil. Although tung oil has been known for many years in the Orient, it has only recently been discovered by Europeans and Americans as a very valuable oil for the varnish maker.

Tung oil differs from linseed oil in several characteristics. It cannot be used successfully in its raw state, and requires preparation with driers and heat treatment varying somewhat from that given to linseed oil. If tung oil is gradually heated to about 204.4° C. (400° F.), the oil changes into an insoluble jelly; therefore, it must be heated with care to avoid this condition. To prevent the jellying or polymerization of tung oil, small amounts of linseed oil or rosin must be heated with it. It is often given heat treatment with about an equal amount of linseed oil. The same metallic driers that are selected for preparing linseed oil for use in varnishes are also incorporated into tung oil.

One method of preparing a quick drying oil is to use two parts of tung oil to one of linseed oil. The linseed oil should be heated first to about 260° C. (500° F.) with a drier such as manganese borate (MnB_2O_4), using about one pound of the drier to each eight gallons of linseed oil, and stirring before heating the oil. The tung oil is then added slowly to the hot linseed oil. The combined oils are heated to 270° C. (518° F.), and then more drier is added, a little at a time, to the extent of one pound of litharge (PbO) to each two gallons of tung oil. The litharge should have about three per cent of slaked lime mixed with it in order to make the oil less acid. An oil of this composition contains a maximum of driers and dries very rapidly. Most prepared tung oils are somewhat similar to the above but usually contain less of the metallic driers.

Chinese wood oil (tung oil) varies in color from a pale yellow in its best grades to a dark brown color in oils of poor quality. It has rather remarkable drying properties, and in this respect is superior to linseed oil, although its iodine number is slightly lower, being about 163 while that of linseed oil varies from about 178 to 185 for the North American oil.

Varnish makers who are using rosin in large quantities as an important resin in their formulas claim that tung oil gives a rosin varnish certain valuable properties that can be obtained in no other way. The makers of rosin varnish use about nine-tenths of all of the tung oil that is used in the United States. Ester gum varnishes also require tung oil as an important ingredient. China wood oil is now used as the only drying oil in many varnish formulas. It gives varnishes waterproofing qualities; and, for that reason, it is found in many spar varnishes. Some rosin and ester gum varnishes which contain tung oil as the only drying oil are waterproof if properly prepared. Many other similar varnishes contain a small amount of linseed oil with tung oil as the chief drying oil.

Tung oil not only dries faster than linseed oil, but films made from it become much harder. This added hardness is just what rosin and ester gum varnishes lack to make them more useful and satisfactory. While it is true that varnishes made from cheap gums and tung oil show up exceptionally well when new, tests show that they are not as durable when exposed to the weather as varnishes which contain fossil resins.

Tung oil weighs slightly more than linseed oil, having a weight of 7.84 pounds per gallon at ordinary room temperatures. The specific gravity of China wood or tung oil is about .941, which is a little higher than that of linseed oil, .931 to .933. The viscosity of tung oil is very high, 20.5, while that of linseed oil is only about 4.00, compared with that of water.

VARNISH THINNERS OR VOLATILE OIL SOLVENTS

Varnishes would be too thick to spread properly with a brush if they contained only resins and drying oils such as linseed oil and tung oil. In order to have proper flowing and brushing qualities, all oil varnishes must also contain volatile oil solvents which thin the mixtures to such a consistency that they can be applied easily. Without proper thinners the modern wood finisher can not apply thick varnishes much more smoothly than did the ancient Egyptian who probably used a spatula, trowel, or flat stick for smearing the heavy bodied preservative finishes over the mummy cases of his day.

The important thinners or volatile solvents used in varnishes are wood and gum turpentine, various mineral oils such as benzine, also called naphtha 54°, heavy naphtha 41° and 48°, varnolene, kerosene 46°, Texaco spirits, and special thinning compounds containing some of the above-named volatile oils with small quantities of other substances.

Turpentine. In the past turpentine was considered the perfect solvent for varnishes. At the present time, because of the hydrogenation of petroleum solvents, chemists are able to vary the solvent powers of these petroleum thinners to equal those of turpentine or effect a greater solvency, almost equal to a full aromatic solvent.

Various reports indicate that from 65 to 75 per cent of the world's supply of turpentine comes from the United States. The turpentines made in foreign countries are slightly different in composition from our own product, because the raw materials used abroad are gathered from species of trees different from those that produce the crude turpentine gum in the United States.

Two kinds of turpentine are manufactured in the United States: (1) gum turpentine, manufactured by distilling a crude gum which is exuded from the longleaf pine (*Pinus australis* or *palustris*) and a few other pine trees of the South; and (2) wood turpentine, obtained through the destructive distillation from "lightwood" or pitchy stumps or logs, or sometimes through the steam distillation of wood and the use of volatile solvents, such as gasoline or benzine, for the separation of the turpentine from the rosin.

Gum turpentine is superior to wood turpentine in various ways, particularly in regard to odor; but wood turpentine is often used in varnishes because it is slightly cheaper. Reports indicate that of all the turpentine manufactured in the United States only three per cent is wood turpentine, and the other ninety-seven per cent is gum turpentine. All turpentines bring such high prices at present that varnish makers are willing to take cheap grades, because even low grade turpentines are considered preferable to mineral oils such as the various petroleum solvents.

Turpentine consists very largely of alpha and beta pinene, and distils at temperatures from 155° C. to 180° C. In addition to pinene, turpentines contain small amounts of other terpenes, and some other products of oxidation. Wood turpentine contains small quantities of another terpene, known as dipentene. Chemically, turpentine is not inert and inactive as the petroleum oils are; but it combines readily with many substances such as oxygen, chlorin, bromin, iodine, hydrogen chlorid, nitric acid, sulphuric acid, and many other substances which are highly active chemically.

When exposed to the air in a thin film, turpentine becomes oxidized through absorption of oxygen, and at the same time gives off hydrogen peroxide in small amounts. The absorption of oxygen from turpentine in an uncorked bottle causes the remaining liquid to turn yellow and become more oily and viscous. The boiling point of turpentine is somewhat raised by the various changes that take place, and small quantities of acetic and other acids are produced. Turpentine may turn dark if left in a tin can, because the acids in the oil may attack the iron of the container.

The reason that turpentine is a superior thinner for varnishes and paints is largely on account of its ability to absorb oxygen from the air, then to act as a carrier and thus to convey to the drying oils the free oxygen they so readily absorb. Turpentine also deposits or leaves a certain amount of resinous residue in paints and varnishes, and this material remains in the films of drying oil as a small amount of solid matter. Turpentine evaporates much more slowly than other oils which are often substituted for it. The slow evaporation of turpentine gives it brushing and flowing qualities that no other oil can give. Benzine dries so rapidly that varnishes containing it must be spread quickly, and with great care, or the films or coatings will show brush marks and spots that will have to be touched up. It is thought by some wood finishers and manufacturers that turpentine has more to do with good flowing qualities than aging or even other ingredients in the composition of a varnish.

Turpentine weighs about 7⅕ pounds per gallon at a temperature of 70° F. At 60° F. it weighs from 7.16 pounds to 7.327 pounds per gallon, varying with the specific gravity of different samples of the oil. At 70° F. the variation is from 7.1234 pounds to 7.2896 pounds, and at 80° F. from 7.086 pounds to 7.2515 pounds to the gallon. The above weights are based on a variation of specific gravity from 0.86 to 0.88. The specific gravity of unadulterated turpentine is usually between 0.862 and 0.872 at a temperature of 70° F. The United

States Government standard for turpentine requires that at least 90 per cent of the oil shall distil below 170° C. (338° F.). Most turpentines boil at about 160° C. (320° F.), and entirely distil under 180° C. (356° F.) leaving practically no residue.

Out of the total consumption of turpentine in the United States, about 45 per cent is used by manufacturers for thinning paints and varnishes, and 40 per cent more is used by painters and wood finishers. The other 15 per cent is used in various industries.

Varnishes vary in the amount of drying oils in proportion to the turpentine or other thinners contained. Turpentine is now so expensive that it is not often selected as the sole solvent for varnishes. A "short oil" varnish containing 100 pounds of gum and eight gallons of drying oil would require about 25 gallons of turpentine, while a "long oil" varnish with the same amount of resin and 30 gallons of drying oils would contain about 32 gallons of turpentine. Sometimes a quick-drying "short oil" varnish is made of 100 pounds of resin, five gallons of drying oil, and about 38 gallons of turpentine. Such a varnish might be used as a very thin polishing varnish, but it would not be very durable even though it contained high grade resins and good drying oils. Many varnishes at present contain heavy naphtha 48°, benzine, or varnolene in place of part or all of the turpentine.

Turpentine Substitutes. Several mineral thinners are used as substitutes in part for turpentine in many good varnishes. These less expensive thinners have practically replaced turpentine in most varnishes. They cost only one-fifth to one-quarter as much as turpentine, and add fluidity, flow, and brushing qualities quite similar to those furnished by turpentine. Some manufacturers claim that mineral oils are satisfactory thinners and are practically as good as turpentine in varnishes.

The mineral substitutes are manufactured with the same flash points and distillation ranges as turpentine; therefore they can be placed in hot varnishes at about the same temperature as that used for turpentine. The mixing temperatures are often about 176.6° C. (350° F.), but they may vary somewhat either up or down. The solvent power of petroleum distillates is considerably lower than that of turpentine, rendering the gums in the varnish more liable to precipitation with an excess of thinner. Turpentine gives somewhat better flowing and brushing qualities than can be obtained from the mineral substitutes.

The turpentine substitutes most commonly used in varnish in the United States are: benzine, which is the same as naphtha 54°; naphtha 41° and 48°; petroleum derivatives, manufactured by most oil companies; and kerosene 46°. The ordinary naphthas are too volatile for use in varnishes and cause them to set too quickly and to dry too fast.

Turpentine substitutes for varnishes are often made by compounding two or three of the above named mineral oils. Sometimes a small amount of turpentine, usually wood turpentine if available, is added to the mixture. Moisture and free acid contained in such compounds can be removed by using very small amounts of plaster of Paris and slaked lime.

Driers and Their Functions in Oils, Varnishes, and Japans. The drying oils, such as linseed oil and tung oil, do not dry fast enough in varnishes and paints for most practical purposes; consequently, metallic driers are added to accelerate the drying process which is largely chemical in nature and consists to a great extent of oxidation. The substances used to hasten the drying action of oils are salts of various metals. Such salts are called driers or siccatives.

Salts of various metals, such as calcium, iron, and zinc, have at least slight drying properties; but only those from three metals—cobalt, lead, and manganese—are satisfactory for commercial use. Lead and manganese driers are very commonly used in varnishes; but cobalt is rarely used, though occasionally it is found in the form of a cobalt linoleate, and very recently it has been employed in combination with the acids of other organic oils than linseed.

The function of a drier is largely that of a catalyser, which in this case means that a siccative acts as an oxygen carrier for the oils, which for a time actually gain in weight. The powerful driers, such as the drying salts of lead and manganese, are said to have the capacity of forming two sets of compounds with oxygen, the first of the newly formed substances having only half as much oxygen as is found in the second or final compound.

Driers give up half of their oxygen while in the drying oil; then they absorb an equal amount of oxygen to replace that which was lost, and obtain it from the air. The oils in drying again take oxygen from the driers when they are exposed in films. In this case the driers really act as oxygen carriers from the air to the oil, and increase the rapidity of the oxidation or drying of the film of oil or other finish, such as paint or oil varnish, which contains the drying oil.

The lead driers seem to be more satisfactory than those derived from manganese, even though the latter metal is said to have greater oxidizing power. It is known by the chemists that the oxidizing capacity of a drying oil cannot be correctly measured by its power to absorb oxygen. Some think that the glyceryl radical has its function in the setting, the oxidation, and the polymerization of drying oils.

The changes which take place when oils dry are not very clearly understood by the chemists, partly because it is so difficult to study reactions in the films. It is known, however, that the metals which are the most active as oxygen carriers in oils are those that have more than one oxide, and that this is especially true when the lower oxides form salts that are more stable than the higher oxides.

The amount of driers that rosin or linseed oil will take up before saturation varies greatly with the different drying salts. One gallon of linseed oil, which weighs about $7\frac{3}{4}$ pounds, will absorb $5\frac{1}{4}$ pounds of lead acetate crystals, or $3\frac{1}{10}$ pounds of litharge, or $3\frac{1}{6}$ pounds of red lead, or $1\frac{1}{5}$ pounds of manganese dioxide. Rosin will absorb vastly more of the driers before becoming saturated; for example, 100 pounds of it will take up 36.92 pounds of litharge, or 37.40 pounds red lead, before reaching the saturation point.

The chemical theory of the use of driers as oxygen carriers or catalysts does not seem to take all the reactions into account, and it is evident that part of the phenomena are to some extent physical. There seems to be a greater activity or reaction in a drying film at its surface than elsewhere, and it is probable that a portion of the drier moves to the surface and forms a greater concentration of drying forces just at the place of contact of the air with the film.

The cobalt driers which are sometimes found on the market or which are made in factories are cobalt acetate, cobaltous oxide, cobalt resinate, and cobalt linoleate. Until quite recently cobalt linoleate was the only cobalt drier commonly used, but now combinations of cobalt with some of the other organic oil acids are considered excellent driers.

The lead salts and compounds used as driers are: litharge, which is lead oxide (PbO); red lead, which is called the sesquioxide (Pb_3O_4); lead acetate, ($Pb(C_2H_3O_2)_2 + 3H_2O$), also called white sugar of lead; lead borate, ($Pb(BO_2)_2$); lead resinate, ($Pb(C_{20}H_{29}O_2)_2$); lead oleate, ($Pb(C_{18}H_{33}O_2)_2$); and lead linoleate, ($Pb(C_{18}H_{31}O_2)_2$).

The various manganese driers that can be used are: manganese dioxide (MnO_2); manganese borate in dry form (MnB_2O_4); manganese sulphate ($MnSO_4 + 4H_2O$); and occasionally manganese chloride ($MnC_2 + 4H_2O$). Besides these, the linoleates, resinates, and tungates of manganese are also used as driers. The manganese driers discolor varnishes but little, being much superior to the lead driers in this respect. The lightest in color of all of the manganese driers are the sulphate and the borate; consequently, these salts are often selected as driers for very pale varnishes.

Umber, a ferric oxide containing manganese oxide and clay, receives its drying properties from the manganese content mainly; therefore, it should be considered as a manganese drier rather than an iron drier. Manganese driers are superior to lead driers in resisting moisture; and partly for this reason, they are used with lead driers in waterproof varnishes.

In addition to these driers, a number of the so-called rare earth driers are being used in increasing quantity. They promote the efficiency of the old standard metal driers. Cerium, zirconium, and lithium are examples of these newer, rare earth driers.

For use in paint mixtures manufacturers often select an oleate of lead and manganese which contains about two parts of lead to five parts of manganese. In fact, oleates or resinates made from the two metals just named are commonly used in driers. Driers containing both metals in compounds are often preferred to those made from one of the metals alone, because manganese driers are said to expand in drying while lead driers react differently and are thought to contract.

TABLE VI.

GENERAL FORMULAS FOR OIL VARNISH

Class of Ingredients	Name of Ingredients	General and Chemical Information	Amount Used	Special Function in Varnishes
SOLIDS Varnish Resins or Gums	VARNISH RESINS (General characteristics)	Resins are free acid gums containing resenes. Resins commonly used are hard fossil gums; or rosin, ester gum, or a mixture. Hard resins are not easily soluble cold. They are heated till reduced sometimes 25% in weight, making them more soluble; and then are mixed with hot oxidizing oils. Usual heat about 287° C. (550° F.).	Varies greatly. Spar varnishes often have 27 to 48 gallons of mixed oils to 100 pounds of gum. A very short oil varnish may contain only 4 gallons of oil with 20 gallons of turps to each 100 lbs. of gum.	To furnish solids for films which are about 1/750″ thick. To give resistance to atmosphere and moisture. To produce stableness and gloss. To fill surface cells and stop capillary action. To give hardness to the films.
	PONTIANAK	Melting point 226° C. (440° F.). Semihard. Milky, yellow to reddish-brown. Partly soluble in turpentine.	In spar varnishes, about 100 lbs. gum to 30 gallons of oil and 30 of solvents.	To give waterproof qualities to coach and spar varnishes. To produce hardness in polishing varnishes.
	HARD MANILA (Fossil Copal)	Melts at about 242° C. Quite hard. Dull white, yellow-red, or brown in color.	In polishing varnishes, 100 lbs. gum, 10 gallons of oil, and 36 of solvents.	To produce satisfactory cheap varnishes for inside use. To give good rubbing and polishing qualities to films.
SOLIDS	KAURI	Fossil from New Zealand. Medium hard. Melts at 265° C. (509° F.).	For a coach varnish, 100 lbs. gum, 40 gallons of oil, and 50 gallons of solvent as turpentine.	For durability and to give rubbing and polishing qualities. For use in high-grade varnishes.
	CONGO	Widely used. Fossil. Hard Belgian copal melts at 266° C. Partly soluble in turps and benzine.	For a quick rubbing varnish, 100 lbs. of gum, 8 gals. of oil, and 25 gals. of solvents.	To produce a very light colored hard varnish. To give quality and hardness rather than cheapness.
Varnish Resins or Gums	ROSIN or COLOPHONY	Widely used. Cheap. Melts at 130° C. (266° F.). Slightly soluble in turpentine. Becomes hardened and improved if heated to 200° C. with lime or zinc oxides and becomes a resinate.	For an architectural varnish, 100 lbs. of gum, 30 gallons of tung oil and 90 gallons of solvent.	To lower the price of varnishes. To produce a very level surface. To use in small quantities in high-grade varnishes to cause them to cure quickly. To make varnish films flow easily.
	ESTER GUM	Made by heating common rosin with glycerine to 280° C. (536° F.) thus combining part of the abietic acid with the glycerine. Cheap gum used with tung oil. Melts at 160° C. (320° F.).	For a furniture rubbing varnish, 100 lbs. gum, 10 gallons of tung oil, and 30 gallons of solvent.	To furnish a gum in quantity having a less acid reaction than that of rosin. To produce a waterproof varnish with tung oil that is quite elastic.

TABLE VI.—Continued

GENERAL FORMULAS FOR OIL VARNISH

Class of Ingredients	Name of Ingredients	General and Chemical Information	Amount Used	Special Function in Varnishes
VEHICLES or DRYING OILS		Drying oils form films of a solid elastic nature by oxidation in the air. Linseed and tung oil are the typical drying oils. Drying or oxidation can be accelerated by "driers." Drying oils are "fatty oils" of vegetable origin, and are glycerides which are saponifiable. Oxidation of drying oils is accompanied by heat and danger of spontaneous combustion under certain conditions.	Varies from about 4 gallons up to 52 gallons per 100 lbs. of resin. Rosin and ester gum varnishes contain mostly tung oil with small amounts of linseed oil.	Drying oils act as binders for the resins and make varnish films more elastic. They dry by oxidation instead of evaporation, and make oil varnishes easy to spread. They can be mixed with almost insoluble resins at high temperature and hold them in solution after cooling.
	LINSEED OIL	Is a complex mixture of the glycerides of several vegetable acids. Is extracted from flaxseed by pressure. Varies from light yellow to yellowish brown in color. Flash point is 260° C. Soluble in turpentine and ether. Dries quicker after boiling with driers.	Varies from 8 to 52 gallons of oil to 100 pounds of resin. Long oil varnishes have 25 to 52 gallons of oil to 100 lbs. of resin. Medium oil varnishes—12 to 25 gallons of oil; and short oil, less than 12 gallons to each 100 lbs. of resin.	Drying or oxidation of glycerides of unsaturated acids. Mixed with resins it forms a tough elastic film which is not easily soluble. It provides proper drying qualities which can be varied by the heat treatment of the oil and the driers used in it.
VEHICLES or DRYING OILS	TUNG OIL or CHINA WOOD OIL	Is extracted from the nuts of a Chinese tree by pressure. Dries in two-thirds the time needed for linseed oil. Durability of treated tung oil is greater than for linseed oil. Usually heated to about 205° C. with rosin or linseed oil to prevent jellying. Most of it is used in rosin varnishes.	In spar and marine varnishes, usually 32 to 44 gallons with 4 to 8 gallons of linseed oil to 100 lbs. of resin. In short oil rubbing varnishes, 4½ gallons of tung oil with 4½ gallons of linseed oil, to 100 lbs. of resin.	It gives unusual durability to varnishes with cheap resins. It is very impervious to water when used even with rosin and ester gum. It dries harder than linseed oil, and furnishes hardness to films of rosin varnishes. It dries very rapidly, and is therefore valuable in quick drying varnishes.
VOLATILE SOLVENTS	SOLVENTS or THINNERS	They should have a distilling range similar to that of turpentine which boils at 160° C. and is all distilled at 180° C.		Thinners make varnishes more fluid, blend the mixtures of resins and oils, and furnish brushing qualities.
	TURPENTINE (Two kinds: Gum Turpentine and Wood Turpentine.)	Best known varnish solvent, but is not obtainable in the quantity needed. It is used in part as a solvent for most high-grade varnishes, but is not often found in the cheapest varnishes.	With each 100 lbs. of resin when 8 gallons of oil are used about 25 gallons of turps are added. When 30 gallons of oil are used about 32 gallons of turps are added.	It helps in oxidation of the oils. It leaves a slight residue. It gives exceptional flowing and brushing qualities because of slow evaporation.

TABLE VI.—Continued

GENERAL FORMULAS FOR OIL VARNISH

Class of Ingredients	Name of Ingredients	General and Chemical Information	Amount Used	Special Function in Varnishes
VOLATILE SOLVENTS (*Cont'd*)	NAPHTHA and BENZINE	Various heavy naphthas such as naphtha 41°, 48° and 54° (benzine) are used.	May contain up to 80 gallons in long oil varnishes, with 52 gallons of oil to each 100 lbs. of resin.	They are used in low-cost thinners to add brushing qualities.
	HYDROGENATED NAPHTHAS	Various semi-aromatic naphthas, ranging in solvent strength from turpentine to xylol.	As a 10-25% blend with naphtha and benzine.	They improve solvency and permit increased solids content at equal viscosity using straight naphthas.
	KEROSENE 46°	Solvents for low-grade varnishes.	Used in small quantities, 4 to 16 gallons to 100 lbs. of resin in cheap varnishes, especially baking varnishes.	Very cheap turpentine substitutes. Acts as a retarder.
METALLIC DRIERS	LITHARGE	Lead monoxide (PbO). Often used with other driers, such as manganese borate, red lead, and lead acetate.	Varies greatly, 1½ lbs. to 16 lbs. to each 100 pounds of resin in varnishes.	To accelerate the rapidity of drying of the drying oils.
	RED LEAD	Also called minimum (Pb₃O₄). Often used with manganese sulphate and borate.	Varies up to 16 lbs. per 100 lbs. of resins in varnishes.	To act as an oxygen carrier for drying oils.
	LEAD ACETATE	Also called sugar of lead (Pb(C₂H₃O₂)₂ + 3H₂O). Often used with red lead, and manganese borate or sulphate.	Usually about 8 lbs. to 100 lbs. of resins.	To accelerate the drying qualities of oils.
	MANGANESE DIOXIDE	Black oxide of manganese (MnO₂). Used with red lead and sometimes other driers.	Often 2 to 2½ lbs. to 100 lbs. of resin in varnishes.	Chiefly to increase the thorough drying of the complete film thickness.

Concentrated driers may contain as much as twelve per cent of metallic drying salts when compounded in liquid form, while weaker driers sometimes are manufactured with only two per cent.

Painters' japans are liquid mixtures of driers, and usually contain a varnish gum or resin in addition to the other ingredients ordinarily found in driers. The gums used in japan driers are among the cheapest of the varnish-resins such as rosin especially, and sometimes shellac, and kauri. A present-day thin liquid japan drier might be made up of 100 pounds of rosin, with ten pounds of manganese dioxide, and 15 pounds each of litharge and red lead, with about 10 gallons of linseed oil. These materials are given heat treatments similar to those used in manufacturing varnishes, and then the hot liquid is thinned with heavy naphtha 48° after the mixture has been partly cooled.

Another slightly different japan drier, known as a grinding japan and often used as a vehicle for grinding various pigments, is rich in varnish gums and drying oils. Such a japan must have a composition that will admit of its being thinned with drying oil and turpentine. Grinding japans are very strong in lead driers, and cannot be thinned with unlimited quantities of drying oils without the percipitation or clouding of certain component parts of the liquid.

Shellac grinding japans are made in various ways, one of which is as follows: heat linseed oil (27 to 30 per cent of the total) to about 115.5° C. (240° F.), and gradually add driers such as red lead, litharge, and manganese dioxide, to about 8⅔ per cent while the temperature is being increased to 232.2° C. (450° F.). About 3½ per cent of orange shellac of the T.N. (truly native) grade is slowly stirred into the hot liquid after removing the kettle from the fire. The shellac is cooked into the mixture; and, after cooling somewhat, a thinner of wood turpentine and heavy naphtha 48° is added.

Chapter XII

Natural Fossil-Gum Varnishes (2)

Types of Varnish. A complete list of oil varnishes now used would be long because some manufacturers make over 200 kinds. For the average wood finisher it seems best to group them into a few important classes based upon use. Following are some of the most important groups of varnishes: architectural, baking, cabinet, chair and pew, color, dipping, exterior, enamel, finishing, flat, flat mixing, floor, flowing, furniture, gloss oil, grinding, heatproof, insulating, interior, long oil, marine, mixing, piano, polishing, rubbing, sizing, short oil, spar, spraying, steel car, and waterproof.

Varnish makers vary the ingredients that are selected for incorporating into varnishes according to the purpose for which the varnish is intended. There is no such thing as an "all-purpose varnish," and no one would want such a finish if it could be manufactured.

A brief description of the types of varnish most commonly used by the wood finisher follows:

Architectural Varnish. This term is used to include varnishes that can be used satisfactorily for decorative work, and also on the interior and exterior of buildings.

Baking Varnish. Such varnishes have compositions which enable them to be dried by heat above normal, usually in ovens. They are intended for use over either wood or metal. Baking varnishes are most frequently dipped or sprayed on art-metal objects, parts of automobiles, and fine machines, such as typewriters. Temperatures of from 90° to 220° F. are used in the drying rooms and ovens. Such varnishes contain more than the normal amount of drying oil, but not more than 24 gallons to the 100 pounds of gum; and when baked on they produce a very elastic finish that is usually durable and smooth.

Rosin varnishes, unless hardened rosin is used, will not stand baking at high temperatures, because rosin softens at about 154° F. (67.7° C.). Most good baking varnishes will stand a temperature of 160° F. for an hour. A hardened dammar varnish will stand baking at 220° F. Congo and kauri varnishes are not injured by a temperature of 180° F. No oil varnish will endure a temperature of 300° F. without turning yellow.

Exterior Varnish. This name is given to oil varnishes which are intended for outdoor use on doors, stores, and the exteriors of buildings. They are made to resist the elements of destruction under exposed conditions, and contain more than the usual amount of drying oils.

Enamel Varnishes. Specially prepared varnishes are manufactured for use in enamels. Formerly, very white or transparent varnishes manufactured from dammar gum as a resin were selected for use in white enamels, because such varnishes do not contain linseed oil which may turn yellow with time. Enamel varnishes, especially those made for use with white enamel, must be without color when new, and should not discolor with age. Dammar varnishes are not durable, and are going out of use, because satisfactory, clear, and transparent oil varnishes which are durable have been prepared recently for use in even the whitest enamels.

Varnishes intended to be used with white enamel are generally of the short oil type, and are often made from properly treated rosin and pale magnesia linseed oil. A better varnish for enamel manufacture, however, is a short oil, pale, ester gum compound.

In order to secure very perfect leveling qualities and durability, manufacturers generally select long oil varnishes that are made by the use of low heat and a short cooking of pale oils and a pale gum, such as glycerine rosin which is manufactured from a water white rosin. The cooking of such varnishes should be done in an aluminum kettle to prevent the discoloration which is apt to follow heating in an iron or copper kettle. Long oil varnishes for use in enamels sometimes contain as much as 40 gallons of drying oil to each 100 pounds of varnish gum.

The varnishes used in baking enamels are medium oil varnishes. It has been found that quick-drying varnishes which contain 24 or more gallons of drying oil to each 100 pounds of rosin cannot be used, because this excess of oil causes the enamel to lose its gloss or even to become wrinkled during the baking process. Some of the varnishes which are made for use with baking enamels contain China wood oil, others contain linseed oil, and in still others both oils are found.

Many of the black varnishes used in baking enamels are manufactured from special gums, such as gilsonite, parolite, asphaltum, and manjak. The favorite black gum seems to be gilsonite, a brittle black substance which produces a very high luster. The black baking varnishes are manufactured through heat treatments of the special black gums, usually with manganese treated linseed oil. The thinners commonly used in compounding these black varnishes are 46° kerosene and 54° benzine.

Finishing Varnish. This term refers to a last coat varnish for furniture, such as pianos. These varnishes are manufactured with such a composition that they can be rubbed lightly with pumice stone, yet be more tough and elastic than the other coats under them. Finishing varnishes have a medium oil composition, and can be polished to a high gloss. Some finishing varnishes have as much as 50 per cent of drying oils and are very durable.

Flat Varnish. The name flat varnish is given to varnishes that dry without luster, sometimes producing what is called a "matt" surface, which is dull. They are intended for final coats for furniture, and produce a soft attractive effect without the expense of hand or machine rubbing. Flat varnishes are manufactured in various ways. One method is to add to a varnish containing tung oil some aluminium stearate jelly, which is made from aluminum stearate heated with turpentine and then cooled. Tung oil itself under certain conditions has a tendency to make a "flatted" effect. Aluminum stearate has remarkable qualities for destroying gloss, but it must be used with turpentine rather than benzine as a solvent; and, if used in excess, it may cause the varnish to "liver" or become thick.

Some flat varnishes are made from a soft black Indonesian gum melted at very low heat, sometimes at about 150° F. or 175° F. (73.9° C.). This low-temperature melting process, sometimes called "slack melting," destroys the luster of the gum unless higher heat of 200° F. to 300° F. (148.8° C.) is used later. In such a case the soft Indonesian gums treated with high heat will produce gloss varnish similar to that manufactured from gum from the Congo when a heat of about 550° F. (287.7° C.) is used in cooking the varnish.

Some of the "Satin Finishes" are flat varnishes which are made entirely from the soft Indonesian gum. Such a varnish is quite soft, and is affected by heat at about the some temperature as that which softens rosin varnish. In order to secure reasonable hardness, a certain amount of hard gum varnish is added to the "slack melt" soft gum varnish; yet a flat effect is left if the proper proportion is used and the mixture is hard enough for satisfactory service. Some manufacturers claim that the best flat varnishes are made from gloss varnishes which are "flatted" by the use of aluminum stearate. Occasionally, zinc stearate, calcium stearate, and aluminum resinate are used in place of aluminum stearate.

Flat varnish should not be made by adding beeswax to a gloss varnish, because the flatness secured from the wax is not permanent, and additional coats of varnish will not adhere well if it is ever necessary to refinish the surface. Wax finishes must be entirely removed with turpentine, gasoline, or benzol, and sanded before revarnishing is attempted. It is very difficult to remove the wax from a varnish wax or a varnish "flatted" with wax after it is spread on a surface except through a laborious sanding operation or the use of varnish removers.

Flat Mixing Varnish. Mixing varnishes that will dry flat belong to a rather new type. They are used to mix with pigments, especially lithophone, in the manufacture of flat wall paints for indoor use. The flat varnish helps in binding the pigments together; yet it gives no luster or gloss. Flat enamels are also "flatted" through the use of flat mixing varnishes. Ordinary "gloss" mixing varnishes are often made from heat treated tung oil, with relatively small amounts of other varnish ingredients, such as rosin, driers, and thinners. Mixing varnishes are made into flat mixing varnishes by the addition of aluminum stearate jelly and turpentine, stirring the latter substances slowly into the mixing varnish at ordinary temperatures.

Mixing varnishes for use in paints have a high content of drying oils, largely Chinese wood oil (tung oil), the amount often varying from about 25 per cent to 45 per cent of the total weight of the ingredients. On the other hand, mixing and grinding varnishes for use in enamels are generally "short oil" varnishes and are not as durable for outside use.

Floor Varnishes. In order to be satisfactory for finishing floors, varnishes must have several of the important characteristics of spar varnish; yet they should have only a medium oil content, and must dry hard enough overnight to make walking on them possible, and, finally, they should dry much harder than spar varnishes do. Floor varnishes must be elastic and tough in order that they may be scratched as little as possible under the furniture.

Sometimes floor varnishes are made by blending together other varnishes. In composition floor varnishes often have a drying oil content of about 35 to 38 per cent, the oil used being largely tung oil. This amount of oil with properly treated gums, driers, and thinners, produces varnish that is largely water proof and which does not turn white with water even though rosin be used as the chief or only resin.

Floor varnishes are sometimes used for inside finish of buildings, such as the "trim" and stairways, but they are often objectionable for use on light colored unstained woods because they may be too dark in color.

Flowing Varnish. Whenever a high gloss is desired without rubbing and polishing, a flowing varnish should be selected—at least for the last coat. Such a varnish when flowed freely over a surface will not show brushmarks because it will level itself though the coat be rather thick; consequently, such a finish is not apt to show runs and sags. Flowing varnishes do not set very quickly; therefore they dry with a very smooth lustrous appearance which is devoid of all brush marks.

Furniture Varnishes. There are many grades of varnish that might come under this classification. Such varnishes must dry very hard and quickly, and give a brilliant luster when rubbed and polished. In general they are short oil varnishes containing often only about 13 per cent of drying oils—partly tung oil, and partly bleached heavy bodied linseed oil. Some of the hard gums, such as hard manila resin or a mixture of rosin and kauri, are preferable to the soft gums in the manufacture of furniture varnishes.

Gloss Oil Varnish. This group of short oil varnishes represents a very cheap mixture of ingredients of low grade. Gloss oils are used for sizing canvas, plastered walls, and ceilings, for grinding barrel paints, and as blending varnishes with grinding oils for barn and freight car paints. Some of the gloss oils are employed as grinding mixtures for use in baking enamels and varnishes to add luster to the finishes.

The composition of gloss oil varnishes varies, some mixtures having ingredients that blend well with turpentine varnishes, while others are of such a nature that they should be used with benzine varnishes. Gloss oils are really low grade quick-drying varnishes, manufactured from rosin, cheap thinners, such as benzine or kerosene 46°, with driers, and sometimes relatively small amounts of drying oils. They are quite similar in composition to some of the cheap short oil varnishes, and dry with great rapidity, usually becoming hard in from about 20 to 50 minutes. Gloss oils are rich in rosin and contain driers and drying oils in small amounts. Many gloss oils are made from rosin, slaked lime, a thinner, and sometimes caustic soda.

Grinding Varnishes. Grinding liquids are hardly true varnishes because they often contain little or no rosin or other varnish gums. In this case, they resemble japans more than varnishes. When they contain rosin they are somewhat similar in composition to gloss oils, but they are relatively weak in rosin.

Grinding varnishes and japans are used as liquid grinding mediums for grinding various paint and varnish pigment colors. They must be of such a composition that they will blend well with pigments, and the various thinners and driers used in japans and gloss oils, which are similar in general composition to the grinding varnishes. The chief uses of grinding varnishes, grinding japans, and gloss oils are quite different, however.

A neutral grinding varnish that will dry very hard may be made from glycerine rosin, tung oil, metallic driers, such as manganese borate and litharge, and a thinner—heavy naphtha 48° often being selected for the purpose. Linseed oil is also used in connection with tung oil, and a more expensive solvent such as turpentine, especially wood turpentine, may replace part of the heavy naphtha.

Grinding japans and grinding varnishes can not be very

clearly distinguished from each other judging by the ingredients. Many grinding japans, however, contain shellac as the resin, while grinding varnishes are commonly made from rosin, and contain smaller amounts of metallic driers. The distinguishing feature between grinding japans and grinding varnishes is in the relative proportion of the ingredients used—the grinding japans containing vastly more driers than are found in grinding varnishes.

Hard Oil Varnish. This name represents an old type of varnish that came into use a few years ago in an imitation of a rubbed linseed oil finish. Hard oil varnish is a term which is now given to almost any cheap varnish that is suitable for interior use only.

Heatproof Varnish. Machinery and surfaces that are liable to become heated require a rather unusual quality which resists heat. Such varnishes often contain menhaden oil, or some other fish oil, because these oils are not so easily affected by heat.

Interior Varnish. Such varnishes are intended for use on the inside of buildings. Various varnishes are selected for this purpose, such as cabinet varnish, hard oil finishes, interior spar, spirit varnishes, such as shellac and dammar, flat varnishes, and possibly enamels which are hardly true varnishes. Interior varnishes usually run from 22 to 35 gallons of oil per 100 pounds of resin. The result is a harder film than that of the spar varnishes, and yet one that has sufficient flexibility, good water resistance, and other film characteristics, enabling it to last for years.[1]

Insulating Varnish. Electric conductors, especially insulated wires, often need added insulation in motors, generators, and other electric machines in order to prevent short circuits. Shellac and some types of varnishes, often baking varnishes of low electric conductivity, are used as insulating varnishes.

Long Oil Varnish. Any varnish that has a rather large proportion of drying oil relative to the gum is known as a long oil varnish. An excess of drying oil retards the drying of a varnish, but makes the film much tougher and more elastic. Spar varnishes are long oil varnishes. A varnish with 39 per cent of drying oil would be ranked as a typical long oil varnish. The

---

[1] Fisher, E. M., What You Should Know About Paint, Chp. 5, page 91.

amount of drying oil contained in long oil varnishes varies in the formulas from 40 to 55 gallons of such oils to each 100 pounds of resins.

Marine Varnish. Steamboats, yachts, motor boats, canoes, and all craft and utensils intended for use about or in water, especially salt water, or which are exposed to marine atmosphere, require a special varnish designed to withstand such conditions. Marine varnishes are long oil varnishes, sometimes called spar varnishes. They often contain about 38 per cent or more of drying oil—largely tung oil, together with smaller quantities of linseed oil. Some of the hard gums are desirable as ingredients for use in marine varnishes, but rosin properly treated with tung oil may be used successfully. A good marine varnish should have a high luster, dry in about eight hours, and finally become very hard and waterproof. Such a varnish contains about 48 gallons of drying oil to each 100 lbs. of gum.

Mixing Varnish. In order to add luster and hardness to paints and enamels, certain types of gloss varnishes are mixed with them. Varnishes adapted to this purpose are known as mixing varnishes, and contain no objectionable ingredients that prevent them from forming satisfactory mixtures with paints or enamels.

Mixing varnishes for use in paint, especially for outside use, are long oil varnishes containing a large amount of tung oil; while varnishes for use in enamels are apt to be short oil varnishes, usually containing less than 12 gallons, of drying oil to each 100 pounds of gum. The short oil mixing varnishes often contain about eight to ten gallons of drying oils to each 100 pounds of resins, which may be of various kinds, such as water white rosin, japan rosin, kauri seeds, Indonesia Nubs, or hard manila gum. Cheap short oil mixing varnishes may, however, be made in which only about two and one-half gallons of China wood oil are used as the drying oil, with 100 pounds of rosin prepared with proper driers.

Enamel mixing varnishes of the long oil type for use in enamels containing colored pigments are sometimes made with as much as 36 gallons of drying oils, mostly China wood oil, to each 100 pounds of varnish gum.

Piano Varnishes. The high luster and brilliant effect of surfaces which can be perfectly leveled and polished necessitate the use of special varnishes which dry with great hardness and possess unusual flowing and rubbing qualities. High grade polishing varnishes, manufactured from hard gums, such as congo, together with special polishing oils, largely tung oil treated with rosin and driers, are often used as piano varnishes. Such varnishes should dry very hard, and are usually "short oiled," some of them containing only six gallons or less of drying oils to 100 pounds of gum. Piano varnishes are finishing or last coat varnishes; consequently, they should be tougher and more elastic than is necessary in case of undercoat varnishes.

Polishing Varnishes. Very hard varnishes that will take a high polish after being rubbed with pumice stone and polished with rottenstone, are known as polishing varnishes. They are preferably manufactured from hard gums such as congo, kauri, hard manila, or pontianak. While polishing varnishes are similar to rubbing varnishes, they are usually harder, and are of such a composition that it is possible to give them a more permanent and higher polish. Polishing varnishes are made for inside use and must be very hard; therefore, they are preferably of the short oil type, containing from five to eleven gallons of drying oils to each 100 pounds of resin, mostly the hard gum type though 10 to 20 per cent of rosin is often mixed with the more expensive gums. Polishing varnishes are finishing varnishes that are to be used over other varnishes.

Rubbing Varnishes. Undercoat varnishes that are hard and rather heavy bodied, and which are suitable for rubbing with either water or rubbing oil without softening or other damage, are called rubbing varnishes. Congo gum, a hard resin of excellent abrading qualities, together with China wood oil as the chief drying oil, are favorite ingredients for use in manufacturing rubbing varnishes. Other hard gums such as kauri and pontianak are also used. Various amounts of hard rosin or pale ester gum are sometimes incorporated into rubbing varnishes with the hard gums, together with varying proportions of linseed oil which is often properly treated manganese oil.

Rubbing varnishes dry rather slowly, because they contain small amounts of driers. Long oil varnishes are too soft, and do not rub well because they gum up. Rubbing varnishes are usually of the short oil type, but they must be so compounded that they will not cloud or turn white when rubbed with water and pumice stone. Rubbing varnishes are rather brittle, and must not be spread on top of softer more elastic varnishes, such as spar varnishes, because some form of cracking is liable to occur if this is done.

Varnishes which are not true rubbing varnishes can usually be rubbed with sandpaper or pumice stone sufficiently to remove the gloss and permit of the application of another coat.

Sizing Varnishes. In order to seal the pores of plastered walls and stop the penetration of paints, low-grade varnishes are sometimes used instead of glue sizing. The varnishes selected for this purpose are cheap rosin mixtures, which are often called gloss oils. Such sizing-varnishes are manufactured from rosin with heat treatments, and thinned with benzine and sometimes kerosene 46° as solvents. Small amounts of drying oils are contained in some, while other formulas contain no oils except the solvents.

Sizing varnishes dry very rapidly—the time required often being about 45 minutes, the slow-drying kind hardening in two or three hours. The rosin is given heat treatments similar to those used in manufacturing other varnishes. Slaked lime and sometimes caustic soda in small quantities are heated with the rosin to neutralize the acid in the gum and harden the rosin itself.

Temperatures of from 260° C. (500° F.) to 287.7° C. (550° F.), or slightly higher, are sometimes used in melting the rosin with the lime, caustic soda, and driers if any are used. If a drying oil is used it is also heated with the rosin. The thinners are added as the melted mass cools down—kerosene at about 232.2° C. (450° F.), or slightly less, and naphtha 54° (benzine) at about 160° C. (320° F.).

Short Oil Varnishes. If a varnish contains less than about twelve gallons of drying oil to each 100 pounds of gum, it is classed as a short oil varnish. Many varnishes manufactured for inside use, such as rubbing varnishes, are of this type. Various kinds of gum are used, and the other ingredients contained in short oil varnishes are similar to the materials ordinarily found in medium oil and long oil varnishes. Some of the quick-drying short oil varnishes contain only three and one-half to four gallons of drying oils, such as tung oil and linseed oil, to each 100 pounds of resin. Varnishes for use in white enamel are sometimes of this type. Such varnishes will not cause white finishes to turn yellow with the lapse of time, because they contain little linseed oil, the usual cause of discoloration.

Spar Varnish. A typical long oil varnish, which is highly resistant to dampness and the destructive action of water, has been made for many years for coating the spars of ships, hence the name, spar varnish. Elasticity, toughness, and resistance to water are its chief characteristics. Spar varnishes dry slowly, do not become very hard, and possess only a moderate luster. They are intended for outdoor use, about windows, sinks, in bath rooms, and wherever resistance to moisture is necessary.

Hard gums, especially pontianak, are preferable for manufacturing the best grades of spar varnishes. Cheaper gums, such as hardened rosin and ester gum, together with heat-treated China wood oil, are also sometimes used in the manufacture of cheap spar varnishes. China wood oil (tung oil) has very largely displaced linseed oil in the manufacture of some spar varnishes which usually contain a very high percentage of drying oil. Tung oil gives water-resisting and quick-drying qualities, while linseed oil is more elastic and enduring under extreme variations in temperature especially for outside exposure. For these reasons, a blend of the two oils is preferred for use in varnishes for outdoor use. Tung oil is more expensive than linseed oil, and is used in spar varnishes because of its excellent qualities, and not as an adulterant.

Spraying Varnishes. Factories which formerly used the brush method of applying finishes introduced the air gun pressure process. In order to apply varnishes effectively, special spraying varnishes are available, which are, in general, very similar to other varnishes, but often somewhat thinner. Many of the ordinary brushing varnishes can be used satisfactorily with an air gun. Other varnishes should be thinned with turpentine if they are too heavy bodied.

The turpentine should be added several hours before using the varnish or it will not become well incorporated into the mixture. It is preferable, however, to thin varnish with ready-prepared very thin varnish that has been mixed with additional turpentine several days previously. In the manufacture of varnish, turpentine is poured into the mixture of gum and drying oils while the ingredients are still very hot, often at temperatures of about 210° C. (410° F.). In this way the turpentine is thoroughly blended into the mixture. Varnishes also should age for several weeks or months before use in order that there may be a perfectly homogeneous mixture when they are used. Some varnishes need additional stirring before use. For the reasons just given, it will be understood that, if varnishes are thinned for spraying, all mixtures must be thoroughly stirred and time allowed for cooling in order that the cold turpentine may become properly incorporated into the complex mixture of hot materials.

Spraying varnishes and dipping varnishes should have a viscosity within the range 8 to 16, measured by the Scott Viscosimeter, while brushing varnishes come within the numbers 16 to 24, though they often can be applied with a brush with a viscosity of about 36.

Waterproof Varnishes. Long oil varnishes manufactured from a hard gum have been considered the only good waterproof varnishes. Since China wood oil has become known to the varnish makers, the kind of gum used has become less important. Formerly, it was thought that rosin varnishes were unfit for exposure to water, but it has been discovered that rosin, properly heat treated, with China wood oil in large quantities, can be used in waterproof varnishes.

Ester gum, which is a synthetic gum, made by treating rosin with glycerine at a temperature of about 275° C. (527° F.), is superior to treated rosin as a gum for water proof varnishes. The films of varnishes manufactured from ester gum and China wood oil are water proof, and will not turn white in water. A long oil varnish consisting of 100 pounds of ester gum and 40 gallons of China wood oil, heat treated at from 275° C. (527° F.) to 296.1° C. (565° F.) for from 15 to 30 minutes will be water proof, and gas proof if the higher temperature is used.

A long oil varnish from ester gum and linseed oil is also reasonably water proof. Short oil and many medium oil varnishes which contain rosin as the chief gum are very apt to turn white in water. Some varnishes that contain considerable hard gum, especially pontianak gum, are somewhat water proof, though ranked as short oil varnishes which contain less than 12 gallons of drying oil to each 100 pounds of gum.

Working and Thinning Properties of Varnishes. The work-ing properties of varnishes vary greatly with their composition, the method of application, and the temperature of the air in the room or place where the varnishes are being applied. In addition, the conditions for work, such as a clean room con-taining as little dust as possible, a clean brush which has not stood in the varnish a long time, clean varnish which has not stood open in a dusty room, and clean, properly dusted sur-faces—all enter into the problem, and affect the success of a job of varnishing.

Varnishes are judged as to their working characteristics by variations in reaction after application, such as the follow-ing: (1) flowing qualities, (2) leveling properties, (3) time of setting, (4) ability to stay in place, and (5) thickness of the film.

The *flowing qualities* are felt by the finisher when the brush does not stick or pull, even with a reasonable amount of brushing.

Good *leveling properties* are shown when a varnish can be cross brushed twice; yet possesses enough fluidity to flatten out leaving no brush marks.

The *time of setting* varies with the temperature. Varnishes set quickly on a hot day, or if artificially warmed. They are stiff, and do not spread well, if colder than about 70° F. The amount of time required in cross-brushing a varnish film until it will no longer flatten out to a level surface free from brush marks shows the time of setting.

Staying in place is an important property of a varnish; otherwise, vertical and oblique surfaces show sags, runs, and other defects which unfortunately appear on varnish films that do not stay where they are placed.

The *thickness* of a varnish film is sometimes called its "full-ness," or measurement of "body." Long cooking and high tem-peratures change the characteristics of an oil gum mass. High temperatures and long cooking require more thinner, and a varnish so made will spread out into a thin film and possess less "body" or "fullness." The thinner itself practically all evaporates; therefore, a varnish containing a large amount of thinner brushes on a surface in a very thin film.

The mixing properties, or amount of thinner that a varnish

will incorporate into itself and remain clear, vary depending upon the amount of drying oil in the varnish. In general, long oil varnishes absorb turpentine, benzine, and benzol freely. Short oil varnishes become cloudy, or the gum may be precipitated, if an excess of benzine be used as a thinner. Turpentine can generally be used in almost any desired amount without affecting the gum in the varnish solution. Many varnishes contain light naphtha, which is called 54° benzine, or the heavier naphtha 48°; but these thinners can be added only in limited amounts to varnishes if they are cold, especially below 70° F.

Luster, Elasticity, and Color of Varnishes. These qualities are given to varnishes largely by the materials used in manufacture, though cooking may modify them somewhat, especially in the color.

Luster in a varnish depends largely upon the gums or varnish resins incorporated into the mixture for heat treatment in the manufacturing process. Rosin seems to give a higher gloss than any other gum used in varnishes, but it is not durable unless heat-treated and neutralized somewhat with lime or some other flux, in order to reduce its acidity and harden it. Heat treatments of rosin or other gums with oils in varnish making reduce the luster to some extent, especially if high temperatures be used.

Elasticity in a varnish comes largely from the drying oil constituents, especially being dependent upon the amount of drying oils in the mixture, and somewhat upon the kind of gum or gums selected. Ester gum is preferred to hardened rosin where an elastic varnish is desired. Long oil varnishes are considerably more elastic than are short oil varnishes. Many of the elastic varnishes are made with about 35 gallons of drying oil, usually linseed oil, to 100 pounds of gum—hard manila or pontianak gum being preferred. Elastic varnishes are intended chiefly for outside use, because they are less affected by the weather, and allow slight changes in expansion or contraction of the surfaces without checking or cracking of the finishing films.

Color in varnishes is due to colors in the gums, the drying oils, and sometimes to the driers that are used. High temperatures and prolonged cooking darken varnishes, and are avoided in the manufacture of pale varnishes. Pale varnishes are made of pale gums, very light colored drying oils, and driers that do not discolor, umber especially being avoided.

Necessary Preparations for Varnishing. This discussion has made it clear that there are many kinds of varnishes, and that the ingredients which are incorporated into these oleoresinous finishes are numerous and vary greatly in cost and quality. Some varnishes are suitable for one purpose, but are not satisfactory for certain other uses. Waterproof long oil varnishes should not be applied to furniture, because they dry too slowly, are too soft, lack high luster, and do not rub well. Short oil varnishes which dry hard and quickly, and have a brilliant luster, are preferred by the furniture finisher. The wood finisher's problem at first is the selection of a suitable varnish.

The experienced wood finisher is particular about the brush or brushes used in spreading varnish. A brush of the proper size, with well-set bristles of medium stiffness, should be selected. Either flat or oval-shaped brushes may be used; oval brushes being preferred for large surfaces where big brushfuls of varnish are necessary for rapid work. An old brush which has been used with paint or shellac is unsatisfactory. Even a high-grade new brush, "set in rubber," requires preliminary treatment before it is ready for use on a last-coat job of varnishing. A new brush should have the dust and loose bristles removed before it is fit for varnishing. It is best to use a new brush for undercoat work for a while, until all loose bristles are removed or fall out; then, after a careful cleaning in turpentine, it is ready for finishing work.

All surfaces should be examined to find out whether they are properly dry before varnishing is begun. Trouble will follow if a second coat is applied over a partly dried undercoat.

Dusting and cleaning the object to be varnished just before varnishing is begun are very important operations that the amateur may overlook. Dust is continually settling, and should be removed just before spreading the varnish. If there is much dust on a piece of furniture or some other object which is to be varnished, it is preferable to take the article away from the varnish room for dusting, in order to avoid scattering dust into the air of the finishing room; because some of it is very apt to settle on a newly varnished surface and spoil the finish.

After removing the loose dust with a dusting brush, the surfaces should be wiped with a piece of cheesecloth or chamois skin dampened with water. A piece of muslin or cheesecloth may be dampened with benzine or turpentine for cleaning a surface which has an undercoat on it, or a "tack rag" may be made by dampening a dustless and lintless rag in very thin varnish. Such a "tack rag" if nearly dry, will take up all dust and leave a surface ready for varnishing. All fragments of sand and dust must be removed from the cracks, corners, and pockets in the cells of the wood, or these waste particles will be dragged out by the varnish brush in flowing on the varnish, and will spoil an otherwise perfect finish.

Old surfaces which are to be revarnished should be washed thoroughly with moderately strong soapy water, then rinsed and wiped, preferably with a chamois skin dampened in clear water. After washing and drying, all old varnished surfaces which are to be refinished should be smoothed down with fine sandpaper which also removes the gloss; then they should be carefully dusted and wiped to make them clean and dustless.

Old wax finishes, or surfaces that have been treated with a varnish remover containing wax, should be cleaned properly with benzine, turpentine, or even high test gasoline. Such surfaces should be wiped, after treatment with the wax solvents, in order to remove all traces of wax. New films of varnish will not adhere satisfactorily to surfaces having even a small amount or a very thin layer of wax upon them.

The finishing room and the clothes of the wood finisher should be as free from dust as possible. Sometimes the floors in finishing rooms are sprinkled with water to lay the dust. The rooms should be dry, however, because varnish does not dry well on damp days. When the weather is damp or rainy the windows of the finishing room should be closed. Ventilation without drafts is desirable because fresh air helps oxidation of the drying oils in the varnish, and speeds up the evaporation of the solvents and thinners.

The temperature of a varnishing room during the winter time should be between 70° F. and 80° F., and certainly never below 60° F., because warm varnish spreads more satisfactorily. If varnish has been seriously chilled by exposure to very cold weather, it should be warmed by placing the container in warm water, and finally strained, particularly if it is not properly mixed or has separated into its original ingredients to some extent.

Varnish should not be thinned by the finisher, because the manufacturers put as much thinner in the mixture as it will stand and yet give satisfactory service. If a thinner varnish is required, the container may be placed in warm water, or a small amount of turpentine added. If thinner is added to a varnish, at least twelve hours should be given in order that the ingredients may become properly mixed.

Application of Oil Varnishes. Experienced finishers flow all oil varnishes over surfaces with the point of the brush. The brush should be held in a position nearly perpendicular to the work, but leaning slightly in the direction of the brush stroke (Fig. 12-1). At the beginning of a varnishing operation the brush should be well loaded, dipping it far enough into the varnish to cover most of the bristles, and wiping off the excess varnish from the brush in order to prevent dripping. One should, however, remember to avoid unnecessary wiping of the brush, especially on the side of the container, because this operation allows air-bubbles to enter the varnish in the brush. A clean wire stretched across the top of the container makes the best possible wiper for removing excess varnish from a brush.

Varnish should be applied by using brush strokes with the grain of the material which is being finished. Slow-setting varnishes are often cross-brushed, and then evened over lengthwise of the grain. After a varnish has begun to stiffen, it should not be brushed because, under this condition, brush marks made in the film will always show.

Panels should be varnished by starting with a brushful of varnish near the middle of one end of the panel. The ends and corners should be covered; then the varnish on the entire panel may be cross brushed, and finished by using light strokes lengthwise of the grain, with a brush containing only a small amount of varnish. It is good practice to spread the soft varnish film from the middle toward the ends of the panel when doing the final brushing lengthwise of the grain; always using long, rather light strokes, in order to leave the surface in as smooth a condition as possible.

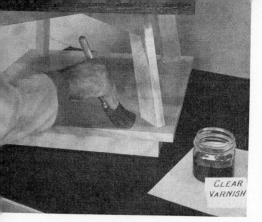

12—1. In varnishing, hold the brush in a position nearly perpendicular to the work, leaning slightly in the direction of the brush stroke. 12—2. Finish a varnished surface with light, feathering strokes, using the very tip of the brush.

Many varnishers do not use the cross brushing method. They spread the varnish lengthwise of the grain, and rebrush the entire surface in the same direction after a few minutes, in order to remove the bubbles, and to make sure that the entire surface is evenly covered with a thin coat of uniform thickness (Fig. 12-2).

First coats of a heavy-bodied varnish, when used as undercoats, usually should be thinned with from 14 to 25 per cent of turpentine. Varnish rather than shellac undercoats should always be used whenever the object is to be exposed to dampness, because shellac is very apt to turn white if it comes in contact with moisture. The preliminary coat is really only a durable sizing, which has the function of stopping the capillarity of the wood cells and making a foundation for later finishing coats.

Second coats, or any of the later coats of varnish, must never be applied to a surface until the undercoats are absolutely dry; otherwise there may be cracking, checking, flaking, or "crazing" later on. Varnishes must never be applied over undercoats of any kind without removing the gloss, because varnishes do not adhere properly to such surfaces. The gloss of the undercoats should be removed by the use of No. 00, No. 000, or No. 0000 sandpaper, always applied with the grain, and held over the fingers or stretched over a soft felt pad (Fig. 12-3). Fine steel wool or pumice stone is sometimes employed to cut off the gloss of undercoats. All traces of sand

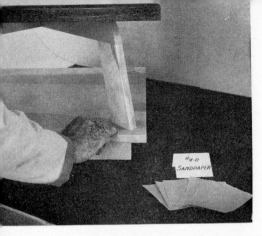

12—3. After the first coat dries, remove the gloss by careful sanding with No. 3/0 or 4/0 finishing paper.

and dust from the undercoats must be removed before revarnishing is attempted.

While it is true that undercoats should be applied in thin coats and spread about as thin as possible in covering the surface, it should be noted that any succeeding coats may be somewhat thicker, and should not be brushed out as thin as possible with a dry brush. On vertical or oblique surfaces the varnish must be flowed on in a thin coat, because an excessively heavy coat may show sags or tear drops. All runs and sags can be caught and brushed out with the grain if the work is inspected and touched up every few minutes.

Wrinkling is usually the result of applying too much varnish, especially on horizontal surfaces. Thick films or coats of varnish do not dry evenly from top to bottom, because the outside layer forms a skin, and expands through the taking on of oxygen before the lower or inside portion of the film hardens. Wrinkles are the result of the expansion of the outer skin of a film, which hardens or oxidizes and expands while the lower portion is still soft.

Three or four coats of varnish are often applied if a satisfactory finish is expected, the varnish being spread out thin by careful work with the brush.

The covering power of varnishes varies greatly, being modified by the temperature, the amount of drying oils and thinners, and also by the skill of the finisher. Spar varnishes, which are long oil varnishes, will spread out over considerable surface, usually from 500 to 550 square feet to the gallon for one coat. If floor varnishes are spread thin, they will usually cover from 450 to 500 square feet to the gallon. Flat varnishes are apt to be rather stiff, and one gallon often covers only 400 to 450 square feet.

Rubbing the Coats of Varnish

Special varnishes known as rubbing varnishes should be selected whenever a rubbed finish is desired. Rubbing varnishes dry hard as they are short oil varnishes which preferably contain a considerable amount of hard gum, such as congo, manila, kauri, or pontianak. Long oil varnishes do not rub well, because they make relatively soft films without a high luster. Varnishes which are used for rubbing usually contain from six to twelve gallons of drying oil to each 100 pounds of resin.

Plenty of time for thorough drying or hardening should be allowed before rubbing is attempted. Very few varnishes dry hard enough to rub under two days, and usually it is preferable to allow from three to six days for drying. If heated drying rooms are used, the time of drying may be reduced.

Several methods are employed in rubbing varnish: (1) very fine waterproof sandpaper, water, and a wet felt pad; (2) fine sandpaper and rubbing oil; (3) rough rubbing with lump pumice stone and water; (4) rubbing with water and pumice stone powder to produce a dull finish; and (5) rubbing with a special rubbing oil and pumice stone powder to make a satin finish. Brush rubbing, or what might be called scouring, with a very stiff flat brush such as is used for wall brushing with pumice stone and rubbing oil, is also sometimes used on coarse work to remove the gloss of varnish.

Every one of the three or more coats applied in producing a rubbed varnish finish must be rubbed in order to produce a satisfactory level and smooth finish of soft luster. On coarse woods the wood filler largely fills the openings in the cells, and this plugging of the open pores tends to stop capillarity or suction of the many cell openings upon the varnish-coats. Undercoats of shellac varnish are applied, and should be sandpapered, in order to smooth the surface for later coats of finish, and to improve the adhesion of these films which must firmly attach themselves to the undercoats. Each additional coat of varnish, if sandpapered smooth, tends to add to the level and even effect of the final finish, because all openings below the general level of the surface are finally filled with the varnish while all high spots are cut off each time to the general level of the surface. The first coats of varnish are at present very commonly rubbed by the wet sandpaper method, while the final coats are usually finished by rubbing with pumice stone.

Rubbing with Waterproof Sandpaper. Excellent waterproof sandpapers having a very fine abrasive attached to hard, nonabsorbent paper with waterproof glue are on the market. Rubbing with waterproof sandpaper and water is more expensive in cost of materials than is the old method of rubbing with pumice stone, but much faster, and more satisfactory work can be done between coats of varnish than is possible by the older method.

The sandpaper should be of a fine grit, such as No. 5/0 to No. 8/0, and should be soaked for a moment in water and used over a soft block or wet felt pad. A very dull surface is produced by waterproof sandpaper, though smoother and more level than that produced by the use of pumice stone. The rubbing must be done carefully in order to have all the strokes lengthwise of the grain, and to prevent cutting through the coats of varnish and stain on corners and other exposed places.

Rubbing with Oil and Sandpaper. Varnish films other than the last one are often rubbed between coats with very fine sandpaper and rubbing oil. This method smooths the surface satisfactorily, and is helpful in protecting the workmen from the danger of breathing sand dust which is injurious to health. Rubbing with oil is apt to darken very light woods somewhat. The sandpaper and the surfaces should be cleaned by the use of benzine.

Dull Finish Rubbing with Pumice Stone Powder and Water. An attractive dull finish is produced by rubbing with powdered pumice stone and a thick felt pad, the abrasive being wet with water. This process is commonly used in furniture and piano factories to make a perfectly smooth level surface preparatory to the application of a final flowing or polishing coat of varnish. A coarse rubbing is often given first by the use of a medium pumice stone powder, such as No. ½ or the finer grade No. 0. Felt pads from 1″ to 2″ thick, and of convenient size to hold in the hand, and of coarse or fine texture, are used as rubbing blocks. Home made rubbing blocks can be prepared by securing pieces of felt of various grades of fineness and attaching them to wooden blocks of various desired sizes by means of waterproof glue, such as any of the

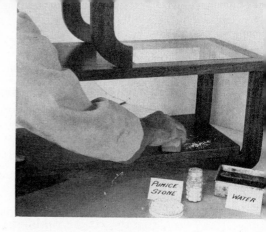

12—4. To produce an attractive, dull, satin finish, rub with pumice stone and water. Use a felt-covered rubbing block.

casein glues. The felts should not contain water soluble dyes which will dissolve into the rubbing paste and discolor the surfaces.

Various procedures are used by wood finishers in rubbing varnished surfaces. Some finishers prepare a paste in a flat, large, open container, mixing sifted pumice stone powder with water, and wetting the rubbing felts in the mixture. The end grain of large tops or other exposed portions of articles of furniture should usually be rubbed first. There is danger of cutting through the finish on corners (arrises), by using too much pressure on the pad. Carvings or surfaces of unusual and varied shapes should be rubbed with special rubbing brushes. Round or curved surfaces can be rubbed with burlap or thin flexible felt pads. Flat surfaces may be rubbed more easily if sponged with water, with a small amount of pumice stone powder sprinkled evenly over the glossy varnish. On flat surfaces the rubbing must be done very evenly, and straight, or lengthwise of the grain (Fig. 12-4).

One should remember that pumice stone is really an abrasive, and makes small scratches that are practically invisible when they run lengthwise of the grain, but which show if the rubbing is done across the grain or with circular strokes. The same amount of pressure should be used during the entire rubbing process, and the whole surface should be rubbed evenly. There is a tendency to rub harder in the middle of a long stroke than at the ends, which portions often require additional rubbing with short strokes. The felt pads should be kept wet with the paste and plenty of water, in order to prevent heating or burning. Prolonged rubbing should be avoided or too much of the varnish film may be removed.

The condition of the rubbed varnish should be inspected from time to time by washing and wiping a portion of the surface. This is a check on the finisher's work which will prevent underrubbing or overrubbing of the varnish.

The rubbing felt should be examined often, and any hardened varnish that has adhered to the felt should be removed. Fragments of varnish on the face of the felt are apt to scratch and damage the surface.

After the coarse rubbing is completed, the surfaces should be washed and wiped clean, then allowed to dry for twelve hours or longer.

Fine pumice stone powder, FF or FFF, with a fine soft felt is often used in finishing rubbed surfaces. The fine rubbing follows the coarse rubbing after the varnish has been allowed to dry and harden for 12 to 24 hours.

Much time can be saved by doing all first rubbing with No. 8/0 waterproof sandpaper, followed by No. 300 crocus cloth. In using these two grades of abrasives, the result is quite similar to that obtained when using pumice stone.

Satin Finish with Rubbing Oil and Pumice Stone. Rubbing with oil is a slower process than rubbing with water, and produces a surface that is different in general effect because a varnish film rubbed with oil has a higher luster. The oil rubbed surface is often called a satin finish. In appearance it is between the very dull effect produced by rubbing with water and powdered pumice stone and a highly polished finish, such as is used on a piano.

The satin finish is produced by scratching very fine lines on a varnished surface by rubbing with oil and very fine pumice stone of about FF or FFF grade. The finisher should make a series of very fine straight lines that are parallel to each other by careful rubbing lengthwise of the surface. The fine, lengthwise scratches on wood do not show, if made carefully, but any cross, oblique, or circular scratches can be seen, and will spoil the finish. Water-stained finishes are particularly sensitive to scratching by careless rubbing. The proper oil for use in rubbing is a neutral mineral oil or a paraffin oil, rather than linseed oil. Prepared rubbing oils are sold on the market by most of the wood finishing supply houses. Some expert rubbers use a crude petroleum oil for rubbing, while still others prefer kerosene because very fast rubbing can be done with it.

The pumice stone should be thoroughly cleaned from the surface with naphtha, benzine, or some other cheap thinner and a rag after the work is finished. For inspection, small portions of each surface should be cleaned from time to time. This can be done by wiping or cleaning with the palm of the hand or with a rag.

The oil rubbing method should not be used between the various coats of varnish, because the later coats will not adhere well to such a finish. Oil rubbing is for the final coat only and often precedes polishing.

In factories machine rubbing has taken the place of hand rubbing. The machines are operated by air pressure or small electric motors which cause two oscillating felt covered pads about 4″ or 5″ square to do the rubbing (Fig. 12-5).

POLISHING PROCESSES

The brilliant polish which is often placed on high-grade

12—5. Rubbing with a two-pad rubbing machine. Back-and-forth movement of pads is supplied by air pressure.

pianos is not often used in the finishing of furniture and the woodwork of houses. The satin finish which is produced by rubbing a coat of varnish with a mineral rubbing oil is, however, sometimes polished with rottenstone, and is in this manner given much additional luster. A dull surface that has been produced by rubbing with water and fine pumice stone powder may also be polished to a considerable extent.

Piano polishing is usually done on a final coat of polishing varnish, a short oil varnish that dries very hard and has a high luster. Polishing varnish when used should be applied as a last coat over surfaces that have been well filled, if the wood is porous. As a foundation for the polishing varnish there should be several undercoats of rubbing varnish, properly sandpapered or rubbed with water and pumice stone between coats. A person should not attempt to polish a varnished object unless perfectly level surfaces have been prepared with several coats of varnish.

Polishing a varnished surface with rottenstone after it has been rubbed with pumice stone removes the fine scratches that were made on the surface by the pumice stone, and produces a very level smooth surface, with a high luster that varies somewhat with the composition of the film of varnish on the surface.

Three methods of polishing varnished surfaces are used by wood finishers: (1) polishing with rottenstone and water; (2) polishing with rottenstone and oil; and (3) "spiriting off" or French polishing with alcohol.

A much higher luster can be produced by any of the methods if a polishing varnish is used for the last coat. Polishing may be done, however, with either oil or water, over rubbing varnish or polishing varnish. Long oil varnishes are usually too soft to receive a high polish.

Polishing with Rottenstone and Water. The method of putting a quick but rather low polish on the rubbing varnish itself, after fine rubbing with pumice stone and water and a redrying of the surface of at least twelve hours, is very commonly used on ordinary furniture. If the preceding rubbing with pumice stone has been done with water, the polishing can also easily be done with water and rottenstone. Carefully sifted rottenstone does not scratch, but it may contain grit

12—6. After rubbing with pumice stone, a varnished surface is next rubbed with rottenstone and oil.

that makes fine lines. In order to avoid scratching it is wise to rub lengthwise of the grain of wood for the final polishing when water is used with rottenstone for polishing. Some polishers rub across the grain to remove the pumice stone scratches when the polishing process is started with rottenstone. Other skilled finishers use a circular motion in polishing. The final polishing, however, is usually done by rubbing carefully lengthwise of the grain. A very fine piece of felt of convenient size to hold in the hand and about ¼″ thick makes an excellent polishing pad. The final polishing is often done with the hand.

Polishing with Rottenstone and Oil. The oil method with rottenstone is preferable for finishing surfaces that have been rubbed with pumice stone and oil. A thin, fine, soft piece of felt is generally employed as a pad in the oil-polishing process. A pad of cotton waste dampened with water than with oil polish is often used. Rottenstone in the form of a brick may be rubbed on the pads, or very fine sifted powder of the same material may be mixed with the polishing oil itself or sprinkled over the surface which is to be polished. There are many rubbing oils, polishes, cleaners, and furniture renovators on the market (Fig. 12-6). Every polisher is apt to have a favorite formula which he has learned how to use. Numerous liquid furniture polishes are for sale, ready for use. Some of these polishes are very satisfactory though rather expensive.

The oil polishing liquids vary somewhat in ingredients, but usually they are made up from mixtures of oil, such as raw linseed, boiled linseed, or golden oil, together with de-natured or wood alcohol, vinegar or acetic acid, and antimony trichloride ($SbCl_3$), called butter of antimony. The chief purpose of using acetic acid or vinegar in a polishing oil is because of its strong cleansing action. If the work is newly varnished, or if an old surface has been washed thoroughly with soap and water, there is little or no necessity for acetic acid in a polishing oil, though its activity on the surface possibly makes the polishing process more rapid.

Lemon oil, made from the rind of lemons, is thought to possess unusual virtues by some polishers who use it in a mixture of 2 ounces to the gallon of neutral polishing oil. Olive oil, also called sweet oil, is thought to be the best polishing oil by other finishers. Linseed oil is often used, especially in polishes for old furniture. Its drying properties are such that there is danger of spontaneous combustion if rags saturated with it are left in masses where they can heat and catch fire. Felt polishing pads containing linseed oil from a furniture polishing liquid should be cleaned with benzine or some other volatile thinner after they are no longer needed for the day. Unless all linseed oil is removed by cleaning, or the pad is kept wet in a thinning fluid, the pad may become heated through oxidation and catch fire. Cotton waste polishing pads that have been used with oil polishing liquids should be placed in a fire proof waste can and removed from the building daily.

Polishing Oil Formulas. Some polishing oil formulas recommended by experienced wood finishers are as follows:

Formula No. 1.
1¼ oz. oil of cedar,
½ pint pure turpentine,
½ pint paraffin oil,
¼ to ¾ oz. oil of citronella,
2 oz. sifted rottenstone powder.
Shake the mixture thoroughly, and allow a few days for assimilation.

Formula No. 2.
1 pint raw linseed oil,
1 pint light golden oil,
1 pint 5 oz. distilled water or rain water.
Mix the above, and add
¼ pint acetic acid,
1 oz. antimony trichloride ($SbCl_3$) (butter of antimony),
⅛ pint denatured or wood alcohol,
3 oz. sifted rottenstone powder.

Formula No. 3.
½ pint olive oil,
½ pint denatured alcohol,
2 oz. sifted rottenstone powder.

In repolishing old varnished surfaces it is desirable to include acetic acid in the formula, because it cleans the old varnish and hastens the action of the polish. The following formulas are well adapted for this purpose:

Formula No. 4.
½ pint turpentine,
½ pint boiled linseed oil,
½ pint strong vinegar,
1 to 3 ounces of sifted rottenstone may be added, if it is desired to polish rather than clean and renovate.

Formula No. 5.
1 quart paraffin oil,
1 quart denatured alcohol,
1 pint to 1 quart strong vinegar,
3 to 6 ounces of sifted rottenstone may be added if desired.

Spiriting Off or French Polishing with Alcohol. An oil polished surface is sometimes given a very high luster by "spiriting off" the varnish with denatured alcohol. The method is expensive, and is not often used except on high-grade furniture that requires a very brilliant luster.

After a satisfactory polish has been secured on a polishing or finishing varnish by use of rottenstone and an oil composed of ¼ to ½ oz. of lemon oil to a pint of neutral oil, the surface should be thoroughly cleaned. The human hand, if the skin is in good condition and without callouses, makes the best polishing pad. The hand should be wet with polishing oil at the start of the process, and nearly dry at the finish. After rubbing carefully with the lemon oil polish, using a circular motion, the surface should be cleaned in order to remove any particles of rottenstone. The surface may be wiped off with a lemon oil polish which contains no rottenstone.

"Spiriting off" may be done with a soft wad of cloth which has been dampened but is not wet with denatured alcohol (Fig. 12-7). The excess of alcohol should be wrung out of the polishing rag. Great care must be taken in "spiriting off" the surface, or the alcohol will burn through the varnish and spoil the finish. The polishing pad should be kept moving in circles, and not allowed to come to a rest for a moment on the sur-

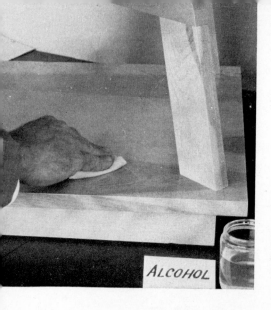

12—7. "Spiriting off" is a method of cleaning an oil-polished surface. A high luster is secured by moving a soft cloth, slightly dampened with alcohol in a circular motion over the surface.

face. Some finishers dampen the rubbing cloth with water, then wring it dry. They next dampen the rag with alcohol slightly and wring it nearly dry in order to reduce the strength of the alcohol by putting it on a moist rag instead of a dry one. The quick wiping in the "spiriting off" process cleans the polishing oil from the surface and leaves a clean brilliant luster.

Varnish Removers. Certain liquids when applied to varnished surfaces possess strong enough solvent action to soften the dry and hard films in such a manner that they can be scraped off (Figs. 12-8, 9, 10, and 11). Some of the solvent liquids commonly used in varnish removers are denatured and wood alcohol, benzol, acetone, amyl acetate, butyl acetate, fusel oil, strong caustic soda solution with water, and ammonia and other alkalies.

Many varnish removers contain paraffin wax in various amounts, sometimes in quantities sufficient to make the remover appear like a thin paste. The wax is used to keep the

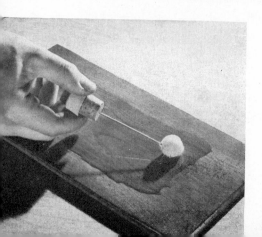

COURTESY HILLYARD SALES CO.
12—8. Apply varnish remover with a brush or swab. Wait a short time until the remover softens the finish.

12—9. A good varnish remover reacts to a finished surface like this.

volatile liquids from evaporating too rapidly from the varnish coatings. Such thick paraffin removers are especially useful on vertical and oblique surfaces. Every trace of wax, such as paraffin, must be removed before the surface can be refinished because shellac and varnish will not adhere or dry properly to material that has wax on it. Benzine, gasoline, or turpentine can be added to dissolve and remove the paraffin.

12—10. When the reaction of the remover to the finish is complete, the old finish is removed with a dull scraping tool.

COURTESY HILLYARD SALES COMPANY

12—11. While many removers are highly inflammable, the one used here is non-inflammable, a distinct advantage in the paintshop.

Acetone is often an important ingredient in the better grades of varnish removers, while cheaper solvents, such as alcohol and benzol, are the chief ingredients in inexpensive removers.

Many formulas for varnish removers contain liquids that will burn the skin, and all such mixtures must be applied with rubber gloves, or with care to keep the liquid away from the hands entirely.

Varnish removers that contain alkalies are liable to darken the wood to some extent. The amount of darkening is not usually serious or very objectionable except on very light-colored woods.

Formulas for Paint and Varnish Removers.

Formula No. 1.

1 qt. denatured alcohol (high proof—188° or 190°),

1 qt. benzol (90 per cent quality),
¼ lb. paraffin wax.

The wax should be melted first, and poured into the benzol after taking both of these *away from the fire*. Then, while stirring, pour the benzol into the alcohol.

Formula No. 2.
½ gal. benzol (90 per cent grade),
1 qt. acetone,
1 qt. wood alcohol,
½ lb. paraffin wax.

Formula No. 3.
1 qt. strong ammonia (26° or 28°),
1 pt. turpentine.

Mix the ingredients together by shaking thoroughly in a bottle.

This formula is useful for the removal of paint rather than varnish, because the irritating ammonia should not be used indoors, and it tends to darken the wood somewhat. The discoloration can be removed to some extent by sandpapering the surface with No. ½ sandpaper.

Many prepared varnish removers are for sale on the market, and these preparations are generally more satisfactory for use in schools than are those which are homemade. Some of these removers are wax-free.

Cleaning Varnish Brushes. The solvents used as thinners in varnish can be used in most cases as cleaners for varnish brushes. In school shops, turpentine is often employed as a cleaning fluid. Varnish brushes that have been neglected until gum partly hardens about the ferrule can be cleaned more satisfactorily by the use of amyl acetate, or butyl acetate,

12—12. After cleaning a varnish brush with turpentine or some other brush cleaner, give the brush a thorough washing with liquid soap and luke-warm water. 12—13. After a brush has been cleaned, wrap it in a paper towel and allow it to dry thoroughly.

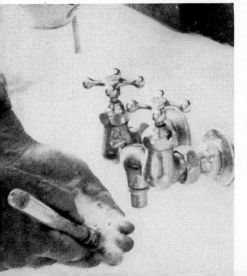
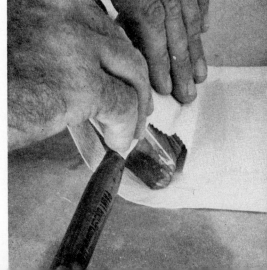

which is cheaper though not quite so good a solvent (Fig. 12-12 and 13).

Many liquid varnish removers are also satisfactory for use as brush cleaners. Varnish removers containing strong alkalies damage the bristles of the brushes, and must be avoided or used with great caution. Varnish removers should be cleaned out of brushes by a final washing in turpentine, especially if the brush is to be put back into varnish in a wet condition.

SELECTED REFERENCES, CHAPTERS XI AND XII

Natural Fossil-Gum

Chatfield, H. W., "Ideal Varnish Solvent," *Paint, Oil and Chemical Review,* 112, pp. 20-22, Aug. 4, 1949.

Conrad, G., "Stripping Finishing Materials," *Organic Finishing,* 8, page 13, June, 1947.

Deniston, G. L., *The Science of Modern Woodfinishing,* "Finishing with Varnish," Chapter XI, pp. 156-178, 1949.

Ibid., "Rubbing and Polishing of Organic Coatings," Chapter XIII, pp. 208-229, 1949.

Fisher, E. M., *What You Should Know about Paint,* "Varnishes," Chapter V, pp. 80-92, 1952.

Gibbia, S. W., *Wood Finishing and Refinishing,* "Varnish," Chapter VI, pp. 82-100, 1954.

Mattiello, Joseph J., *Protective and Decorative Coatings,* Volume 2, "Varnishes," Chapter VIII, pp. 193-249, 1942.

McGee, R. A. and Brown, A. G., *Instructional Units in Woodfinishing,* "To Apply an Oil Varnish," Chapter IV, pp. 290-335, 1950.

Ibid., "To Rub Down and Polish a Varnished Surface," pp. 40-47, 1950.

Soderberg, G. A., *Finishing Materials and Methods,* "Paint and Varnish Removers," Chapter XVIII, pp. 116-118, 1952.

Ibid., "Coated and Polishing Abrasives," Chapter XIX, pp. 119-132, 1952.

Chapter XIII

Varnish Evolution

Importance of Synthetic Resins. Important steps forward
in science and the making of new products valuable to man
have characterized the century. Various fields of human activity have contributed offerings of utility; among those of
very great need and value being the resinlike materials which
have been discovered and perfected in the laboratories of the
chemists. The uses of these new resins, often resembling amber
in appearance, are now in the thousands, and their value is
beyond that of the fondest dreams of the research workers of
a few years ago. These purely synthetic materials are widely
used for molding plastics, for various laminated objects, for
valuable cements; for coatings for fabrics, for telephone fixtures, for numerous automobile parts; and for a thousand other
purposes, among which are new, much needed resins for the
varnish maker. Synthetic resins add a new speed to the setting of the so-called four hour varnishes, in addition to decreasing the time needed for the hardening of coatings made
from such varnishes.

One large manufacturer of synthetic resins has stated that
greater improvements in surface coatings have appeared during the past 35 years than during the previous century. Formulas for making varnishes were considered to be of great
value and were kept secret until the new synthetic resins
appeared and the trained chemist took over the manufacture
of varnishes. Today, a scientist who is a specialist in physical
and colloidal chemistry is at the head of an experimental laboratory where all formulas are tried out. Many manufacturers
of synthetic resins publish suggestive varnish formulas for the
use of varnish makers, and such formulas are available to almost any one who is interested. A varnish formula is probably

251

of much less importance than when the old fossil resins and linseed oil were used, because great changes in the final product turned out can be brought about by variations in the heat treatments of the synthetic resins and oils used in varnish manufacture of the new quick drying type of finishes. Details of procedure in the varnish kettle are more likely to be kept secret by manufacturers than any listing of proportions of ingredients such as are found in a varnish formula.

Classes of Varnish. Three classes of varnish are mentioned in Chapter XI, "Classification of Varnishes," p. 195. Actually, from a *drying* point of view, there seem to be four rather distinct classes. The types are distinguished by evaporation of the thinners and solvents and the method of hardening of the films made from the varnishes. The four classes might be named as follows: (1) spirit varnishes; (2) linseed oil fossil-gum varnishes; (3) China wood oil with fossil-gum varnishes; and (4) synthetic resin varnishes.

1. Spirit varnishes dry entirely by *evaporation* of the solvent. The most common types are: (a) shellac containing an alcohol solvent, and (b) dammar varnish, which is made with a volatile oil such as turpentine or a turpentine substitute which is often petroleum spirits.

2. Fossil-gum, ester gum, and limed rosin varnishes dry in two ways: (a) by *evaporation* of the volatile thinner or solvents, and (b) through the *oxidation* of the vehicle or drying oils—generally consisting of specially treated boiled linseed oil in the standard slow drying varnishes. These are the old types of oil varnishes which have been used for hundreds of years and were almost universally employed for permanent finishes until recently.

3. The China wood oil types of slow drying varnishes are made from fossil gums, ester gum or specially treated rosin. Such varnishes contain China wood oil as the chief drying oil of the varnish vehicle and dry: (a) partly by the *evaporation* of the thinner, (b) partly by *oxidation* of the drying oil or oils, and finally (c) through the *polymerization* of the China wood oil which has peculiar drying characteristics that are different from those of linseed oil previously used as the chief drying oil in oil varnishes.

4. The synthetic resin and China wood oil type of four hour or quick-drying varnishes dries in three ways as follows: (a) through *evaporation* of a volatile thinner, such as varnolene (a petroleum product) and xylol (a high boiling coal-tar product); (b) through a modified amount of *oxidation;* and (c) through a new factor or reaction called *polymerization* or gelatinization of both the China wood oil and the liquefied synthetic resins. These combined processes of setting and drying produce a speed in surface setting previously unknown and a considerable acceleration in complete hardening or drying of films made from such varnishes. Attention should be called to the fact that synthetic resins are chemically a product of reactions such as polymerization or condensation, and that the molecules are quite complex and of somewhat indefinite structure. Various factors used in manufacturing synthetic resins may change the final resin product, though the materials from which the resins are made may be identical. The varnishes which are sold on the market as rapid-drying or four-hour varnishes are made entirely or largely from synthetic resins and contain considerable amounts of China wood oil, which dries rapidly, partly by polymerization.

Spirit Varnishes. The old types of spirit and volatile oil varnishes, such as shellac and dammar varnish, are still used for numerous purposes. See Chapter X for detailed information. Spirit varnishes are made cold or without great heat by dissolving the resin in its best solvent, such as grain alcohol for shellac, and turpentine or more commonly a turpentine substitute for dammar and mastic. Shellac substitutes, which are cheap, inferior finishes, also belong in this group if they contain alcohol as a solvent. Some of the synthetic gums similar to those used in lacquers are also soluble in volatile oils, and varnishes from them belong in this group because they dry by evaporation.

The user of shellac years ago bought orange flake shellac in the form of thin scales varying in size up to about three-quarters of an inch in diameter. Wood alcohol was the solvent which the shop finisher used in preparing his orange shellac. White shellac was made from chunks of bleached shellac which dissolved with difficulty in wood alcohol, especially if the shellac was old and had been exposed to the air for some time. Today, either orange or white shellac in liquid form of various strengths dissolved in denatured grain alcohol can be obtained from any dealer in finishing supplies. Some of the cheaper liquid shellacs of today are made with a solvent which is a mixture of grain and wood alcohol. Such a shellac produces a disagreeable odor when it is being applied.

Shellac varnishes may be thinned with cold denatured alcohol and can then be used in a very short time. Coatings of shellac varnish dry very quickly and produce a low gloss or semilustrous finish. Shellac varnish is often used on floors and for some other finishes. Shellac coatings will turn white if exposed to the weather or spotted with water. Contractors often prefer shellac as a floor finish because it is easy to apply, dries quickly, and produces a good effect. Shellac is generally unsatisfactory for floors because it does not wear long or well, and turns white if water comes in contact with it. Shellac somewhat diluted is often used for an undercoat or as a sealer. It should be sanded well before another finish is applied over it in order to secure smoothness and aid in the adhesion of the next coating.

Oil Varnishes with Linseed Oil. Varnishes made from fossil resins, ester gum, or treated rosin, which can be melted to liquid form at great heat and then combined with linseed oil in large part, have been the standard slow drying varnishes that have been in use in some of their forms for centuries. Metallic driers of several types have usually been added in small amounts to speed up drying or oxidation. An excess of drier cannot be added to increase the drying speed because of various difficulties that are impossible to overcome. In the old oil or oleoresinous varnishes, turpentine was placed in the mixture as a thinner or volatile solvent; but, for some years, this excellent solvent has been replaced very largely by some mineral spirit or a cheap petroleum volatile oil.

It is through the *evaporation* of the thinner or solvent, and the slower changes in the drying oil, which the chemists say is largely *oxidation,* that a linseed oil varnish including fossil resin dries out and changes from a liquid to a solid film. There is a rather marked chemical change during the oxidation of drying oils, such as linseed oil, and the new substance formed has molecules which contain additional atoms of oxygen. The oxidation of a varnish film begins at the surface, which forms a skin on the outside and dries out more slowly inside because of greater difficulty in obtaining oxygen from the air about the film.

The standard thinner for practically all of the high grade oil varnishes of the hard fossil gum type was turpentine, which almost entirely dried out by evaporation, leaving only a very small residue. Other volatile thinners have more recently been substituted for turpentine since Congo resin and kauri have become scarce and expensive. Other resins have replaced the hard fossil resins at least in part.

Great variations in the speed for drying of linseed oil varnishes made with hard fossil gums are possible. Quick-drying or four-hour varnishes, however, are not produced from these materials. The drying times of most fossil-gum varnishes vary from about two days to about a year. The very slow-drying type is sometimes used on fishing rods in order to secure a very flexible finish. Heat treatments of the linseed oil produce great changes in the oil, and variations in the speed in drying of varnishes made from oils of different heat treatments are very great.

Slow-Drying Oil Varnishes with China Wood Oil. The demand for varnishes has gradually increased from year to year while the supply of good fossil resins has slowly decreased in amount. The result has been substitute resins, such as ester gum and specially treated limed rosin. Cheap varnishes made from untreated rosin proved to be very unsatisfactory. So ester gum varnishes gradually came into favor. Then China wood oil was tried with lime-treated rosin and a better varnish was obtained than could be made from rosin and linseed oil.

The discovery of some of the possibilities and advantages derived from the introduction of China wood oil in oil varnishes was the first gold mine that was to bring about a great "rush" in varnish chemistry and a new era in varnish manufacture and use. Varnishes with resins, such as ester gum or even heat-treated limed rosin, were made with properly heat-treated China wood oil. They were inexpensive and possessed most of the good qualities of the famous old linseed oil varnishes manufactured with fossil resins.

China wood oil varnishes dry out both physically and chemically by somewhat different reactions from those common with linseed oil. Drying of the China wood type of varnish is: (1) by *evaporation* of the thinner; (2) by chemical *oxidation* of some of the oils; and (3) by *polymerization* of the China wood oil to some extent.

Polymerization is a very technical term that is hard to understand by anyone who is not a trained chemist. In brief, polymerization is a change in the molecules of a substance into new molecules which have the same percentage of each component but which possess a higher molecular weight that is always a simple multiple of the original atomic weight. The physical change as a result of polymerization is very marked and striking, and the drying reactions also differ to some extent from those of the linseed oil types of varnishes. Films that dry largely by polymerization seem to dry at a rather uniform rate from top to bottom instead of skinning over on top as is common with the linseed oil fossil-resin type of varnishes.

Drying oils are placed in varnishes in order to produce more elasticity, furnish greater toughness, and to add waterproofness to coatings made from them. Spirit varnishes, such as shellac or dammar varnish, contain no drying oil and lack elasticity, toughness, and waterproofness which are essential characteristics for floor varnishes and for all finishes for outdoor exposure.

China wood oil is reported by some varnish authorities to be used almost exclusively in the manufacture of modern architectural varnishes. Small amounts of linseed oil are, however, necessary in the preparatory heat treatment of the China wood oil.

The fatty acids found in linseed oil and China wood oil are quite different. In linseed oil the acids are: palmitic 9%, oleic 15%, linoleic 41%, and linolenic 35%. China wood oil is said to contain palmitic acid 5%, oleic 15%, and eleostearic acid 80%. The fatty acids are quite different and their drying characteristics also differ widely. The very valuable properties of China wood oil are said to come from its exceptionally high content of eleostearic acid, which is not a component part of linseed oil. The two oils both contain palmitic acid, and many of their properties are quite similar.

China wood oil must have very carefully controlled heat treatments in order to prevent it from polymerizing into an insoluble jelly, which is useless as varnish. Also, to assist in control of the oil, small portions of linseed oil, rosin, and a very little litharge are added during the heat treatment of the China wood oil. The oil treatment takes place before the cooking of varnish resins and oils in the kettle in making varnish.

The chief change that takes place in the "drying" of varnish oils is generally oxidation, which means that the unsaturated acids in the oils absorb oxygen from the air.

Some of the following chapters in this book will give information about synthetic resins, describe their characteristics, and finally give suggestions about their application.

SELECTED REFERENCES, CHAPTER XIII

Varnish Evolution

Deniston, G. L., *The Science of Modern Woodfinishing*, "Finishing With Varnish," Chapter XI, pp. 156-178, 1949.

Kappelmeier, C. P. A., "Chemistry in the Evolution of the Modern Varnish Industry," *Paint Oil and Chemical Review*, 112, pp. 18 plus, July 7, 1949.

Mattiello, Joseph J., *Protective and Decorative Coatings*, Volume 1, "Introduction, Paint and Varnish Industry," pp. 1-56; 1941.

Neidig, C. P. and Burrell, H., "Paint, Varnish and Lacquer Industry in 1947," *Chemical and Engineering News*, 26, pp. 25-27, Jan. 5, 1948.

Von Fischer, W. and Bobalek, Edward G., *Organic Protective Coatings;* Reinhold Publishing Corp., 1953; 387 pages.

Chapter XIV

Synthetic Resins

Synthetics Revolutionize Varnish Making. Outstanding progress in the world's industry has followed the discoveries of the chemist and physicist in thinking out important problems and improvements for the benefit of man. A limited list of these problems would include: (1) the generation and use of electricity; (2) the vulcanization of rubber; (3) methods of making nickel and chrome steel; and (4) the discovery of processes for making synthetic varnish resins from materials that are cheap and plentiful yet which resemble the valuable old fossil resins, possess most of their good qualities, and, in addition, have some previously unknown virtues.

Last but not least, we should mention the recent development of atomic and nuclear power. Time will tell whether these two will serve or help destroy mankind.

Synthetic resins have almost completely revolutionized the ancient art of varnish making and very markedly reduced the time needed for the drying of finishes—making drying speeds for varnish that are somewhat similar to those for lacquer.

Synthetic resins indicate a great step forward in man's progress, being greatly needed because the natural resins seem to be largely exhausted. Synthetics can be produced in large quantities, and have greatly increased the use of varnishes and varnish enamels, which now compete with lacquers to a very considerable extent. The cost of the resins is reasonable, and films made from them dry with great rapidity. The quality and permanency of the films are excellent compared with similar properties of other varnishes.

Meaning of Term "Synthetic Resins." In appearance synthetic varnish resins somewhat resemble natural or fossil resins, which are formed by natural processes through long years and are dug out of the ground. Synthetic resins are not chemically the same as natural resins but are manufactured products that can be substituted partly or entirely for them. The old varnish formulas are usually greatly modified when synthetic gums are used. Synthetic resins are manufactured resinlike materials which are made from chemicals that are usually simple in form and, through treatment and processing, are converted into new chemical compounds which somewhat resemble natural resins though often with greatly improved and changed properties.

The known synthetic resins at present are numerous, though only a few of them are really important commercially. The various resins have a molecular structure that is somewhat indefinite as a result of polymerization or condensation reactions. The final synthetic resin varies with such factors in manufacturing as the following: (1) relative amounts of the original materials used; (2) the acid or alkali chosen as a catalyst which forms new unstable compounds; (3) the temperature and length of time allowed in processing the materials; and (4) the amount and kind of other substances that are incorporated into the mixtures during manufacture.

Types of Synthetic Resins Used. Several types of synthetic resins are manufactured that might be listed as follows:

1. Resin esters or ester gums which are partly synthetic. They are produced by the reaction of such natural resins as rosin with glycerine or some other higher alcohol. Chemical treatment or processing greatly changes the properties and reactions of the final product—ester gum—from the original rosin, which is highly acid. Ester gum is really a glyceryl ester of rosin. Fig. 14-1 pictures various types of this gum.

2. The phenol formaldehyde resins, which are purely synthetic, are called phenolics, and are really condensates of one of the phenols with formaldehyde. Many resins of this type are really modified phenolics and are combinations often with ester gum, and sometimes with rosin or some fatty acid. The following resins belong in this group of pure and modified phenolics: Bakelite, Amberol, Beckacites, Paranol, Durez, and Durite.

14—1. Ester gums. Various types of ester gum are now substituted for fossil resins which are scarce. Ester gums make much better varnishes than can be produced from rosin.

The pure phenol formaldehyde resins vary in characteristics, depending on the relative amounts of phenol and formaldehyde which are used and whether an acid or alkaline catalyst is employed. Some of these resins are always soluble in alcohol and are fusible. Another group to which Bakelite belongs is soluble in alcohol in the early stages of condensation, yet becomes insoluble on higher heat treatments. Resins that are soluble in drying oils, or which can be made soluble through heat treatments or processing, are needed for oil varnishes. In order to secure such oil solubility more complex phenols are sometimes substituted for the ordinary phenol in the manufacture of phenol formaldehyde resins. Cresol is a chemically related compound which sometimes replaces phenol. Another method of making a phenol formaldehyde resin oil soluble is to introduce into the mixture some soluble substance, such as rosin or a fatty acid which will dissolve in drying oils or mineral thinners.

The manufacturers of pure or 100% phenolics claim that several years of experience with varnishes made from such resins have shown that they are superior under outdoor exposure when tried where moisture was excessive and salt spray was possible. The reaction to chemicals such as acids, alkalies, and gases was not rapid.

3. The alkyd groups include the Glyptals, Rezyls, and Teglacs especially, together with some of the modified Amberols and Beckasols. The Glyptals of the General Electric Company are important resins which are chemically glycerol phthalic anhydride condensates. Some of the Beckasols are of the straight alkyd type, while others are modified, especially with phenol.

The phenol alkyds are a composite type of important resins that are sometimes placed in a separate group or type. Good examples of the modified phenol alkyd type are some of the Beckasols, which in pure form are alkyds; and some of the Amberols, which in unmodified form are of the phenol formaldehyde class.

Experience with the alkyd resins has shown that they are valuable in films that must retain colors—especially all whites and light tints.

4. The Cumar or Coumarone type of resins is based on the polymerization of indene, coumarone, and similar compounds found in some of the coal-tar naphthas. The Neville resin, called *Nevindene*, is an example of the Coumarone type.

5. Other groups of synthetic resins might be mentioned, such as urea and melamine resins, vinyl resins, chlorinated diphenyls, and toluol sulfonamide resins, and stirenated alkyds.

The urea resins are valuable for use in plastic moldings in the formation of colorless glass. In varnishes they lack the needed waterproofness, but they produce films of unusual transparency and good gloss.

In synthetic enamels they have proved satisfactory for general use and in fortifying the chemical and solvent resistance of alkyd resins. They are of the baking type, used in the finishing of home appliances such as refrigerators, stoves, and washing machines.

The vinyl resins have been used to some extent as binding material in molding plastics, but their general use is limited. These resins can be manufactured in an almost colorless and

14—2. Amberols. The pale amberol shown in the photograph is now
used in various quick-drying varnishes. It is frequently mixed with other
resins in varnish making. Synthetic resins vary greatly in color and often
are darker than natural resins or ester gum.

transparent form. Varnishes have been made from vinyl resins
for use on objects of metal and sometimes for fabrics.

The Important Synthetic Resins. Many new synthetic resins
have been produced, but only a few of them are of much
value. The few that are valuable at the present time are really
very precious because they are needed to replace natural resins
which are now scarce and more expensive. A few of the best
known synthetic resins will be mentioned and described here.
Others of some value are known and are being used to some
extent.

Amberols. The amberols, Fig. 14-2, are of the phenol formaldehyde type but are often modified or used in combination
with other resins which supply qualities not found in the pure
resins. The resins commonly chosen to modify the 100% resins
into various Albertols or Amberols are often rosin, rosin esters
or ester gum, and sometimes natural resins. The addition of
cheap, common rosin to the pure phenol formaldehyde resin
produces a new resin characterized by hardness, better oil
solubility, greater durability, and less tendency to turn yellow
in transparent films. Several grades of Amberol are manufac-

tured having varying characteristics of hardness, different acid numbers, and other physical properties, such as oil solubility and the temperatures used when dissolving in oils. The important Amberols, except No. 226, are not soluble in alcohol, but they are soluble in most of the usual varnish solvents, as turpentine, mineral thinner, and toluol.

Bakelite. The synthetic material known as Bakelite is the discovery of Dr. L. H. Bakeland and has been used in some of its forms for half a century (since 1909). He discovered that an amber colored, resinlike material could be produced from phenol and formaldehyde by joining them under certain conditions. Bakelite is well known for its use in plastic and molded material—for the telephone and parts of the automobile, for example.

Bakelite resin is now made by placing definite quantities of phenol and formaldehyde—colorless liquids—in a closed and jacketed kettle and allowing them to react under steam for several hours. Then in the kettle a layer of resinous material in a molten state will be found below and water above. This resin when separated from the water is known as Bakelite resinoid. The initial resinoid can be processed into six quite different materials or classes having different properties: (1) resinoids for transparent materials, as cigarette holders; (2) molding materials to be used with wood flour, as telephone receivers; (3) laminated products made from sheets of paper or cloth treated with Bakelite in alcohol; (4) liquid varnishes of the baking type and cements; (5) synthetic resins for air drying finishes, as the two- and four-hour varnishes;

14—3. Bakelites. Synthetic resins are now made in various grades and colors. The pale Bakelite is used in pale varnishes. The other, shown at the left, is used in darker varnishes. Such resins now replace kauri and Congo copal resins, formerly used in high grade varnishes.

and (6) special resinoids as bonding material for abrasive products, such as grinding wheels.

The Bakelite resins which are used in paints and varnishes are of three types: (1) the pure or 100% phenolic resins without modifications with oils or other resins; (2) pure Bakelite resins that have been modified with a drying oil; and (3) pure Bakelite resins modified by mixture with other resins (Fig. 14-3), page 263.

Varnishes made from Bakelite possess certain very valuable properties, such as durability, exposure ruggedness, and resistance to abrasion—lasting qualities in connection with salt water, soap, and corrosive agents. The Bakelite varnishes used are of the short oil and medium oil lengths; that is, from 10 gallons to 35 gallons of oil. Long oil varnishes are not needed with Bakelite resins and would be less durable because drying oils are less durable than the Bakelite resins. It should be remembered that Bakelite resins of somewhat different compositions are placed in quite a number of types of varnishes requiring different formulas. On account of their real merit Bakelite varnishes are used on the decks and other parts of ships in place of spar varnish, on floors which receive hard wear and washing; about schools, public buildings, and homes, as metal priming coatings; for furniture; and also for baked on finishes over metal furniture and various metal parts and objects.

Other Phenol Formaldehyde Synthetic Resins. The Paranols, Paraduras, and Esterols form a group of synthetic resins which are modified phenolics that are prepared for use in interior and exterior varnishes. They have high melting points and excellent solubility.

The *Durites* consist of a pure 100% type of phenolics made from some phenol condensed with formaldehyde and unmodified by any mixture with other resins.

Durez resins are also of the unmodified phenolic type that are oil soluble in kettle treatments. Varnishes made from Durez resins are said to have high gloss, even though highly pigmented, and also to possess excellent adhesion to surfaces.

The *Beckacites* are of the phenol formaldehyde type of resins that melt at temperatures between 225° F. and 275° F., which is a rather low varnish making temperature. The resins combine easily, especially with China wood oil, and form varnishes that dry hard with good gloss and make films of good durability.

The *Rauzene* resins are partly phenolic resins of the modified type and are often combined with fossil resins. Some of them are non-phenolics made especially for lacquers.

Alkyd Groups. *Glyptals.* These resins are highly complex chemically and are formed through polymerization of glycerine with the mixed esters of phthalic acid and vegetable drying oil acids, such as are found in linseed oil or China wood oil. Resins of this type are now preferred for use in certain lacquers, paints, and varnishes. Some of the modified glyptals have been used in insulating varnishes and for a binder for laminated mica.

A resin of the glycerol phthalate type with China wood oil and soya bean oil, a semi-drying oil, is at present used in millions of gallons of enamel now being furnished annually for finishing automobiles. The du Pont Company developed the finishes and the Ford Company worked out the technique of application. Finishes of this type are far more durable than were any of the earlier varnish-enamel or lacquer finishes. The coatings are more susbtantial and require less polishing. It might be added that the automobile trade in general has adopted somewhat similar finishes of spraying enamels for use on all cars.

Alkyd finishes made with a China wood oil modifier will air dry in about 16 hours. Usually, alkyd finishes are made, in part at least, with soya bean oil, which is slow or almost non-drying; and, in this case, a baked on finish is required. The baking type placed on metal requires for drying only 1 to 1½ hours at a temperature of 275° F. to 325° F. The Ford factory some years ago was using sprayed on enamel finishes of the alkyd type and baking them on under both heat and light by use of thousands of 260 watt electric lamps. The bodies passed through tunnels or moving ovens powerfully lighted for both heat and light lumination during the drying process. Some repair shops "spray on" enamel and dry it out under a big lamp or group of lamps.

At present the alkyd or phthalic type of enamels are used for baked on metal finishes, such as automobiles, articles of tin, and refrigerators. Alkyd resins are primarily a constituent of most present day lacquers.

The *Rezyls* and *Teglacs* are other alkyd resins made by using modifying agents which are generally fatty acids. The Rezyls are used in house paints, lacquers, and in some baking enamels. The Teglacs are also modified alkyds, which are combined with some natural resin acid as the modifying agent.

Nevindene Resins. It is from reactive chemicals known as coumarone and indene, which are found in certain coal-tar naphthas, that the cumar type of synthetic resins called *Nevindene* is obtained. Reactions of coumarone and indene through treatment with polymerizing agents produce the Nevindene resins which are manufactured in several grades. The most valuable seem to be the hard grades. Though not soluble in alcohol, they are soluble in varying proportions in the light coal-tar solvents and petroleum naphthas. The Nevindenes blend well with some of the needed drying oils, with other synthetic resins, and also with fossil resins sometimes mixed with them for special purposes. It has been found, however, that the phenol modified indene types of resins are most easily blended with other varnish ingredients; consequently, they are especially valuable for use in plastics, adhesives, chlorinated rubber coatings, and varnishes. The Nevindene resins are used in blends sometimes to reduce the acidity of the mixtures, being almost neutral or containing practically no acid themselves. Another reason for blending with other resins is because Nevindene sells at a lower price than most resins of other types. The Neville resins are manufactured for use in varnishes, bronzing liquids, and paints; and such finishes are resistant to moisture, alkali, and acids. The earliest types of Nevindene resin varnishes and enamels showed after yellowing, which made them unsuitable where white enamels and transparent light finishes were desired. This quality has been somewhat improved recently by use of purer materials.

SELECTED REFERENCES, CHAPTER XIV

Synthetic Resins

Deniston, G. L., *The Science of Modern Woodfinishing*, "Lacquers, Synthetics and Their Application," Chapter XII, pp. 179-207, 1949.

Fisher, E. M., *What You Should Know About Paint,* "Other Synthetic Resins," Chapter VI, pp. 93-100, 1952.

Gibbia, S. W., *Wood Finishing and Refinishing,* "Varnish," Chapter VI, pp. 97-100, 1954.

Mattiello, Joseph J., *Protective and Decorative Coatings,* Volume I, "Alkyd Resins," Chapter XIII, pp. 338-359, 1941.

Ibid., "Synthetic Drying Oils," Chapter V, pp. 151-161.

Ibid., "Phenolic Resins," Chapter XII, pp. 311-337.

Ibid., "Vinyl Resins," Chapter XVII, pp. 433-446.

Ibid., "Urea-formaldehyde Coatings Composition," Chapter XV, pp. 391-415.

Von Fisher, W., and Bobalek, E. G., *Organic Protective Coatings,* "Vinyl Resins for Organic Protective Coatings," Chapter IX, pp. 167-209, 1953.

Wampler, Rollin H., *Modern Organic Finishes,* pp. 5 and 13, 1946.

Chapter XV

Quick-Drying Varnish Characteristics
and Ingredients

Origin and Purposes of Drying Speed. Acceleration or speed in the hardening of the rapid drying or four-hour varnishes and enamels comes chiefly from the use of synthetic resins and partly from the proper heat treatment of the drying oils which are used together with suitable driers. Synthetic resins are manufactured for a great number of purposes, including use in clear varnishes for furniture, floors, and outside use; as well as for incorporating into enamels for finishes on wood and metal, for air drying and baking, and to be applied with either brush or spray gun.

It should be remembered that heat treatment in the varnish kettle may change the characteristics of a varnish to a very considerable extent. In making an ester gum varnish with China wood oil, it is important to give the oil proper cooking; consequently, temperatures of 525° F. to 560° F. are often used in the kettle. It should be noted that when synthetic gums are employed the China wood oil and resins are heat treated at much lower temperatures than are needed for the proper cooking of ester gum or fossil gum varnishes.

Meaning of Term "Quick-Drying Varnishes." It might be well to state that the term "quick-drying varnishes" is quite inclusive in meaning and is generally somewhat misleading. It would possibly be better to call them quick-setting varnishes because they set very quickly; but they dry hard only in perhaps about half or three fourths the time needed for slow drying fossil gum varnishes. Coatings of the so-called four-hour floor varnishes can sometimes be walked upon very carefully after four hours, but they are not really dry and should not be sandpapered and recoated for several hours more. The finisher should wait until such varnishes are really hard—usually 24 to 48 hours for floor varnishes—before sandpapering and recoating them.

Factors in Quick Drying. The quick-drying ingredients—synthetic resins chiefly—can be placed in various types of varnishes for numerous purposes, such as short oil furniture and trim varnishes, medium oil floor varnishes, and spar varnishes that are not very long in oil. Both gloss and flat surfaces are possible, as well as modification of these two types. It has been found that some of the synthetic resins are very durable in themselves, and that the addition of a large amount of drying oils to make a spar varnish for waterproof use is unnecessary. Medium oil, synthetic resin varnishes can be made that are more durable than fossil gum, long oil spar varnishes of the old type.

In drying speed the synthetic resin, quick-drying varnishes are in a class by themselves. They come between the fossil gum or ester gum varnishes and nitrocellulose lacquers in speed of drying hard and especially in rapidity of setting. The quick-setting characteristic is usually of considerable value to the varnisher because less dust will settle into the sticky surface and fewer flies and insects will be caught than when slow drying varnishes are used. Then, too, articles can be moved and carefully handled much sooner than with the slow setting type of varnishes. It is difficult to generalize, however, because the speed in drying of synthetic varnishes at present varies widely; some of the most rapid types, even, almost equal the rapidity of lacquer, though this is not usual. Varnish manufacturers have discovered that the drying speed of synthetic resin varnishes can be varied considerably by selecting certain types of synthetic resins, and can be decreased by use of the modified type of synthetics which may contain fossil resins, ester gum, or limed rosin. There are other factors that enter into quick drying, such as the type of thinner that is used, the vehicle of drying oils selected, and their heat treatments. Turpentine is less used in the new varnishes and has been replaced by cheaper mineral thinners which vary quite widely in their time of evaporation. The thinners actually used are usually petroleum products, such as mineral spirits.

Several factors have already been mentioned in connection

with the drying of synthetic varnishes. Such varnishes do not dry by the rather simple processes of evaporation and oxidation, as is the case with fossil resin varnishes. New and additional factors enter the drying process when synthetic resins and China wood oil are used. The new factors are called polymerization and jellation. The drying, in case of synthetic resin varnishes, quickly takes place on the surface. A protective coating of rather hard varnish is quickly formed on the outside, but there is not a corresponding rate of hardening throughout the entire thickness of the film.

Driers may also affect the rate of drying of synthetic varnishes. In general, the four-hour varnishes do not really need drier, and very little is used. More drier should not usually be added in order to speed up the setting and drying of varnish coatings because too much drier may upset the balance of ingredients in the varnish mixture. In the past, when unusual speed with fossil or ester gum varnishes was desired, more drier was used and the amount of drying oil was reduced. These changes are not needed when synthetic gums are chosen for varnish manufacture. Driers have usually been salts of cobalt, manganese, zinc, and lead. Some driers known as "Naphthenates," "Octoates," and "Oilsolates" are being employed. The chief purpose of driers is to accelerate the oxidation process through the taking up of oxygen from the varnish drying oils, which are really fatty organic acids. Large quantities of driers in varnish tend to cause brittleness of films and to reduce their resistance to alkalies.

Qualities of Varnishes. Various tests and standards have been demanded by interested agencies, such as the Federal Government, several states, large cities, and by varnish buyers. These requirements have much in common though they are not standardized.

A complete list of the various qualities of varnishes would be long, and a discussion in detail about them would probably not be profitable in these pages. A list of the chief qualities will be of interest to some readers, also a few brief remarks about some of them. Among the most important qualities are: good working and flowing properties, hardness, color, drying time, viscosity, moisture and gas proofness, weather exposure test for one year, also resistance to hot or cold water, gasoline, and acids or alkalies; clear transparent color, proper body, sufficient elasticity, and exemption from both checking and flatting.

Experience has shown that flat varnishes show a cloudy effect, especially when they are placed over very dark woods, such as walnut or mahogany, or over woods stained in these colors. In fact, it has been found that flat varnishes do not furnish as clear and transparent effects as come from clear varnish, rubbed finishes. Another objection to flat varnish is that it is less waterproof than are clear varnishes in general. Usually the use of flat varnish is satisfactory for inside use because it is applied only as a final coating, the other coats being of more waterproof gloss varnish.

"Aging," which was formerly thought to be of great value in varnish making, is still practised unless the varnish is forced through a press filter. It has been found that one important advantage of "aged" varnish is that it is clearer because through a period of a few months in tanks a certain amount of very finely undissolved suspended matter remaining in the varnish gradually settles, leaving a clear varnish which is better for use. At present some manufacturers have a system of press filtering their varnishes which clears them about as well as storage and aging. Because it has been found that the important properties or qualities of varnishes remain largely unchanged by aging and that press filtering will remove the small particles that usually settle if given time, it has been decided that aging is not as important as it was formerly thought to be. Aging seems to remove fine sediment through settling, but the other properties which are important, such as durability, drying, waterproofness, body, and working qualities, seem to remain unchanged by storage and aging.

In addition to precipitation of solid impurities that will never dissolve, other effects may be possible in some kinds and grades of varnish. Ripening through aging is thought to be of real value for high grade varnishes, especially for use on automobiles, coaches, and for architectural work. It is thought that in some types of varnish the chemical reactions in the liquids are slow and that there may be gradual changes, partly physical and partly chemical, through a period of months. There also may be some evaporation of rather volatile liquids which will change the varnish in some respects.

The need for an aging process is said to depend somewhat on the type of driers used in the varnish. The use of some of the new "non-sludging" driers is said to have made aging of less importance.

Ingredients in Varnishes. The formulas for varnish making that are being used in manufacturing our present day varnishes are considerably different from those used with fossil resins or even ester gum of previous years.

The ingredients selected for the manufacture of the new synthetic varnishes, though somewhat different from those used just a few years ago, come under the same general classification; namely, (1) resins, (2) drying oils or vehicle, (3) solvents or volatile oils, and (4) driers. The real composition of the new varnishes is much different from the old, however, because of great differences in most of the classes.

Synthetic resins, described in another chapter of this book, are now used for making the quick-drying varnishes. The slow drying varnishes are made of fossil gums, ester gum, and limed rosin. Many varnishes contain a mixture of resins. Sometimes fossil gums are added to the solution containing molten synthetic resins or ester gum in order to produce certain types of varnish films.

The drying oil or vehicle has gradually been changed from linseed oil formerly used in all varnishes to China wood oil, also called tung oil, which requires special treatment but which possesses valuable and quite different qualities from those found in linseed oil.

It is from the inclusion of synthetic resins and China wood oil that the new quick-drying varnishes obtain the peculiar drying principle known as polymerization, which causes rapid setting and a reaction through the film something like that of the formation of a jelly.

Turpentine, the solvent and thinner formerly placed in the fossil varnishes of a few years ago, has been mostly replaced by xylol and cheap mineral thinners, such as Varnolene and other similar solvents which are petroleum products. Turpentine is known to be a more active oxygen carrier than are the petroleum thinners; but its cost is usually four or five times as much, and it leaves very little valuable residue after evaporation. Turpentine causes the varnish oils to flow and spread easier under a brush because it evaporates more slowly than do the substitute oils. The lack of turpentine is the cause of the stiff brushing or pull that is noticeable when applying synthetic varnishes.

The mineral thinners which are now almost exclusively employed for thinning varnishes are often called mineral spirits, though special terms such as Varnolene or solvent naphtha are sometimes used. The thinner chosen enters into the problem of spreading varnish, but it evaporates quickly and leaves little residue; consequently, most varnishes contain only cheap mineral spirits, either entirely or in large part.

Thinning Synthetic Varnishes. Persons who have felt the easy flow of varnishes of the past are tempted to thin any synthetic varnish that they have in order to make it spread easier—more like the varnishes of a few years ago. Thinners should not be added to quick-drying varnishes because there is danger of precipitation of the gums and serious varnish trouble. Manufacturers prepare them for use just as they are found in the cans. No addition of thinners of any kind is allowable without danger, except when mixing and dipping varnishes are being used.

Cold varnishes do not spread easily. The remedy is heat. Place the varnish pot on a hot brick or in a container of hot water some minutes before use and the flow under the brush will be greatly improved.

Varnish Cooking. The methods of cooking fossil resin and synthetic gum varnishes vary to some extent, but heat treatments are necessary in making all of the drying oil varnishes. Fossil resins in general must be heated to a very high heat and held at some high temperature until about 20% of the molten liquid has been driven off by evaporation. Temperatures of 600° F., or above, are commonly used. This heat treatment or melting changes the fossil resins and causes them to be soluble in drying oils—usually linseed and China wood oil—which are poured into the hot resin mixture away from the fire, the temperature of the oil varying with different types of varnish. The batch of resin is then recooked in order to cause the resin mixture and drying oils to combine thoroughly.

Ester gum varnishes do not require any prolonged cooking or high heat. China wood oil must be cooked at a temperature between 525° F. and 560° F. preferably with part of the ester gum. Later on, the remainder of the ester gum is put into the kettle and the batch is properly recooked, though at a lower temperature. When partly cooled, the varnish is thinned with mineral spirits or some similar cheap, volatile liquid.

Synthetic resins are usually cooked at the top heat with suitable drying oils, especially China wood oil with a small portion of linseed oil; but a considerably lower cooking heat is employed for them than for fossil resin or ester gum varnishes.

The actual or real properties of varnishes of all types are determined to a considerable degree by the method of cooking used. The same component ingredients can be so modified by different cooking operations that the final varnishes produced may be quite different in their characteristics.

Disadvantages Possible in Synthetic Varnishes. While it is true that synthetic varnishes have many real advantages over fossil resin varnishes of the best grade, most of them also had at first one or more of the disadvantages shown in the following list:

1. There seems to be a greater tendency for synthetic coatings to turn more or less yellow.

2. Synthetic varnish coatings seem to be rather thin or have less body than slow drying varnishes.

3. Heavy synthetic varnish coatings may sometimes wrinkle.

4. The gas checking danger is greater with synthetic varnishes.

5. Synthetic varnishes are apt to be darker in color and not as transparent as are clear fossil gum varnishes.

Synthetic varnishes have been improved since their appearance and most of the disadvantages of these varnishes have gradually been eliminated. The improvements have been in the form of pre-preparation of the oils, in the cooking procedures, and in the use of paler driers. There are also very great differences in the qualities of various makes of varnish. An honest manufacturer or salesman can usually be helpful in the selection of a satisfactory varnish.

Chapter XVI

Application of Quick-Drying Varnishes

Reasons for Varnishing. The purposes of varnish are rather numerous and should be of much interest to people who apply wood and metal finishes. Some of the important purposes which will come to one's mind are: (1) protection of the surfaces from probable injuries; (2) the bringing out of the hidden beauty of grain and color; (3) the development of a gloss or luster; (4) the production of a hard, smooth surface that may be handled; (5) the exclusion of moisture, vapors, and the usual agencies of decay; and (6) the giving of a finished effect or dress that pleases the eye and brings satisfaction to persons who love harmony and things which are fitting.

Quick-drying varnishes are in a class by themselves because of their rapid setting, and also because they harden fast enough for handling or careful service within a few hours. Varnishes made of synthetic resins harden quickly and are now widely used on furniture, on floors, in architectural work, and in quick-drying paints.

Choice of a Varnish. There is no such thing today as an all-purpose varnish. Varnishes are now made for special uses and for particular methods of application. In the classification for use we might mention short oil furniture rubbing varnishes, medium oil floor varnishes, long oil spar varnishes, flat varnishes, insulating varnishes, mixing varnishes, color varnishes, and quite a number of special varnishes. The list of varnishes classified by methods of application is short, but the types differ considerably. Among them might be mentioned: air-drying varnishes, baking varnishes, spraying varnishes, brushing varnishes, and dipping varnishes. The user should always consider both the purpose of the varnish and the method of application which he finds available or most convenient. If a varnisher wishes to apply a furniture rubbing varnish with a brush, he should obtain a varnish made for that particular purpose. A spraying varnish would be too thin. It should be remembered that synthetic varnishes are not easily "doctored" by use of thinners as was possible with the old fossil gum varnishes. Synthetic gum varnishes do not mix properly with varnish thinners when cold. A factory prepared varnish for each type of work and each method of application is necessary for best results.

General Preparations for Brush Varnishing. There are several preliminaries to a successful job of brush varnishing. The following are some important preparations:

1. The varnish room should be cleaned and dusted during the afternoon of the day before the varnishing is to be done. A clean room is needed, not a dusty shop used for woodworking.

2. Prepare all surfaces to be varnished—smooth, sandpaper, and dust. Do this work in another room, not the place where varnishing is to be done. When revarnishing, it is very important to remove any old wax polish, furniture polish, grease, oil from handling or dirt by washing, preferably with turpentine. Rough undercoats should be removed or smoothed properly.

3. Have a revolving varnish stand, if possible, because the varnishing light will always be at its best when the stand is properly turned.

4. Always use a clean varnish pot or container. A drip or wipe wire across the top is very helpful. Clean tin cans make cheap and satisfactory varnish pots, which can be thrown away daily.

5. It is important that varnish be kept properly warmed during cold weather. Place the varnish pot on one or two hot bricks, or stand the pot in a vessel of hot water some minutes before the varnishing is started.

6. Do not try to thin or reduce quick-drying varnishes. They do not mix or thin well when cold.

7. Wipe off all dust from the object to be varnished by the use of a "tack rag" moistened in very thin varnish just before the varnishing is started (Fig. 16-1).

16—1. Just prior to varnishing, wipe off all dust by the use of a "tack rag." Such a rag is lightly moistened with very thin varnish or turpentine.

8. Make sure that all undercoats are properly dried before varnishing.

9. The varnisher should wear dust free and reasonably clean clothes, or dirt and lint may get into some newly varnished surface.

Brush Application of Quick-Drying Varnishes. There has been a shift to dipping and spraying of varnishes in factories; but, in architectural work and in home shops, varnish is largely applied with a brush. When fossil gum varnishes of the old slow drying type were used, varnishing with a brush was about the easiest of all of the wood finishing operations. Now, with synthetic resins incorporated into thinners and solvents somewhat like those used in lacquers, synthetic resin varnishes of the rapid drying type require a new and somewhat different technique in application. The new four hour varnishes spread

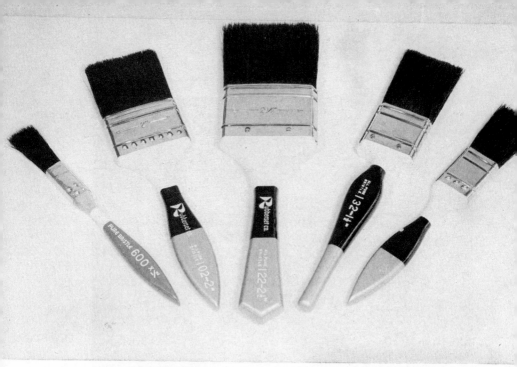

PHOTO BY ROBERT C. SMITHERAM, JR.

16—2. Pure bristle varnish brushes of various sizes.

more like brushing lacquer or shellac. There is apt to be something of a pull by the varnish instead of an easy, smooth, gliding of the brush. Formerly, cross brushing of large varnished surfaces was frequent; now it is not so common because the varnish often sets too quickly. Do not use cross brushing if the varnish sets or stiffens so quickly that brush marks are left.

The following suggestions for the brush application of quick-drying varnishes may be of value:

1. Brushes for use in such varnishes should be selected from the soft and thick but chisel type of special varnish brushes. Either oval or flat brushes are satisfactory (Figs. 16-2 and 3).

2. Put a new brush into varnish while dry and several minutes before use. Brushes that have been used, and which will be needed frequently, should be kept in a "brush keeper" which contains enough "brush keeper varnish" to cover the bristles of the suspended brushes (Fig. 16-4). Linseed oil and turpentine are not considered good for "keeping" brushes used in some kinds of quick-drying varnish. New brushes are improved by use, if given proper care. Old brushes which have

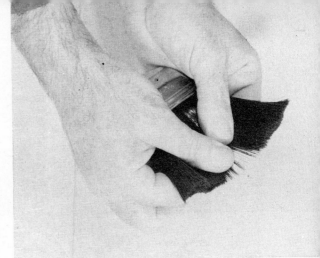

PHOTO BY
ROBERT C. SMITHERAM, JR.

16—3. Examine a brush like this. Individual bristles of a good brush have "flagged" ends.

split bristle points are not satisfactory for particular work. It is wise to work a brush into the varnish very thoroughly before attempting any particular work. Some paint and varnish manufacturers now supply brush keepers and a special brush keeper varnish which will save varnish brushes. Brush keeper varnish is really a thin finishing varnish manufactured without driers, and does not oxidize rapidly. It is considered to be almost nondrying.

3. Learn how a skillful varnisher holds his brush. Usually, hold the fingers well down on the brush ferrule. Avoid too much pressure which will bend the brush and prevent the varnish from flowing from the ends of the bristles (Fig. 16-5).

16—4. When placing a brush in a container partly filled with "brush keeper," all bristles should be submerged, but must not touch the bottom of the container.

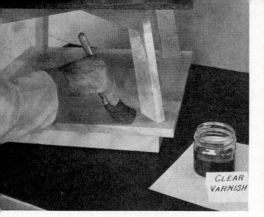

16—5. In varnishing, hold the brush well down on the brush ferrule.
16—6. Finish a varnished surface with light, feathering strokes.

4. A good varnish technique is to start at the ends of the surface and brush toward the middle, finishing with light feathering strokes that will leave no marks (Fig. 16-6).

5. A panel is best covered by varnishing about the margins at the start; then proceed by stroking from the ends toward the middle, lightly lifting the brush when the surface is covered. The varnisher should finish all varnishing by brushing with the grain of the wood. It is often best to varnish edges with the side of the brush.

6. Do not apply very heavy coats of varnish or attempt over brushing in order to secure thin coats. Heavy coats may cause runs or sags, especially on vertical or oblique surfaces. Too much brushing may roughen varnish coatings that have partly set or hardened. All runs and sags should be corrected just as soon as possible. This means that a varnisher must frequently inspect his work.

7. Surplus varnish left on the edges should be removed promptly. The side of a rather dry brush is most convenient for smoothing edges (Fig. 16-7).

8. While varnishing, a person should stand in such a position that the light will be reflected from the freshly varnished surfaces. Unless this is done it is probable that some portions will be skipped or only partially covered. A revolving varnish stand is a very important part of the equipment and is very helpful to the workman in covering all surfaces and inspecting promptly before the varnish has set.

9. If a dull gloss or satin finish is desired, a dull varnish or satin coating should be applied over a properly sanded last

coat of gloss varnish. Unless the final coat of dull or satin varnish is applied carefully in good light, spots of gloss varnish are apt to show through, and another coat of varnish will be needed.

10. If the can contains clean varnish, do not pour back into the original container partly used varnish which has been in contact with the brush. Put such unused varnish in a can labeled "Varnish from the Pot." Pouring unused varnish into the original clean varnish may contaminate the whole stock in the container with dust or dirt. Keep the varnish container very tightly closed to avoid dirt and prevent evaporation of volatile liquids.

11. The place for starting and the order for procedure in varnishing an article of furniture should be considered very carefully. A rather general rule is: The article of furniture, such as a table, should be turned upside down and the under parts should be varnished first (Fig. 16-8). Then the object should be turned to its usual position and the upper portions should be varnished first, followed by application to the under portions, gradually working downward. This procedure will prevent drops of varnish from falling on finished work. Such drops are sometimes hard to smooth out.

16—7. Remove any excess varnish on edges with the side of a rather dry brush. 16—8. When varnishing a project, varnish all underparts first. Turn the project upside down if necessary—and possible.

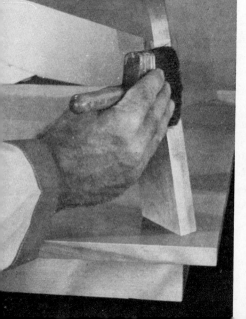
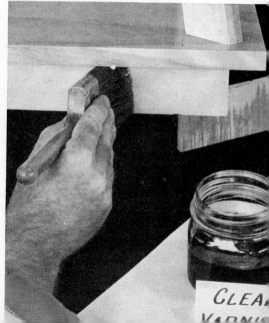

Varnish Troubles. Good varnish and good weather conditions will generally mean no trouble for a skillful varnisher. If there be trouble, the cause is often underneath the coat of varnish. The most common causes are apt to be found among the following: (1) oily or greasy surfaces were not properly cleaned; (2) some of the undercoats were not perfectly dry and hard; (3) excessive moisture or atmospheric humidity which caused "bloom" and sometimes poor spreading under the brush; and (4) a poor varnish which contained too much resin. Sometimes the varnish trouble may be a combination of the above listed vexatious annoyances.

Several of the common and bothersome varnish difficulties which follow varnishing, with suggested remedies, are:

1. *Blistering.* Small spots appear where the varnish raises. Remedy: Remove grease or oil from the surface by proper cleaning, and do not apply varnish in very humid weather or in direct, hot sunshine. Avoid all shellac undercoats when the varnish coats are to be exposed to water, especially hot water.

2. *Bloom.* A cloudy effect in blotches which discolors the finish. Remedy: Varnishing in moist conditions should be avoided. "Bloom" generally dries out and disappears unless caused by ammonia in the air.

3. *Crazing.* Minute cracks appear. Remedy: Varnish only when the temperature is about 70° F. or above. If the varnish was applied in the cold, then the varnish is too hard and inelastic.

4. *Crawling.* The varnish does not spread smoothly and evenly. Remedy: Avoid low temperature during application and drying, unusual moisture, grease, oil, and dirt from handling. Cleaning old surfaces which are to be revarnished is important. Benzine or turpentine may be used. A varnish of too great viscosity for the conditions may be the cause of the trouble.

5. *Deadening.* A gloss varnish may lose luster, often in spots. Remedy: Only well seasoned lumber should be used. Undercoats should not be porous and should be thoroughly dry. Coal gas sometimes causes partial clouding.

6. *Runs and Sags.* A common trouble caused by applying too heavy, poorly spread coats of varnish which are insuffici-

ently brushed—especially on oblique or vertical surfaces. An elastic brush is helpful. Remedy: If the varnish has not set, spread it with a rather dry brush. If brushing causes roughness to fresh varnish, then wipe off the coat with turpentine or a synthetic varnish reducer on a rag. If the coat is to be rubbed, allow the runs and sags to dry with the varnish, then rub them down even with the rest of the surface.

7. *Sweating.* Luster sometimes appears in spots on a rubbed varnish surface. The cause is improperly dried undercoats. Allow plenty of time for the hardening of undercoats. The only remedy is a new varnish job.

8. *Spotting.* The cause is sometimes severe chilling of a freshly varnished surface, sometimes by splashes of water. Discolored spots appear. The constituents in the varnish may separate, causing a loss of transparency. On vehicles the color usually returns if the spotted surface is washed and dried, preferably in the open air and sunlight.

9. *Tackiness.* Coats of varnish over improperly cleaned old surfaces that are greasy, dirty, or have been much handled, sometimes remain tacky and will not harden. Remedy: Remove the tacky coating with paint and varnish remover and revarnish after proper cleaning. The best cleaning is a rub down with pumice stone and water. Improper drying conditions or the use of an unsuitable type of varnish may cause varnish coatings to remain tacky. Nondrying oils, or some improper thinner placed in a varnish, may cause coatings from it to remain tacky indefinitely. *Warning:* Quick-drying varnishes cannot safely be thinned when cold, or mixed, or reduced in any way. This is also true of some of the fossil resin varnishes of recent manufacture. It is best to allow the varnish manufacturer to thin varnishes.

10. *Livering in the Can.* To leave varnishes standing in the original can unopened and exposed to extreme cold, may cause "livering," which means a separation of the ingredients. Remedy: None. Always store varnishes in a moderately warm room during cold weather. (Sometimes cheap varnishes of poor mixtures "liver" into viscous, paintlike masses as a result of chemical reactions. The manufacturers should be notified of such conditions.)

11. *Skinning.* Sometimes varnish in cans that have been

16—9. Specks are readily removed by screening the varnish through a piece of old
nylon hose.

opened and not tightly corked or sealed forms a crust or skin
because of surface oxidation and evaporation of the volatile
varnish thinner. Such varnishes will cause "seeds" or "specks"
in all varnish coatings made from them unless the varnish is
carefully strained. A quart of varnish will not keep well in a
gallon can. It will be helpful if the varnish is poured into a
quart can which is tightly closed to exclude the air. This will
reduce the amount of oxidation, evaporation, and "skinning."

Specks. These are usually caused by dirty brushes or by
skin that has formed on varnish exposed to air. To avoid specks
keep a varnished object in a clean room, away from dust.
All brushes must be kept in a "brush keeper," hung by the
handle, and properly immersed in "brush keeper varnish." It
is very important to keep all brushes, varnish pots, and the
drip wire absolutely clean and free from specks of hardened
varnish. The "brush keeper" should have a cover that is as
tight fitting as possible. The ends of the bristles of all brushes
should not touch the bottom of the "brush keeper" or they will
curl to one side and never again be really useful for the proper
spreading of varnish back and forth. All brushes should be
carefully cleaned and put away dry if they are not to be used
frequently or in the near future. Store them in such a position
that the bristles will not be bent. Remedy: Specks may be removed by screening the varnish through fine cheese cloth or
a piece of old nylon hose (Fig. 16-9).

Cleaning of Brushes. Success in the brush application of all finishes depends to a considerable extent upon the brush used and its condition. The brush should be clean, soft, pliable and elastic. Selection of a brush always should depend upon the kind of finish to be applied, and also upon the size and material to be covered. Brushes of a good grade are set in cement or some rubber composition. Brushes set in shellac or glue will not hold their bristles when used in some finishes.

The general rule for brush cleaning is: Use the same solvent for cleaning the brush that was used in thinning the finishing material. It is a puzzle sometimes to know just what to use for cleaning brushes that are saturated with synthetic varnish. One of the large manufacturers states that he uses turpentine in his brushing synthetic varnishes, and that brushes used in such varnishes may be cleaned in turpentine. The same manufacturer says that "equipment or brushes used in spraying synthetics should be cleaned in synthetic reducer." Probably many varnish brushes will be saved by keeping some synthetic reducer on hand, because many synthetic varnishes do not contain turpentine, and brushes used in such varnishes should not be cleaned in turpentine. You should obtain a synthetic reducer from the manufacturer of the synthetic varnish that you are using.

Lacquer thinner or lacquer remover in general should clean lacquer brushes and possibly brushes used in synthetic varnishes. A lacquer brush cleaner made of grain alcohol and acetone is good for lacquer brushes, but it is not good for synthetic varnish brushes because most of the synthetic varnish resins are not soluble in alcohol or acetone.

The solvents used in thinning synthetic varnishes are in general a coal-tar product, which evaporates slowly, such as xylol, together with a petroleum thinner, such as mineral spirits or Varnolene. With this in mind a synthetic varnish brush cleaner that is made of Varnolene and xylol, half and half, probably will be satisfactory. Another similar formula would be mineral spirits and toluol. Oleum Spirits and Hydrogenated Naphthas No. 2 or No. 3 are also recommended. Such cleaning solvents for brushes should be considerably cheaper than lacquer thinners and better for removing the varnish.

Undercoats for Quick-Drying Varnishes. The same types of undercoats that are used under slow-drying varnishes may be employed when four-hour varnishes are used. Ordinarily this means stain, filler, and shellac. Many expert finishers and some of the best manufacturers recommend shellac as a sealer undercoat in preference to an extra coat of varnish.

Shellac has some rather outstanding advantages as an undercoat. Some of the advantages of shellac as an undercoat are: it provides a very smooth nonabsorbent foundation; it dries hard quicker than most varnishes; it sands very easily to a very smooth and clean surface; it does not stain or darken the surfaces as much as is done by varnish if white shellac is used; and, although thin in films, it seals well and prevents the varnish coats from sinking into the filler or the wood itself. When using shellac as a sealer under varnish, it should be applied as a thin coat. A good mixture is 4-lb. cut shellac thinned with 4 or 5 equal parts of denatured alcohol.

Moisture or water ruins a shellac finish by turning it white. It is necessary, therefore, to omit shellac coatings on all outside exposure finishes, on window sills, and especially on floors. Coats of waterproof varnish will blister badly over shellac, yet stand up well without the shellac coating if treated with boiling water.

For a high degree of waterproofness shellac should be omitted entirely, and a coat of quick-drying varnish may be applied directly over the other undercoats, which should be very dry or they may be somewhat "lifted" by the varnish coating.

Shellac undercoats should always be very carefully sanded before coats of varnish are applied over them. Careful sanding seems to improve the adhesion of varnish coats to shellac undercoats, and it also provides a smooth and better foundation for the finishing coats.

Varnish can be applied over lacquer sealer in a single coat. The kind of sealer used has a lot to do with the adhesion and toughness. It is well to avoid high-stearate, easy-sanding sealers. For best results a sealer should be used that is designed especially for use under varnish. Toughness of the sealer coat is affected by the length of time that the sealer dries before the varnish is applied. For good results, apply the varnish the same day as the sealer—the next day at the latest.

SELECTED REFERENCES, CHAPTER XVI

Application of Quick-Drying Varnishes

Gibbia, S. W., *Woodfinishing and Refinishing*, "Varnish," Chapter VI, pp. 89-93; 1954.

Ibid., "Rubbing," Chapter VIII, pp. 123-137; 1954.

Ibid., "Producing a Luster, Polishing the Surface," Chapter IX, pp. 138-155; 1954.

Kinney, Ralph Parsons, *The Complete Book of Furniture Repair and Refinishing*, "Refinishing," Chapter V, pp. 122-156; 1950.

McGee, R. A. and Brown, A. G., *Instructional Units in Woodfinishing*, "To Apply an Oil Varnish," Unit 4, pp. 29-35; 1950.

Soderberg, George A., *Finishing Materials and Methods*, "To Produce a Varnish Finish," Chapter XXVII, pp. 211-213; 1952.

Chapter XVII

Enamels and Enameling

Paint Enamels and Their Functions. The term enamel is loosely used in naming various compounds which usually contain paint, pigment colors, and varnish. The word may also refer to fused enamels, sometimes called glazes. Paint enamels are sometimes called varnish paints or colored varnishes. In this chapter the word enamel refers to paint enamels exclusively. Enamels are generally defined as being either pale air drying or baking varnishes which contain white paint pigments and very often coloring matter. Color in paint enamels usually comes from pigments which are ground in varnish, oil, or japan; but in some cases may be derived from coal-tar and azo-type dyes. For white enamels titanium dioxide is the pigment that is most satisfactory, ground in a special very pale or transparent varnish.

Enamels possess good body, and this means opacity or power of obscuration, commonly called covering power. In general, however, they do not have the opacity of oil paints. Enamels are very tough and elastic, and usually wear far better than oil paints under similar conditions. Many of them are made with a high gloss which resists very severe exposure; others have semigloss or dull effects.

The drying time for enamels is similar to that of oil varnishes, being from 12 to 18 hours. Industrial enamels are now made to set in 2 to 4 hours.

The chief function of enamels is to give a very high grade finish which is hard, smooth, and long lasting for inside use and resistant to weather when used outside. Enamels are primarily finishing materials, not undercoating substances. They are used for the last one or two finishing coats only, on account of their great beauty and good wearing qualities and their superiority to paint.

Composition of Enamels. The ingredients selected for the manufacture of enamels are numerous, because of the many uses to which enamels are put and the grades and types that are in demand.

The pigments used in enamels are ground very fine, in varnish, or alkyd resin solutions, and sometimes in linseed oil or in japan. In the case of white enamels of high grade, only titanium oxide is used, and it should be ground in a very transparent or pale enamel varnish.

Many manufacturers use an elastic, long oil varnish as a vehicle, even in the production of white and ivory enamels. The varnishes selected for this purpose are special enamel varnishes, however, and are almost transparent because they are made from pale resins and bleached linseed oil.

The medium or vehicle for carrying the pigments in enamels is usually a soya or safflower-oil modified alkyd resin for very pale or transparent varnish. For white enamels such as used on the interior of refrigerators, a good grade of dammar varnish formerly was selected for the purpose, but new films made from it are more brittle, being rather markedly less elastic than those from the best of the pale oil varnishes. Some American manufacturers have used dammar varnish, because it produces the whitest and probably the most satisfactory snow white enamel known.

In the preparation of interior enamels, manufacturers now strive for good color retention. For this reason, linseed oil has been practically eliminated from the better grades of enamel, using soya and safflower as substitutes. Zinc oxide, in small amounts, can be used for further improved color retention. The marked physical changes, of course, are the result of chemical changes in the oil itself that follow the absorption of oxygen. In this case the linseed oil loses its power of cohesion to a great extent, and its function as a binder for the pigments ceases to exist. Crumbling, disintegration, and scaling of a paint film gradually follow when the particles in the mass of the coating are no longer held firmly together by the adhesiveness of the binder. In enamels, however, it should be remembered that varnish instead of oil is used as a medium or vehicle for carrying the pigments.

The inclusion of resins greatly increases the adherence of

the particles of pigment in the enamel. If the pigments are ground to very great fineness and mixed in a proper varnish medium, a condition that is somewhat colloidal is the result.

The best volatile solvent and thinner to use in enamels is undoubtedly American gum turpentine, called spirits of turpentine or oil of turpentine. If too much turpentine is added to a prepared gloss enamel in an attempt to thin it, some of the high luster will be lost and a flatting effect will result. Some manufacturers sell a specially prepared enamel reducer which consists of a large per cent of turpentine with a small amount of the same varnish gum used in the enamel.

On account of the high price of turpentine, other thinners are often substituted, such as benzine; also toluol, which is closely related to benzol, both being coal-tar derivatives. Acetone is another volatile thinner which is occasionally used in enamels. If only a comparatively small amount of thinner is needed, most wood finishers add turpentine. A less expensive thinner may be made of equal parts of turpentine and benzine. It is poor economy, however, to use very much benzine for the reason that this liquid does not have a very strong solvent action on varnish gums. Benzine does not have the flatting effect on gloss enamels that is objectionable in turpentine; therefore, it is preferred by some finishers, especially where it is desired to preserve a high luster on a surface.

Coloring or tinting of enamels is accomplished by the addition to the titanium white pigment of finely ground colors which are mixed with a specially prepared pale enamel varnish. White enamels, which are already prepared, may be mixed with properly prepared colored pigments, or they may be colored by compounding them with colored enamels. If a finisher knows how to mix colors, he can obtain any desired hue by mixing together prepared colored enamels, or by adding the proper amounts of colors which are ground either in japan, oil, or preferably in a special enamel varnish.

Types of Enamels

Several surface effects or types of finish are needed in enamels. The manufacturers have met these demands, and are now producing enamels having high gloss, semigloss or eggshell gloss, and flat or dull effects. These names refer to about the same surface appearances as those produced by varnishes having similar names.

Other properties of enamels besides surface effects are taken under consideration in the manufacture of enamels, and this has resulted in quite a variety of names for the various products, among them being: polishing enamels, marine enamels, exterior enamels, satin finish enamels, rubbing enamels, eggshell or semigloss enamels, and flat enamels. The user of enamels soon discovers that enamels which are given similar names by different manufacturers are not at all alike in composition and vary somewhat in characteristics.

Gloss Enamels. Gloss enamels vary in composition, the ingredients selected depending largely upon the use for which the finishing material is intended. For example, white refrigerator enamels and some other snow-white enamels occasionally contain a pale, hard high grade dammar resin, which produces the most brilliant gloss or luster that comes from any of the varnishes used in manufacturing enamels. Dammar varnish is a spirit varnish which is made with a turpentine or petroleum solvent, and contains no linseed oil which at times turns to a yellowish tinge after aging. The pigment which is mixed with the pale, very transparent dammar varnish is titanium dioxide for all white and very light-toned enamels. Other oil soluble pigments may be used with enamels of dark hues.

Other gloss enamels are made from very pale oil varnishes and alkyd resins containing specially treated drying oils. Gloss enamels of such compositions are very durable, being unusually waterproof, and suitable for use in most of the rooms of a house, but especially for kitchens, bathrooms, and in such places as dairies, ice cream plants, and parts of hotels, hospitals, and restaurants where much water is used, or where the woodwork is exposed to repeated washings or much dampness.

While gloss enamels are intended for use on the inside of buildings, some will wear well on the outside, and may be mixed with gloss paint, thereby producing a coating that is unusually lustrous, hard, and durable. When gloss white enamel is mixed with outside white paint a very much whiter effect is produced than with white paint alone.

Polishing or Rubbing Enamel. A polishing or rubbing enamel, which is often called a gloss enamel, produces an effect which is similar to that of the gloss enamel just described, the varnish medium being made from a light colored, carefully prepared rosin or a very pale copal gum, a solvent of turpentine or turpentine substitute, and a vehicle of specially treated boiled linseed oil, sometimes called "stand oil," particularly by English writers. Some of the varnishes used are long oil varnishes which contain bleached linseed oil prepared in such a way through heat treatments and the addition of driers that it is almost colorless and darkens the enamel body very little.

Some of the well known enamels contain specially treated tung oil or China wood oil, which replaces at least part of the linseed oil usually contained in pale oil varnishes made for use in enamels. Polishing or rubbing enamels usually dry hard in from 24 to 48 hours. If two coats are used, the surface is carefully sanded with No. 3/0 or No. 4/0 sandpaper after the first coat, in order to produce a smooth surface, and to remove the gloss which is apt to prevent the last coating of enamel from adhering properly to the one previously applied. Polishing gloss enamels can be rubbed with pumice stone and water, which produces an effect similar to that which comes from a rubbed varnish finish. Although polishing and rubbing of enamel coats produce a surface of superior smoothness, these operations are practiced very little because of the high cost. Rubbed-effect finishes can be partly produced by varying the pigment content within the enamel.

Waterproof Enamels. Waterproof enamels, also called marine enamels, are used for finishing parts of boats, water pails, sinks, bathtubs, bathrooms, kitchens, special hotel rooms and other portions of buildings and utensils which are often used in or about water. If made from high grade varnish that contains no rosin, such enamels can be used with both hot and cold water, but they are improved by being properly baked on the surfaces instead of being dried at ordinary temperatures.

Exterior Enamels. Exterior enamels are made from long oil varnishes which dry slowly. They stand the weather more satisfactorily than other enamels on account of their greater elasticity. They are sometimes used on the outside of buildings or portions of buildings which require superior lasting finishes and also on porch and camp furniture.

Satin Finish Enamels. Satin finish enamels, also called eggshell or semigloss enamels, have an attractive appearance with a dull polish similar to that produced on ivory or horn, but with less luster. The final effect of these enamels is much like that of a hand rubbed finish with pumice stone on a gloss enamel. They are very popular for the trimming or interior woodwork of buildings and furniture on account of the soft effects produced, including a sheen or dull luster that is artistic and very attractive. This type of enamels should not be used for exterior surfaces, because of their higher pigment content and do not wear as well outdoors as do gloss enamels.

Flat Enamels. Flat enamels are made in a manner similar to that used in manufacturing gloss enamels; but, in order to reduce the gloss, a higher percentage of pigment is used. Flat varnishes are made by some manufacturers from a soft Indonesian gum by the "slack melting" process, which requires only from 150° to 175° F. of heat for melting the resin, instead of 550° F. required in the manufacture of rubbing varnishes from Congo gum, and are said to be used as a vehicle in the manufacture of some of the very dull enamels which have practically no gloss.

The pigments used in flat enamels are titanium dioxide and titanium calcium pigment, which are ground very fine. The luster of flat and satin enamels varies with the amount of varnish used; that is to say, the more varnish used the greater the gloss. Flat enamels have only enough varnish in the medium to hold the particles of pigment together and act as a binder. In enamels, the amount of linseed oil is limited; or omitted, if dammar varnish is used; and the varnish itself acts as the cementing material which causes the very finely ground particles of pigments to cohere or hold together when a film of the mixture dries after being spread on a surface.

Durability of Enamels. Enamel finishes, while expensive, are very attractive and beautiful because they are always used as final finishes over carefully prepared foundations of undercoats which are invariably sanded in order to level the surfaces before the next application or coating. One reason for using an enamel finish is that it has great durability. Such finishes, if properly applied and made from high grade materials, are enduring because the surface films do not dry up into powder and rub off in the form of dust or scales as paint does.

An enamel finish is as enduring as a varnish finish, the lasting qualities varying, however, with the grade of varnish which is used as a medium. The cheaper enamels are, of course, made from less expensive materials and the cheapening is apt to come from the use of inferior varnish, which is often made from low priced gums such as colophony, a high-sounding trade name for rosin manufactured from crude turpentine gum. Enamels that include varnishes having much rosin in their composition are usually very brittle, and cannot stay in place over a wood surface that expands and contracts to some extent with the varying moisture conditions of the air. The lack of elasticity of such an enamel causes checking, cracking, and scaling off, and the result is a ruined finish.

For exterior use, a gloss enamel that is rather slow in drying, because there is more drying oil in its composition, is preferable unless a snowy whiteness is wanted. Drying oils, such as boiled linseed oil and tung oil, retard the speed of drying and may cause a slight yellowing in white enamels; but they add greatly to the elasticity of the vehicle, and reduce the brittleness of the enamel itself after it has been dried on a surface in the form of a film.

Undercoats and Preparation for Enamel Finishes. The beauty and wearing qualities of an enamel finish depend partly on the quality and handling of the enamel itself; but also, to a large extent, upon the foundation of undercoats which may be either helpful or ruinous to the final outercoatings. The number of undercoats in enamel finishes of the highest class may vary from one to three. Most enamel finishes, however, have from two to three undercoats.

The obscuration of the wood itself, and a proper tone effect of color, should be completed by the undercoats for the reason that not more than two coats of the final material are used, largely on account of the expense, and partly because it is more difficult to make enamel films adhere to gloss enamel than to undercoats of flat paint. Exterior gloss paint is unsatisfactory under enamel for two reasons: (1) because such paints contain too much linseed oil; and (2) because enamels do not adhere well to glossy undercoats.

Woods that are to receive an enamel finish should be carefully prepared by the same methods used for varnish finishes.

In other words, they should be planed, scraped, sanded, and dusted. All holes should be plugged or filled with cabinet-maker's cement. Oil putty should not be used until one coat of paint has been applied to the surfaces. Metal surfaces are best cleaned with benzine or cleaner's naphtha which will remove any oil or greasy spots and dirty places that might prevent the proper adherence of the undercoats. Rusty places on metal must be brightened by sandpaper.

Enameling Specifications and Procedure. Specifications and directions for a superior *enamel finish of six or seven coats* are as follows:

1. A coat of about *one-half strength shellac varnish* should be applied over all knots and spots containing pitch especially. Woods that are quite porous or absorptive of finish should have a coat of shellac over all the surfaces to be finished, in addition to the shellacking for knots and pitch. Some finishers prefer to apply shellac over the first priming coat of paint. Both methods generally give entire satisfaction if the film of

17—1. After knots and spots containing pitch have been sealed with thin shellac, a priming coat of proper color is applied.

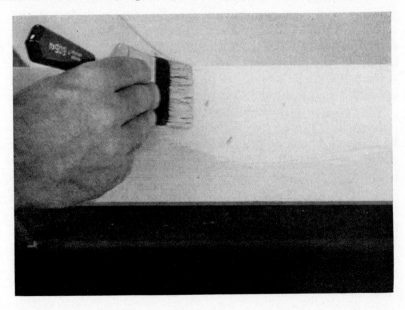

shellac is properly sanded with No. 2/0 or No. 3/0 sandpaper, in order to remove the gloss before the next coat is applied. A shellac sizing coat should be used on yellow pine, basswood, and cypress, but is not necessary for such woods as poplar or birch. If the finish is to be of white enamel, it is preferable to use white shellac, otherwise orange shellac should be selected.

2. A *priming coat* of properly colored paint, made by the use of white lead, pigment colors ground in oil, and a vehicle of equal parts of boiled linseed oil and turpentine, should be applied over the shellac sizing (Fig. 17-1). Some finishers prefer to use raw linseed oil and japan drier instead of boiled oil. If the priming coat is for a white enamel finish, no color should be used, and as little linseed oil as possible.

Usually, a mixture for a priming coat under white enamel should be made of one-third boiled linseed oil and two-thirds turpentine. In order to prevent linseed oil from working up through the undercoats and turning white enamel to a slight tinge of yellow later on, some experts apply the sizing coat of shellac over the priming coat rather than under it. It is preferable to obtain a pale or bleached linseed oil and a white japan drier, if possible, especially for use under a white enamel finish. The ground coating of paint should be spread as smoothly as possible, and two days should be allowed for drying if the mixture is made with boiled linseed oil, and usually three days if raw oil is used. After the paint is thoroughly dry it should be smoothed with No. 0 or No. 00 sandpaper, and the surface should be dusted. If puttying is required the sanding operation should be delayed until the putty is dry.

3. *Puttying* should follow the priming coat of paint. Oil putty, which can be purchased in light and dark colors, should be used. Putty can be prepared in the shop by mixing a factory-made paste of lead in oil with dry whiting until a stiff putty is obtained. Pigments known as dry colors should be kneaded into the putty if colors are wanted. A small amount of japan drier can also be added to the mixture to make a quick-drying putty.

In the application of putty a finisher should use a putty knife and fill all holes, cracks, worm holes, and dents or other defects, and the filling should be done generously, so that all openings shall be overfilled rather than underfilled (Fig. 17-2).

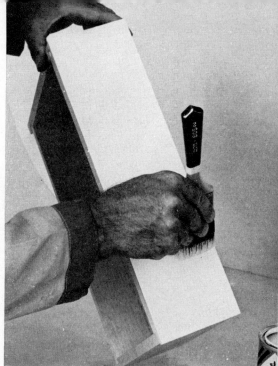

17—2. After the priming coat dries and has been carefully sanded with No. 2/0 sandpaper, fill all holes, cracks and other defects with oil putty or spackle. 17—3. After the putty has dried thoroughly and has been sanded smooth, a special enamel undercoat is applied next.

The putty itself does not shrink much if any in hardening. The excess of material is easily removed flush with the surface with sandpaper after it is thoroughly dry, and presents much less of a problem than an underfilled hole. Putty should be allowed to dry for 24 hours or part of it may be pulled out of place by the brush when the next film of undercoat is spread over the surface.

4. *Flat paint undercoats* should be applied over the priming coat, or over the shellac film in case the latter is spread over the priming coat, as is sometimes done (Fig. 17-3). Two or three applications of undercoating paint are generally used, the number depending upon the perfection of finish desired. Special enamel undercoat paints can be purchased of paint dealers, and these should be tinted or colored with colors ground in japan in order to match the tone of the final enamel hue or effect.

It is not desirable to use linseed oil in the last application of undercoat paint, turpentine being the proper thinner. Under-

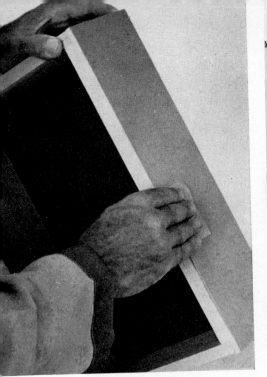
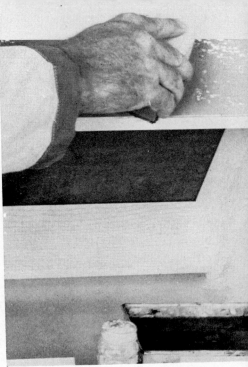

17—4. Two coats of enamel are applied next. Sand carefully in between coats with No. 4/0 sandpaper. 17—5. For a soft, dull finish, rub the final enamel coat with pumice stone and water. A pale rubbing oil may also be used.

coats may be prepared in various ways. Some finishers use white lead ground in oil, taking one part of boiled linseed oil and three parts of turpentine for the first undercoat. The last undercoat should consist of equal parts of titanium white and white lead ground in oil, thinned with 3 parts of turpentine, and one part of white enamel varnish. The enamel varnish may be omitted, and turpentine alone can be used as a medium and thinner.

Dammar varnish is sometimes used as an enamel varnish. Pale oil varnishes are preferred by many finishers because of greater elasticity and permanency. If three undercoats are applied, the second one should contain very little or no linseed oil, and should be much like the last undercoat just described.

Each application or film of the undercoating paint must have approximately three days to dry, and should then be smoothed down with No. 0 or No. 00 sandpaper, and dusted before the next coat of paint is brushed over the surfaces that are to be enameled. Some paint undercoats, under good drying conditions, will dry hard in two days. The speed of drying depends upon the temperature and humidity of the atmosphere and varies from day to day.

5. *Two coats of enamel* are recommended for a high-grade *finish* (Fig. 17-4). The first coat, however, may be a mixture of equal parts of properly colored enamel and undercoat paint. This reduces the expense somewhat, and provides a surface that will receive the finishing enamel coat more readily, and which is more elastic than the final coat of enamel. The most beautiful effect is made by the use of two coats of enamel, the first being very carefully sanded to cut the gloss with No. 4/0 sandpaper after three days or more for drying.

Enamels are more easily applied when rather thin, because such thin mixtures work more easily and do not pull so hard under the brush. Turpentine, or turpentine and benzine in equal parts, may be used as a thinner to a limited extent; but, if thin coats of enamel of half strength are wanted, it is desirable to dilute with a prepared enamel reducer, or to mix one by taking three parts of turpentine and one part of enamel varnish, such as dammar varnish or pale copal varnish. Thinning with too much turpentine dulls a gloss enamel; therefore, instead of using turpentine alone as a diluent, varnish is diluted with turpentine in varnish reducers, which are to be used where much thinning is necessary. Enamels are generally brushed on surfaces with much care, using a rather large chisel-pointed fitch rubber-set varnish brush. Such brushes, made of moderately fine and soft bristles, can be used to touch up a surface by rebrushing the coat with a somewhat dry brush, if this is done very soon after the enamel film is applied, and before the varnish in the medium has set to any great extent. Temperatures for enameling are similar to those for varnishing —between 70° and 80° F.

6. The *last coat* of gloss enamel should be rubbed, not sanded. Very soft dull gloss finishes can be secured from gloss enamels by rubbing the surface with pumice stone and water, or even with pumice stone and a pale rubbing oil (Fig. 17-5). Dark rubbing oil should not be used on a white enamel surface as it may discolor it. Flat and satin-finish enamels should not be rubbed.

7. An *optional finishing coat of varnish* may be applied. A rather light coat of good rubbing varnish is sometimes used over a gloss enamel finish which has been sanded. The final finish is rubbed with pumice stone and water, following the methods used for rubbing varnish. It is not desirable to varnish over a white enamel finish, however, as the color in the varnish is apt to discolor the snowy whiteness of the enamel.

A Commonly Used Enamel Finish. Specifications for a *quickly made enamel finish* are as follows:

1. Prepare the surface of the wood with tools and sandpaper.
2. Apply one coat of properly colored primer paint, or some other enamel undercoating material, purchased already prepared. Puttying and sandpapering should be done between the undercoats. Each application of paint must have at least two days for drying.
3. A coat of equal parts of enamel and undercoating paint should next be brushed on as a foundation for the finishing film of enamel. It should be of the same color as the final coat. Approximately three days are required for drying; then the surface should be sanded with No. 2/0 to No. 4/0 sandpaper.
4. The final finishing coat is of enamel, often in full strength, but sometimes thinned slightly in order to make it flow more easily and evenly with a brush.

Refinishing Old Painted or Enameled Surfaces. The re-enameling of old surfaces which were finished originally with varnish, paint, or enamel often presents rather difficult problems, especially if the old finish be in bad condition. The workman must carefully inspect and scrape the old finish with his putty knife to determine whether it is firmly adhering or clinging to the surface in blisters, scales, or loose fragments. If the former finish consisted of paint or enamel which has become loosened, then paint and varnish remover should be used to take off everything down to the original surface. On the other hand, if the former paint and enamel have not cracked or scaled off in spots, and present a firm, hard, smooth, and level surface after thorough sandpapering, then new undercoats of the proper color can be brushed over the old finish and resanded between coats. Before any new paint is applied, all surfaces should be scraped, sanded, and washed to remove any grease. If wax has been applied over an old varnish, it is very important that it be entirely removed with gasoline, benzine, or turpentine, because other finishes will not adhere to a waxed surface.

In refinishing with enamel, it is often possible to omit the shellacking and priming coats. If they are found necessary after entirely removing an old finish, they should be applied, and the directions for new finishes followed. The number of undercoats depends upon the covering and coloring power of the paint which is being applied, and the grade of finish desired. A good refinishing job can often be obtained by the use of two coats of properly colored undercoating paint, followed by another of one-half enamel and one-half undercoating paint, prepared as described previously in this chapter, together with one coat of enamel of the desired color for the final finish.

Application of Enamels. It is necessary that enameling be done in a place having a temperature of 70° to 80° F. If the temperature is below 70° F., the enamel will not flow freely under the brush, which will seem to stick to the surface or "pull," making it impossible to spread the new coating quickly, evenly, and easily.

Enamel which is too thick spreads with much difficulty, because the brush does not slide freely over the surface but sticks and "pulls," much as it does when the room and material are too cold. The surface is apt to show brush-marks and waves and an uneven surface if a finisher attempts to apply too heavy a coat. Thinning with an enamel reducer, previously described, is the proper remedy.

A rather thick or heavy coat can be applied in a warm room if the enamel is warmed by placing the container in a pan or pail of hot water which has been removed from the fire. A thick enamel may be made to flow on the surface more easily by slightly thinning the mixture with camphorated turpentine, prepared by dissolving one half ounce of gum camphor in a quart of turpentine or a mixture of equal parts of turpentine and benzine. Instead of thinning with camphorated turpentine, some finishers prefer to add small quantities of water-white kerosene, glycerine, or even olive oil or castor oil. On account of their color the oils just mentioned may be objectionable for use in white enamels. All things considered the most satisfactory method of spreading thick enamel is to apply it when it is warm and in a warm place.

Enamels dry much faster in a warm than in a cold room, and present smoother and more attractive surfaces. If a finishing room becomes cold at night, a wet film or coating of enamel dries slowly; consequently, it absorbs more dust particles which are as harmful to such a finish as to a varnished surface.

Success in enameling often depends upon the following factors: having a warm dust-free room, a clean, suitable brush, and an enamel that has been strained to remove all specks, sediment, and dried, hard particles found in old cans of prepared enamel. Stir such enamels, and then strain through a screen of very fine mesh, or through a lintless piece of cloth, such as an old white linen handkerchief or similar material. Old nylon stockings make good screening material.

Covering Capacities of Enamel and Paint Undercoats. The covering capacities of enamels vary somewhat with their fluidity or the relative amount of pigments and other solids contained in the medium, which consists of thinners or solvents and sometimes a small amount of drying oil. One quart of the prepared enamel, without the use of thinners, when spread by an expert finisher in a warm room, will cover from 100 to 150 square feet of surface with one coat. The undercoat paints under similar conditions have about the same covering capacity.

SELECTED REFERENCES, CHAPTER XVII

Enamels and Enameling

Fisher, E. M., *What You Should Know about Paints,* "Enamels, Metal Protection, Lacquer," Chapter IX, pp. 129-138; 1952.

Mattiello, Joseph J., *Protective and Decorative Coatings,* Volume 3, "Paint and Enamels for Interiors," Chapter XI, pp. 333-385; 1943.

McGee, R. A. and Brown, A. G., *Instructional Units in Woodfinishing,* "To Apply Inside Paint and Enamel," Chapter IX, pp. 63-67; 1950.

Soderberg, George A., *Finishing Materials and Methods,* Chapters I, II, and III, pp. 3-32; 1952.

Von Fischer, W. and Bobalek, Edward G., *Organic Protective Coatings;* Reinhold Publishing Co., 1953; 387 pages.

Wampler, Rollin H., *Modern Organic Finishes,* "Oleoresinous and Alkyd Varnishes and Enamels," Chapter I, pp. 3-14; 1946.

Waring, Ralph G., *Woodfinishing and Painting Made Easy,* "Modern Fast Drying Finishes," Chapter X, pp. 118-124; 1940.

Chapter XVIII

Paint and Painting

Brief History of Paint and Painting. The Bible tells us in the sixth chapter of Genesis that Noah was directed to build an ark of gopher wood, and that it was to be covered with pitch both within and without. Whether pitch was some kind of paint is difficult to tell.

Paintings that go back to prehistoric times have been found on the walls of sealed caves in France, Italy, and Spain. These paintings are supposed to have been made many thousands of years ago and in some cases are in three colors—red, black, and yellow.

It is thought that painting had become a dignified art in Egypt as early as 3500 B.C. Numerous earthy colors were manufactured and used at that date. Lampblack was known and was employed by painters as a black paint. The white pigment of the Egyptians was probably made from chalk, and was similar to the whiting which we use for making calcimine and oil putty.

Some of the early historians have mentioned that Egyptian and Cretan artists of about 1500 B.C. had a great variety of colors. These ancient pigments probably were quite similar to those of the present day.

It is also of interest to know that at about 1000 B.C. the Egyptians began to protect paintings on palaces, tombs, and mummy cases with varnish. Many samples of these varnished paintings have been preserved to us through being buried under the dry sands of the edge of the Sahara desert, and kept away from the disintegrating effects of atmosphere and rot-destroying fungi which usually soon ruin wood and other materials over which paint is applied.

Paintings which give us a good idea of the paints of Roman times of about the beginning of the Christian era have lately been discovered through the recent excavations of the ruins of the old buried city, Pompeii.

There is much evidence to indicate that linseed oil and many colors similar to those of the present day were known and used in times of great antiquity. Progress in paint making was slow. Emperical knowledge has accumulated through many ages and has been handed down to later generations. The researches of the chemists of the past half century have, however, brought many changes and improvements in the paint making industry.

THE FUNCTIONS OF PAINTS

The chief functions of paints are: (1) obscuration and decoration; (2) preservation of material; (3) sanitation and cleanliness; and (4) improved lighting effects.

Obscuration and Decoration. The first function of paints is probably obscuration, or the covering of an unattractive surface with an opaque finishing material which will fill up small openings, cover defects, and produce a more level surface. Hiding the surface of the material by opaque paint pigments often produces pleasing tone or color effects that are new, bright, and attractive, and which generally add a decorative touch that appeals to the esthetic sense.

Preservation of Materials. Wood, iron, and other materials can be protected by paint, and thereby preserved from the destructive action of the elements, chemical disintegration, or the growth of fungi. Paint protects various materials, especially wood and iron, from the snow and hail of winter, from rains, sand, and dust, and saves the surface from weathering. Iron on bridges and sheet iron or tin can be made to last many times as long, if kept properly painted. Iron window screen wire will last many years if kept well painted, but it will rust and go to pieces in a short time if it is not protected from the elements which cause oxidation or rusting. Properly seasoned wood, especially that which has been kiln dried, when properly painted lasts a long time because the surface is protected from the elements, particularly rain, and it is far more difficult for rot fungi to get into the cells and start their destructive action. Some paints for outside use contain creosote oil, which preserves wood because it resists rot fungi.

Sanitation and Cleanliness. Most surfaces are cleaned and made reasonably smooth preceding the application of paint. Paint materials are largely or entirely made by passing through heat treatments of various kinds and are therefore reasonably germ proof when they are applied. Paints are said to have antiseptic qualities of their own, especially when they contain turpentine. The most important sanitary qualities of paint are a result of its forming an impervious coating over wood and other materials; consequently dirt and germs are kept from penetrating painted objects. Surfaces that are painted with gloss paints in oil can be washed many times and kept much cleaner than can unfinished surfaces.

Improved Lighting Effects. Paints can be used to secure soft and soothing lighting effects. The decorator varies the colors and general tone to suit conditions of location with respect to natural light and general color schemes. Dark rooms can be made lighter by the use of paints of the lightest tints and of the lightest colors if possible. The artificial lighting effects of halls and rooms, as well as the outside of buildings, can be varied and made attractive by the color schemes employed.

COMPOSITION OF PAINTS

The principal ingredients employed in compounding paints are known as pigments, vehicles, thinners, and driers. Paints are mechanical mixtures rather than chemical combinations or compounds.

Pigments. Pigments give obscuration to paints, and may be composed of materials which add color or roughness, and binding qualities as well as covering power. It is therefore proper to divide pigments into three great classes as follows: (1) white or body pigments, the function of which is to give opacity and body to the paint; (2) colored pigments, which are used largely for their color giving properties, though some have good hiding power, density, and permanency; and (3) extenders, which in some cases increase the durability of the paint, reduce its price, and add roughness which is advantageous especially in undercoats. The extenders are white pigments but are not body or covering pigments.

White pigments used in paints may be divided into two

distinct classes: (1) pigments which remain in an opaque condition after being mixed with drying oils, and (2) inert pigments that offer very little hiding power or obscuration as a body material in paints after being incorporated into mixtures containing drying oils, but which add durability and remain chemically inactive. Inert pigments usually retain their opacity whenever water instead of a drying oil, such as linseed oil, is used as the vehicle. The principal white pigments which remain opaque in mixtures with drying oils are white lead, including both the basic carbonate of lead and the sulphate of lead, zinc oxide, zinc lead, lithopone, titanium oxides, antimonious oxide, which is used as a substitute for white lead in France, and tin oxide, which is sometimes employed in making opal glass.

The white pigments which are largely inert, and show little or no chemical reaction with drying oils, which are acid in nature, are calcium carbonate or whiting, which is apt to saponify unless there is white lead in a mixture with the drying oil, gypsum, barytes, China clay, silica, talc or French chalk, and asbestine. The inert pigments are often called "extenders," because their hiding power or opacity when mixed with oil is very small. The "extenders" are not considered as adulterants, pure and simple, by some manufacturers of prepared paints, who claim that small percentages give protective qualities and improve durability of the more active opaque pigments.

The colored pigments are sometimes subdivided into four classes: (1) colors containing lead, (2) colors from iron, (3) carbon colors, and (4) organic colors. Some of the well known pigments in the lead group are red lead, chrome yellow or lead chromate, and its various modifications called chrome orange and chrome green. The iron colors have been known for ages; the oxides being contained in such earth colors as Turkey red, Venetian red, Indian red, red ocher, yellow ochers, which contain ferric oxide (Fe_2O_3) in varying amounts; the black oxide of iron (Fe_3O_4); the umbers, which contain usually more than 36 per cent of iron oxide (Fe_2O_3); and the siennas which contain from about 55 to 79 per cent of ferric oxide (Fe_2O_3). Prussian blue, sometimes called Chinese blue, also contains an iron salt of a very different kind. The slow-drying carbon black pigments are known as graphite or plumbago, lampblack, carbon black, charcoal black, and ivory or bone black. The organic colors are numerous and diverse in origin. They may be derived from animal, vegetable, or chemical sources.

Vehicles. Vehicles for paints are of three distinct classes: drying oils, varnishes, and water. Vehicles really have two functions in paints: (1) if they be drying oils or varnishes, they act as binders which on drying cement the particles of the pigments together and to the surface, and often penetrate into porous or absorbent materials, and on hardening form anchorages for the film of paint; and (2) they form a fluid that helps to carry the powdered pigments to the places where they are wanted by adding brushing qualities not possible with dry substances. Where water is the vehicle a certain amount of cementing or binding quality should be given to the paint through the addition of glue to the mixture.

The *drying oils* used as paint vehicles are linseed oil; China wood or tung oil; perilla oil, another fine drying oil from the orient; walnut oil, a pale oil used in artists' colors; soy bean or soya bean oil, a poor drying oil which can be treated with driers; menhaden oil, also called fish oil, which is used on smokestacks, roofs, and on hot surfaces; and poppy seed oil, which is a golden oil of slow-drying properties used in artists' paints.

Flattening oils are often made use of by painters who wish to mix their own flat wall paints. Such flatting oils can usually be obtained from paint dealers. In composition flatting oils often contain about one pound of alumina stearate to each 19 gallons of treated oils. The oils are frequently a mixture of China wood oil chiefly with a small amount of linseed oil. The drying oils are given heat treatment with driers, such as lead acetate, at a high varnish making temperature and are thinned down about one-half or more with wood turpentine and benzine. Alumina stearate jelly dissolved in turpentine can be stirred into a cold prepared drying oil mixture consisting largely of China wood oil which has been properly treated as described previously.

Gloss varnishes are also sometimes incorporated into paints to add gloss and cementing qualities. Mixing varnishes and grinding liquids are sometimes incorporated into special prepared paints, such as floor-paints. Varnish is most commonly added to paint for the purpose of hardening the film and increasing its durability and wearing qualities. Exterior paints do not often contain varnish. Enamels are mixtures of paint and varnish; but special varnishes are used in connection with special pigments, such as zinc oxide and lithopone.

Water, the third vehicle for use in mixing paints, is employed in preparing water color paints, such as calcimines and whitewashes.

Thinners. The thinners used in paints are practically the same liquids which are employed for thinning oil varnishes. Turpentine is one of the best and, while expensive, still a much used thinner. Some of the coal-tar thinners, such as solvent naphtha and benzol, are sometimes employed; but they are too volatile for general use. The petroleum thinners, such as benzine, also called naphtha 54°, and the heavy naphtha 48°, are used in many prepared quick-drying paints. Varnish makers and painters naphtha is added to a paint, varnish, or enamel to shorten the setting and drying time of the film. The addition of V.M. and P. naphtha also tends to cause the formation of a thicker film.

Benzine causes the paint to dry without gloss, and does not assist the oil in penetration into the pores of the wood as turpentine does. Petroleum thinners with the exception of benzine should not be added to paints, except in small amounts by expert manufacturers because they are nondrying liquids that are apt to cause tacky, soft paint films that will not adhere well.

Kerosene should be avoided as a thinner, because paint mixed with this liquid nearly always proves unsatisfactory. White paint thinned with kerosene often turns yellow and rarely dries to proper hardness. It is true that benzine should not be used as a substitute for turpentine for exterior work; but, for inside use, it is satisfactory, and does not affect the kidneys nor produce other types of painter's ailments which are ascribed by many people to the use of turpentine.

The functions of *thinners* in paint are: (1) to reduce the thickness of the mixture to such a degree that it has proper flowing qualities when applied with a brush; (2) to increase the penetrating qualities of the paint, and enable it to enter deeper into the material over which it is being applied, thereby anchoring the coating more firmly to the surface and preventing scaling or peeling off after the film has set or hardened; and (3) to deaden the gloss of paints or to add flatness.

Driers. The driers used in paints to accelerate the oxidation or drying process, are similar to or exactly the same as the driers used in oil varnishes. The driers prepared by manufacturers for use as oxidation agents are of two distinct classes: one called an oil drier, and the other a japan drier.

The so-called oil driers contain linseed oil or tung oil which has been cooked with metallic drying salts from lead or manganese, or from both. A very concentrated oil drier, sometimes called crusher's drier, is made through heat treatment of linseed oil with 15 to 20 times as much of the metallic oxides of lead and manganese as is ordinarily placed in linseed oil in manufacturing what is commonly called boiled oil. These oil driers should contain no rosin, and do not resemble varnishes. They are very powerful in action, and should be used in small quantities because too large amounts in paints retard drying.

The japan driers are more like rosin varnishes, with an increased amount of lead and manganese drying salts cooked into them. They contain a varnish gum, such as rosin, with lime to neutralize too great acidity, together with driers such as red lead and manganese dioxide, linseed oil properly prepared, and thinners, such as turpentine and benzine 54°. The heat treatments used in making japans are similar to those generally employed in cooking varnish.

White Lead. The most valuable of all the paint-pigments during the past 200 years or more has always been white lead. This "veteran" of the paint industry is often called lead carbonate. It is not a pure carbonate, however, but is what might be called a hydrated lead carbonate. In manufacture, white lead is made from three essential materials: metallic lead, acetic acid (the active portion of vinegar), and carbonic acid gas. The chemical formula usually given for white lead is $2PbCO_3Pb(OH)_2$. The exact amount of the lead hydrate varies somewhat if the action of the carbonic acid is unusually prolonged. In this case more than the usual amount of the hydrate is changed into carbonate.

Various processes are in use for manufacturing white lead. The "Old Dutch process," which dates back to the middle of the seventeenth century, was used in Holland. This method of producing white lead is a very good one, but is slow and expensive.

The Dutch process is based on a reaction of metallic lead and dilute acetic acid in moist air which contains carbon dioxide. The lead is cast in the form of grids called buckles, which in the United States are about 5″ in diameter and ³⁄₁₆″ thick. The buckles are pierced, leaving a plate with a large number of holes resembling a grate. Stamped sheet-metal buckles are not practical, because the metallic-lead particles become too compact to permit proper corrosion. It is for this reason that buckles for white lead making are always of cast lead.

Earthen corroding pots are used as containers for the buckles, which are piled horizontally one on top of the other filling the pot. The earthen pots are glazed on the inside, and are about 6″ in diameter and 10″ high. The lower 3″ of the pot is smaller in diameter, forming a well for the dilute acetic acid, and leaving a ledge just above the small lower cylinder upon which the buckles can rest without being immersed in the acid.

Lead corroding by the "Old Dutch process," the method most commonly used in the United States, is done by placing layers of pots in stacks, called stack rooms. Special buildings for this purpose contain a number of stack rooms which may be of various sizes, but frequently they are about 20 feet by 40 feet on the floor, and perhaps 20 feet to 30 feet in height.

The process of corroding the lead buckles into white lead is simple; but it takes a long time, and the chemical action is not obvious without considering all of the factors. The first operation in filling an empty stack is to place a layer of spent tan bark to a depth of 10″ to 20″ on the floor. A layer which is made up of even rows of pots containing buckles of lead is placed on top of the tan bark leaving a banking of about 18″ of bark around the edge. An opening for an air space leading to a central flue or chimney, is left for ventilation. The flue is temporary and is built of boards, or a ventilating pipe is placed in the middle of the room.

The pots are carefully covered with boards, and on top a new layer of tan bark is filled in to a depth of about 15″ in thickness. The entire room is filled with alternate layers of pots which contain the lead buckles and about a pint of 2½% or 3% acetic acid or acidulated water. The weak acid is sprayed or run into the pots through a hose connected to a tank of acid. The acid is put into the pots just before the layer of boards is placed over the top of the earthen containers.

Chemical action changes the metallic lead buckles in the pots into white lead. The change is very slow and requires about 120 days. Some kind of fermentation takes place in the tan bark, and heat is generated which raises the whole mass to a temperature of from 160° F. (71.1° C.) to 180° F. (82.2° C.). Carbonic acid gas is produced by the decay or fermentation of the organic matter of which the tan bark is composed. The heat which is generated slowly volatilizes the acetic acid that is contained in the pots.

Chemists think that the lead is changed into a basic lead acetate by the action of the acetic acid on the lead. The lead acetate is then changed to a lead carbonate by the carbon dioxide (CO_2) or carbonic acid gas which is abundantly produced by the hot fermenting tan bark. The carbonate is not a pure carbonate, however, the final result being a material called white lead, a somewhat variable mixture usually containing about two parts of carbonate of lead and one part of hydrate of lead.

As already stated, the formula for white lead is usually given as $2PbCO_3Pb(OH)_2$. In case of prolonged action of the carbonic acid gas more of the hydrate of lead is changed into the carbonate, and the formula for the product might be three parts of the carbonate to one of hydrate. A pure carbonate of lead which is not blended with lead hydrate does not make a good paint, because when an uncombined lead carbonate is mixed with linseed oil a mixture is produced that does not have good covering capacity though it is opaque.

The action of the hydrate of lead in linseed oil is, however, very different. The hydrate of lead and drying oil combine to form a sort of transparent varnish which has little power of obscuration. Neither carbonate of lead and a drying oil, nor hydrate of lead in such an oil when used alone, will make a good paint. Lead carbonate and lead hydrate when mixed together in the form of white lead, however, make an excellent covering material which has excellent adhesive qualities obtained from the lead hydrate and oil mixture, and also good obscuration which is derived from the lead carbonate and oil. It is for these reasons that the manufacturers of white lead wish to produce a hydrated carbonate of lead from the buckles in the pots.

After allowing the chemical action on the lead buckles to continue for about three to four months, the stacks are unloaded. Great care is taken to prevent the tan bark from getting into the pots and mixing with the white grids or buckles that have been corroded from pure metallic lead. Sometimes parts of the buckles will not be corroded into the white formation; consequently this metallic portion is removed by mechanical means, and the chunks or powdered portions are washed, ground, and sifted, and finally are made into powdered white lead.

It is very important that the white lead be ground to a proper degree of fineness. The grinding is done in water-mills between horizontal revolving flat stones. After grinding, a thorough washing is necessary to remove the acid which is left by the corroding process. All tan bark must be removed, and also any coarse, improperly ground particles of corroded lead. The last processes are pulverizing and grinding the white lead with linseed oil to make what is often called *keg lead*.

There have been a number of other processes for making white lead some of which are still in use. Very good white lead is made in about twelve days in the United States by the Carter process. The chemical action in all of the processes is somewhat similar to that of the "Old Dutch process," but the procedures vary widely. The composition of white lead made by different processes varies considerably, and this means varying quality and color.

Basic *lead sulphate* is used to some extent in paints. Lead sulphate is non-poisonous, while the corroded carbonate of lead is poisonous to some extent. Lead sulphate has one advantage owing to the fact that it does not darken with sulphur gases while paint made from lead carbonate does darken seriously at times.

Lead sulphate (formula $PbSO_4$) is made by adding sulphuric acid to acetate of lead in a dilute solution. The sulphate of lead is whiter than the carbonate and is non-poisonous, but it has poor covering power, and requires more oil in grinding into paste than does the carbonate of lead. The sulphate of lead makes a paint that is thought to be superior to ordinary white lead for painting steel structures.

Sublimed white lead is similar to lead sulphate, but contains from five to ten per cent of zinc oxide which remains with the lead sulphate in the process of manufacture.

Zinc lead is similar to sublimed lead, but contains equal parts of lead sulphate and zinc oxide.

The hydrated lead carbonate or white lead can be obtained in the form of powder, or more commonly in a paste form which contains about 8 per cent of raw linseed oil.

Properties and Uses of White Lead. The most important of all the white paint pigments during the past two centuries has been white lead in a form similar to that made by the "Old Dutch process." Practically all of the highest grades of paints today contain a high per cent of white lead. This is true especially in paints manufactured for exterior use. White lead is one of the most opaque of the durable white pigments, and forms very stable mixtures in combination with the commonly used drying oils, thinners, colors, and driers.

The most serious objection to white lead as a paint pigment is that it is apt to lose its adhesion and gradually turn to powder. This powder will disappear, or "chalk off" in the language of the painter. Colored pigments used with white lead seem to retard its tendency to turn to powder when it is used as a last coat for outside work. Painters often use zinc oxide and titanium dioxide with white lead for the finishing coat in order to obtain greater hardness and lasting qualities, and to avoid the danger of having the paint come off in powder after a time of exposure to the weather.

Titanium and Zinc White. Two of the most valuable of all of the white pigments of modern origin are titanium and zinc white. They certainly rank just below white lead and titanium dioxide and above other white pigments, such as lithopone. These oxides are manufactured in enormous quantities for use as a paint pigment in England and in the United States.

Lithopone. Many flat wall paints are manufactured in part at least from a new white pigment called lithopone. Chemically speaking we should call lithopone a compound of barium sulphate and zinc sulphide. The chemical formula for lithopone is $BaSO_4 + ZnS$ with the addition, very often, of about one per cent of ZnO, zinc oxide.

Lithopone has greater power of obscuration than any other white paint pigment, and is nonpoisonous which makes it useful for toy painting by children. It is used extensively for inside flat wall finishes or for painting ceilings. It is sometimes used in paint enamels and other finishes for inside use. It does not seem to have very high resistance to weather, and is not suitable for outside use. It is a very white and dense pigment, which is valuable in the linoleum industry and in the vulcanization of rubber.

The cost of lithopone has been less than one-half of that of white lead. For outside painting it lasts only about a year, as it turns to powder and rubs off. It is satisfactory, however, for use on the inside of buildings where a cheap flat paint is needed.

Flat undercoat paint pigments for use under enamels are sometimes made of about 91 per cent of lithopone and nine per cent of zinc oxide. The liquid portion of such an undercoat often consists of about ten per cent of linseed oil together with varnish and mineral spirits.

In grinding lithopone into a stiff paste about twelve per cent of oil is required.

Large amounts of lithopone are used as the chief body-pigment in many cheap paints for inside walls, especially.

Titanium Dioxide.[1] The more modern ready-mixed house paints contain titanium dioxide as the principal prime pigment because, among other reasons, titanium dioxide has the highest hiding power per pound of pigment of any white pigment material so far discovered. Titanium dioxide in paints has other advantages, such as better weathering characteristics of the paint film, and providing a better repaint surface when it comes time to paint again. The old lead-zinc paints failed eventually by checking and cracking, which presented an unsatisfactory

---

[1] Fisher, E. M., *What You Should Know about Paint,* Chapter 1, pp. 6, 7, and 24.

repaint surface. However, titanium paints, properly formulated, fail eventually by erosion, rather than checking and cracking, presenting a good surface for repainting. Also, titanium paints, on account of their slow failure by erosion, present a better general appearance over the next few years because they are less subject to dirt collection.

Of the two major types of titanium dioxide, rutile titanium dioxide gives about six times as much hiding power to a gallon of paint as will a pound of zinc oxide, and a pound of anatase titanium dioxide is about five times as effective in hiding power as zinc oxide. This is due to the greater difference of their refractive index as compared to the refractive index of the vehicle.

Antimony Oxide or White Antimony. Another white pigment which is used on account of its nonpoisonous qualities is antimonious oxide (Sb_2O_3). The pigment makes a good white paste with about ten per cent of oil. It also is an excellent fire retarder.

Paints made from white antimony are like those produced from titanium oxide in that they dry slowly and do not become very hard unless other pigments are included in the mixture.

Barytes or Barium Sulphate. One of the most important of the inert pigments or paint "extenders" is barytes ($BaSO_4$). There are really two forms of barium sulphate: (1) precipitated barytes, which is called *blanc fixe*, an artificial white pigment having a very fine texture; and (2) a natural, rather coarse powder, which is ground from a crystalline mineral known as baryte or heavy spar. The ground mineral powder is usually called barytes, and is less expensive than *blanc fixe*.

Of all of the pigments barytes requires the smallest amount of oil for making it into a paste. Barytes is chemically stable, and causes no chemical reaction when mixed with other materials in paints.

The characteristic of inertness and its lack of color are qualities that make the *blanc fixe* form of barium sulphite a base for making chemical colors such as various "lakes." Green colors can be "reduced" or "extended" with little loss of purity of tone because *blanc fixe* has very little opacity.

Barytes is not ordinarily added to paints by painters, but is often used as a cheap adulterant by manufacturers for extending white zinc and white lead paints. In limited quantities barytes is thought to contribute to the durability of a paint film and to have a tendency to bleach the linseed oil. Very little oil (6 to 9 per cent) is needed in making barytes into a paste, and little or no extra oil is required when this pigment is added to mixtures of other pigments and oil in paste form. This means that a paint made with barytes as an added pigment has more body to the same amount of oil which, of course, is ordinarily desirable. The crystalline structure of the fine particles of barytes presents in a painted surface a very good undercoat quality and makes repainting satisfactory. Barytes is also thought to reduce shrinking and contraction of paint films as they become old.

Barium sulphate is mixed with zinc sulphide in lithopone in the proportion of 71 to 72 per cent of the barium salt to 28 or 29 per cent of the zinc salt. The barium sulphate in lithopone is of the artificial or chemical type. Lithopone is made as a result of a chemical reaction resulting from adding a solution of barium sulphide to an equivalent solution formed of zinc sulphate. A precipitate of fine barium sulphate and zinc sulphide is formed which is filtered and calcined, and later ground to powder.

Whiting or Calcium Carbonate. Whiting is sometimes employed as an oil paint "extender," but it is used chiefly in making calcimine which is a water-mixed paint. It is also the body ingredient of oil putty, which consists of a thick paste of linseed oil with whiting. An excellent putty may be made by mixing whiting in the dry form into a paste of white lead and oil.

Whiting is made from natural chalk, and is calcium carbonate ($CaCO_3$). Chalk is ground by a process of levigation or grinding, several different grades of whiting being prepared which depend upon such qualities as whiteness and fineness. The best grades are called "Paris white" and "gilders white," and it is these two grades which are used as "extenders" in oil paints. These grades of whiting are said to neutralize the acidity of paint mixtures and help to hold the pigment in suspension. The lower grade of whiting, which is a commercial whiting and is given no special name, is the form that is used in calcimine and for manufacturing putty.

Whiting is sometimes placed in oil paints made from white lead, and the combination has proved to be very durable. Whiting requires about 18 per cent of oil to grind it into a paste, and is considered to be a very bulky pigment. The color of whiting is very white. When whiting is ground in oil it does not have much opacity or covering power, but mixtures of whiting and water possess very good body or power of obscuration.

Plaster of Paris is similar to whiting but is a sulphate of lime. Plaster of Paris is manufactured by heating gypsum ($CaSO_4 + 2H_2O$) until it loses part of its water of crystallization, which takes place at a temperature of about 180° to 190° C. Plaster of Paris is used as a cement, for the repair of plaster cracks, and for making casts, but it is not a paint pigment proper.

Magnesium Silicate or Asbestine. In a list of paint "extenders" we should not omit asbestine, which is about as valuable in the paint manufacturing industry as barytes. Asbestine is valuable in paints, especially on account of its structure which is fibrous. This elongated shape of the particles helps in binding paint films together mechanically just as iron rods add strength to reinforced concrete. The light fluffy nature of asbestine aids in holding paint pigments in solution. With asbestine in a mixture, the pigments have less tendency to settle to the bottom. When very heavy pigments, such as white lead or basic lead sulphate, are incorporated into paints a light fluffy "extender," such as asbestine, is very valuable. Cheap paints containing barytes can be kept in solution when asbestine is added to help to float the other "extenders" which have a tendency to settle.

The cost of asbestine is low because it is made out of a cheap material, asbestos. In chemical composition it resembles China Clay, which it has largely displaced as a paint "extender." China Clay is, however, an hydrated silicate of alumina, while asbestine is a silicate of magnesium.

Asbestine is also known on the market under such names as talc and French chalk.

Silica or Silex. Silicon dioxide (SiO_2) is another "extender," which is usually made by crushing quartz rock and grinding it into a fine powder. Other materials such as chert, flint, and sand are sometimes employed as rough material for use in the manufacture of silica or silex.

Silex is the most important body material known for filling the pores of wood, and is widely employed in wood fillers for this purpose. Silex and silica, which are similar substances, are also used in small quantities to give "tooth" or roughness to undercoat paints. The slight roughness added by silex is thought to give a greater hiding power to a second coat of paint because more paint will stick to a rough than to a smooth surface without causing running, sagging, or wrinkling of the film. Some ready-mixed paints include about two and one-half per cent of silex or silica because these substances add "tooth" to the paint. They do not directly increase the covering power of paints because they are almost transparent when mixed with linseed oil. They do add to the obscuration of a film of paint, however, because they make it possible for a surface to hold a thicker coat of paint.

Several paint pigments when mixed with linseed oil are in a smooth and soapy condition, and the addition of a small amount of crystalline material that is somewhat rough and elongated rather than round, tends to add a binder to the film, and improve its surface for repainting.

Black Pigments

The best and most commonly used of the black pigments are lampblack, carbon or gas black, bone black, ivory black, charcoal black, and graphite.

Lampblack. Lampblack is a grayish black pigment which is bulky and very permanent. It is composed of almost pure carbon. Lampblack is soot deposited by burning such substances as mineral oils, or even fats, resins or resinous woods, under conditions which furnish incomplete combustion because of lack of plenty of air or of the cooling action of some substance, such as cold porcelain, which may be placed in the flame. Lampblack in oil dries very slowly, but its drying qualities may be improved by the addition of driers or other colors. It is often used for exterior painting because of its durability. It has a flatting effect when used in black paints and enamels.

Carbon Black. Carbon or gas black is an American black

manufactured by a process similar to one of the methods used in producing lampblack. It is made largely from natural gas flames which strike revolving drums and leave a deposit, called gas black. It produces a color that is far blacker than that obtained from lampblack. Carbon black is preferable to lampblack as a solid black, because it does not produce so dull and grayish a tone. Carbon black has much greater obscuring or hiding power than is possessed by ivory black. It is largely used in printers' inks and in paints. In durability for exterior use it is nearly equal to lampblack.

Bone or Ivory Black. Some years ago real ivory black was made by burning ivory. Today the best grades of ivory black may be made by heating ivory chips and cuttings. The price of a real ivory black is practically prohibitive. Teeth and hard bones are at present used for making the best grades of ivory black. The name, bone black, is given to a black produced from bones from glue factories which are heated or burned in retorts. Ammonia and bone oil are saved by some process through distillation. The bone charcoal which is left as a residue is ground and produces the bone black of commerce.

The terms coach black, drop black, jet black, bone black, and ivory black mean practically the same thing in the United States.

Ivory or drop black is sold to the paint trade in a paste form, which means that the powder is properly ground in oil. The color of ivory or drop black is denser even than that of carbon black. Ivory black has considerably greater opacity than lampblack. Ivory black often seems to have a blue black tinge. Prussian blue in small quantities is sometimes mixed with drop black to modify the color or change its tone slightly.

The amount of oil required for grinding ivory or drop black into a paste is less than that needed in grinding lampblack.

Charcoal Black. Charcoal black is produced from vegetable matter by a method similar to that used in manufacturing ivory or bone black. Charcoal is made by burning such materials as grapevine cuttings, twigs from trees, plum and peach stones, cocoanut shells, or waste from cork, and a black is produced that is used chiefly in water colors for artists.

Graphite. Graphite, also called black lead or plumbago, is a natural mineral form of carbon which is mined as are other ores. An artificial graphite is manufactured from molten cast iron and charcoal. Large quantities of graphite are sometimes found in iron smelting furnaces.

Natural graphite has been known to man from times of great antiquity. Its color is unattractive unless changed in hue by the addition of some other pigment. For this reason it was not extensively used in earlier times.

In composition graphite is often nearly 90 per cent carbon. It contains two or three per cent of volatile matter and several per cent of ash. At one time it was thought to contain lead; hence the name black lead was given to it.

Mixed graphite paints of the present day contain graphite as the chief pigment, but about ten per cent of whiting or a small amount of silica may be added, and the color may be changed with lampblack, or some other black, and red lead. A boiled linseed oil vehicle is used, with a cheap thinner, such as naphtha 48°.

Graphite paints are especially valued for covering machinery and ironwork which is exposed to the weather, because these paints are not affected by exposure to outdoor air, smoke, gases, or destructive climatic changes. Undercoats of red lead are often used under graphite paints on iron roofs and other exposed ironwork. Graphite paints are unusually permanent. They are usually sold in colors, such as red, green, brown, being changed from their natural hue by the addition of other coloring matter, especially the yellow and red oxides of iron.

RED PIGMENTS

The most numerous and important of all of the color giving pigments are the red pigments. They are, in general, rather cheap, durable, and possess good power of obscuration. Some of the red pigments are earth colors, or natural red oxides of such metals as iron, lead, and mercury, while other reds are artificial or manufactured.

Venetian Red. At one time Venetian red was obtained from a natural earth which contained a ferric oxide; but at present this fine red is almost entirely produced artificially. There are various qualities of Venetian red on the market, some kinds being cheap and fading, while the best grades are very durable when carefully ground with linseed oil. The cheap Venetian reds are suitable for roof painting, and for use on barns and box cars. The best grades of Venetian red can be mixed with any of the other pigments and produce bright, attractive, permanent combinations which have good body, especially when made with gypsum as a base or extender. Gypsum is known chemically as a hydrated calcium sulphate. All of the water is removed from the gypsum by heating it to about 200° C. It is this burnt or dead calcium sulphate from gypsum that is used in Venetian red as an "extender."

The Venetian reds sold on the market are composed of an iron oxide (Fe_3O_4) which is a product of calcination of some such substance as ferrous sulphate with slaked lime. Venetian red is really a mixture of ferric oxide, called the sesquioxide, with burnt calcium sulphate ($CaSO_4$). The United States government specifications for Venetian red require that at least 40 per cent of the pigment shall be sesquioxide of iron, which is the real source of color in the pigment.

Indian Red. Red oxides of iron that formerly came from India gave us the name of this pigment. This natural red ocher was calcined in such a manner as to drive off the moisture and produce the desired shade of red. At present most of the Indian red of commerce is manufactured by burning or roasting ferrous sulphate, commonly called green vitriol or copperas ($FeSO_4$), until a material is produced which in the best grades is about 95 per cent ferric oxide (Fe_2O_3).

Indian red is a pigment of unusual permanence in sunlight and mixes well with other colors. It is very opaque and may be "extended" to some extent by inert pigments, such as whiting, barytes, and gypsum, and yet cover a surface very well. It is inexpensive and reliable as a color, and is very widely used.

Various tints of Indian red can be obtained by modifying the heat treatment or by the addition of salt during the calcining process which tends to change the red to more of a purple hue. The characteristic color of Indian red is, however, a brick red.

Tuscan Red. An alizarin lake is used to modify the ordinary Indian red and produce a crimson-toned color called

Tuscan red. On account of its ability to withstand outdoor exposure Tuscan red is used in paints for machinery and implements, and sometimes on steam pipes and radiators. It is a very strong color which is unusually permanent, and can be "extended" with gypsum, whiting, or barytes.

Red Lead. This brilliant scarlet pigment, old in history, was known and used by the ancient Egyptians. In composition it consists of 85 per cent or more of true red lead (Pb_3O_4), and the balance largely of lead monoxide, a drier called litharge (PbO).

Red lead, also called minium, is a powerful drier, and its reactions are often such that it cannot be mixed with paints which are to stand longer than 24 hours before use. High grade red leads which are very fine and 98 per cent pure are made that do not harden with an oil in a container and can be put up in paste form.

The high price of red lead tends to reduce its use, but for over 100 years it has been considered the best possible material to employ for the priming coat on steel and iron as a protection from corrosion. The running gears of wagons and machines are often primed with red lead.

A red lead priming coat may be made from a paste of red lead powder and a drying oil, together with asbestine and barytes "extenders," and a soy bean oil vehicle, together with a cheap thinner such as heavy naphtha 48°. Red lead will not grind into a fine paste with linseed oil on account of its crystalline structure. It is a common practice for painters to mix red lead powder with linseed oil just before the paint is to be applied. Red lead is not mixed into white lead paints. The color is not very satisfactory because it usually fades after a time.

Other Red Pigments. Vermilion, scarlet lake, and carmine are red pigments which are used to a small extent.

Vermilion is a beautiful bluish scarlet pigment that is not very permanent. The English vermilion is a mercuric sulphide (HgS) which is very heavy and settles to the bottom when mixed with oil. It was formerly used extensively, but at present it is expensive, and little valued except by coach-painters for the railroads. The American vermilion is a lead chromate which is fairly permanent to light. It is, however, blackened by sulphides. Vermilion of the American type is used in paints for iron and steel, and is said to be superior to red lead. It is too expensive for general or extended use, however.

Scarlet lake and *carmine* are beautiful red colors made from cochineal. These colors, largely used as stains, are quite transparent, and often fugitive in light. They are employed to some extent in paints to modify the colors of other pigments, but they lack opacity when used alone.

The lakes in general are formed by precipitating a dye, usually a coal-tar dye, upon an inorganic base, such as *blanc fixe*, which is an artificial barytes or barium sulphate ($BaSO_4$). If the dyes are permanent then the lakes are not fugitive; and, of course, if dyes are used that are not light proof, the lakes which are made from them will fade. As a class the lakes are fugitive, especially such delicate colors as rose pine and rose lake.

Orange-Red Pigment. Burnt sienna is a beautiful rather transparent pigment largely used in stains. It is made by burning or calcining raw sienna at a low temperature. Raw sienna is a natural earth color, the best grades of which come from Italy. Painters use the transparent form of burnt sienna quite extensively for graining. Burnt sienna is a mixture of materials, such as silica (SiO_2) about 13 to 20 per cent, ferric oxide (Fe_2O_3) about 65 to 80 per cent, aluminum oxide $1\frac{1}{2}$ to $5\frac{1}{4}$ per cent, together with small quantities of manganese dioxide and calcium sulphate. House painters' burnt sienna is quite opaque, and is used for tinting paints. Burnt sienna makes a good cherry color. It can be changed to a mahogany by the addition of rose pink or some similar color.

Burnt sienna can be obtained on the market in the form of a dry powder or in a paste containing the pigment ground in oil. For tinting oil paints, use the paste ground in oil.

Yellow Pigments

The yellow pigments most commonly used for coloring paints are: yellow ocher, raw sienna, the chrome yellows, Naples yellow, zinc and barium chromate yellow, and a few artists' colors such as cadmium yellow, King's yellow, aureolin or cobalt yellow, and Indian yellow.

Yellow Ocher and Golden Ocher. Natural yellow ochers are earth colors that receive their coloring matter from a certain hydrated iron oxide ($2Fe_2O_3.3H_2O$). Ochers are dug out of the earth in England, France, Spain, the United States of America, and other parts of the world.

A good yellow ocher should have a clear yellow color and contain 20 per cent or more of sesquioxide of iron (Fe_2O_3), and not more than about five per cent of calcium compounds. Ochers vary considerably, depending on where they are obtained and whether or not they have been adulterated. A good French ocher should contain 20 per cent or more of ferric oxide (Fe_2O_3), a silica base often 52 per cent to 54 per cent of the whole weight, alumina (Al_2O_3) to the extent of 12 to 14 per cent, and small amounts of other substances.

The French or French-type American ochers have a silicate base, and are superior; while the old American ochers have an alumina or clay base, and are much inferior. These latter tint well; but their clay base absorbs water, and this moisture is apt to cause scaling and blistering of the paint after it is spread. Ochers should not be used in full strength for priming coats, because they may cause the paint to scale or peel off after a time. If ochers of good grade are compounded with white lead and are finely ground, they may be used in priming coats. Ochers are principally employed by painters in preparing or mixing cream or buff paints for exterior house painting.

Golden ocher is manufactured by adding chrome yellow to an ordinary ocher. Golden ocher has a brighter yellow tone than has yellow ocher at least for a time, but this brilliance may finally be lost with the fading of the chrome yellow which is usually less permanent than is yellow ocher.

Chrome Yellow. On account of their covering power, good body, and high chroma or brilliancy of color, the most valuable of all the yellow pigments are the chrome yellows. In tone they vary from the palest yellow to a rather red hue known as Persian red. The chrome yellows also vary in composition and are sold under such names as Primrose Chrome, Canary, Light or Lemon Chrome, Light Medium Chrome, Middle or Medium Chrome, Light Orange, and Orange Chrome.

The medium chrome yellow is a basic chromate of lead

$(PbCrO_4Pb(OH)_2)$ with a small amount of carbonate of sulphate of lead. The pale chromes contain also either carbonate or sulphate of lead. These substances are precipitated with the chromate of lead and thus form a perfect mixture. Orange chrome consists of a mixture of the basic chromate of lead with the normal chromate of lead $(PbCrO_4)$.

Chrome yellows are slowly affected by atmospheric conditions, but are ranked as fairly durable colors. Pigments, such as ultramarine blue, which contain sulphur in the form of a sulphide should not be mixed with chrome yellows because sulphides darken such yellows until they become almost black. The chrome yellows should not be placed in mixtures which include such ingredients as silicates, lime, soda, or other substances with an alkaline reaction, because there will be a chemical reaction, and the yellow will be changed in hue to an orange or red. Chrome yellows are less permanent than yellow ocher, but they are so much superior to ocher in brilliancy that they are used for many purposes and are generally satisfactory. Decorators find many uses for chrome yellow pigments, but house painters do not use them extensively. The medium chrome yellow is the color most likely to be chosen for outdoor use.

The tinting power of pure chrome yellow is much greater than that of yellow ocher. Owing to its great strength or brilliance of hue a chrome yellow can be adulterated considerably without very great danger of detection by the ordinary painter.

Raw Sienna. The city of Sienna in Italy or its neighborhood furnishes the best raw and burnt siennas that are known. The siennas are earth colors that are very permanent and are old in history, having been used during the glorious days of Rome.

Raw sienna looks like yellow ocher, but it has a slightly deeper yellowish tone. It is a rather transparent color that is useful in oil stains and for graining. Its transparency makes raw sienna less valuable for a body color to give obscuration; but, when mixed with white, good cream tints are obtained which are stronger in hue than are similar mixtures of white and yellow ocher.

Raw sienna receives its color from ferric oxide (Fe_2O_3) which should be included in the earthy matter to an amount of not less than 50 per cent, and it often may exceed 70 per cent.

The other constituents of raw sienna are largely silica (SiO_2) and alumina (Al_2O_3).

Other Yellows. *Naples yellow* is a very opaque pigment which contains oxides of antimony and lead. The color is permanent but rather expensive, and is little used except by decorators and artists. It is considered more satisfactory as an oil color than as a water color, because it lacks proper transparency for use in water color painting.

Cadmium yellow is a sulphide of cadmium (CdS). It can be used to tint white lead without danger of injurious effects or changes as a result of the action of sulphuretted hydrogen. Cadmium yellows are not poisonous; they have good opacity and are permanent. They are little used, however, except by artists because they are high in price. The color known to artists as *Aurora Yellow* is quite similar in composition to cadmium yellow, but its color effect is slightly different.

BLUE PIGMENTS

The most important and extensively used blue pigments of the present day are ultramarine blue and Prussian blue. The copper blues which were formerly used have almost disappeared from the market because they lack good covering power and are fugitive. Cobalt blue is an excellent and very permanent color, but expensive.

Ultramarine Blue. At one time a pretty blue stone called the lapis lazuli was used in the manufacture of the finest of all the blues. During the past century, however, similar blue pigments have been manufactured by chemical processes. This color was used by artists during the middle ages, and has been known generally as ultramarine blue. Colors which are sold to artists under such names as New Blue, French Blue, and Permanent Blue are modifications of ultramarine blue.

Various methods have been used in the manufacture of ultramarine blue which is chemically a very complex compound containing alumina, soda, silicates, sulphur, and other substances.

Ultramarine blue is a very valuable pigment, because it is fast to light, is not changed by sulphurous gases, and can be manufactured in various shades and modifications of hue. The variations have a range from reddish tones to almost violet.

Its opacity is good compared with Prussian blue. It can be used with various mediums such as oils, japans, varnishes, and with water. Calciminers and water color artists prefer it, in general, to most of the other blues. It is not recommended for use with chrome yellow or white lead, however, because the sulphur in its composition has a tendency to react with the lead and darken the color. With zinc white it mixes satisfactorily and safely. Ultramarine blue is often mixed with other pigments, but it is rather too expensive to be used extensively by house painters. It is, however, quite often used with titanium white pigments which are not affected by it except for the change in color.

Prussian Blue. A valuable color which is much used by printers and painters because of its brilliancy of tone is generally called Prussian blue. It is sometimes known as Paris blue. A slightly modified but very similar color is sold as Antwerp blue. Chinese blue is the same in composition as Prussian blue, but it produces a color that is much paler in tone, and has a slight cast of violet or green.

Prussian blue is of rather recent origin. It is extensively used by artists for painting in both oil and water color. It is a very strong color, which makes its use economical; as only very small amounts of it are needed to tint or change the tone of other colors. Prussian blue is a transparent color, however, which is moderately permanent in light. Sunlight modifies Prussian blue, slowly changing it to a greenish tone. The color is often ranked as a rather fugitive color, and it is not satisfactory for exterior painting. Prussian blue is apt to give a dark greenish or a blackish-blue effect that is not as attractive in tone as that produced by ultramarine blue.

Alkalies seem to destroy Prussian blue colors, turning them brown. This makes the use of Prussian blue over newly plastered walls impossible because the color will be destroyed or changed in spots. This blue is extensively used, however, by implement manufacturers in dipping paints, for covering parts of polished steel, especially.

In one manufacturing process Prussian blue is obtained by oxidizing the blue precipitate which is thrown down by the addition of an iron (ferric) salt to a solution containing ferrocyanide of potassium. Chemists give Prussian blue the formula, $KFe_2(Fe_2Cy_{12})$.

Cobalt Blues. Several kinds of so-called cobalt blues are sold on the market. The cheaper kinds are usually nothing but ultramarine blue toned down or reduced in brilliancy by the addition of zinc white.

The genuine cobalt blue is an oxide of cobalt together with an oxide of aluminum. The pigment is prepared by a process of precipitation from a caustic soda solution of alumina by a cobalt chloride solution. This type of cobalt blue is an unusually permanent color which is much too expensive for ordinary painting, and is used almost entirely by artists for fine painting, and to a limited extent for tinting paper for banknotes. It has very limited use in the pottery trades and for tinting pale enamels.

GREEN PIGMENTS

There are really two classes of green inorganic pigments— green earth colors and manufactured green pigments. We might also include a third class, the lakes, which are usually made from coal-tar colors on an inert material, such as *blanc fixe*, an artificial barytes ($BaSO_4$). The most commonly used of all the greens is called chrome green or Brunswick green.

The Earth Greens. The earth greens are rather dull colors, which are known by such names as Terra Verte and Veronese Green. These pigments are ranked as permanent, but they lack body and good covering power; consequently they have largely been replaced by other greens. They make an excellent base material, however, for use in manufacturing certain "lakes," such as Malachite Green, Brilliant Green, and Methylene Blue.

Chemically speaking, the green earths are a magnesium ferrous silicated aluminum oxide. The earths or clays are sometimes called augites.

Chrome or Brunswick Green. The green pigment which is in greatest demand on the market is made by mixing Prussian Blue or Chinese Blue with Chrome Yellow, and is called Chrome or Brunswick Green. It is made up in various shades of green which vary from almost yellow to nearly blue in tone. Chrome greens lack durability, being composed of materials that are not very durable; but they are used extensively, because they possess great brilliancy of effect and have excellent covering power. The wagon and agricultural implement manufacturers are large users of chrome green, and they find it a satisfactory color because it holds its coloring power about as long as the paint lasts.

"Chemically pure" chrome greens are mixtures of the blue and yellow in full strength. Weaker and cheaper chrome greens are made by the use of such "extenders" as barytes or a silicate. Such materials may be used up to about 75 per cent of the mixture with only 25 per cent of color. These poorer grades are called "commercial" green in the paint market.

Other Green Pigments. *Chrome Oxide Green* (Cr_2O_3) is the only true chrome green. It is a very permanent but rather dull color. Although it is an excellent green pigment, it is too expensive for general use because of difficulties in the manufacture. It can be safely mixed with all other pigments, and is not affected by alkalies, acids, or heat.

Cobalt Green is an expensive, rather dull, and nonpoisonous pigment that is very permanent, but it is little used except by artists. It is manufactured through a combination of a zinc salt, such as zinc oxide, with cobalt nitrate.

Viridian or *Emeraude Green,* is a good transparent green that is considered to be permanent, and for this reason it is much used by decorators. Sunlight and sulphuretted hydrogen gas do not affect it. Chemically, Viridian is an hydrated sesquioxide of chromium. It is a stable color which can be mixed safely with any of the other colors.

Permanent Green is similar to Viridian, but it is cheaper because it is diluted or "extended" with an alumina hydrate or some other cheap material.

Brown Pigments

There are only a few brown pigments that are worthy of consideration. The valuable browns of the present day are the raw and burnt umbers, and Vandyke brown—all of them earth colors. Sepia, a color much used by water-color artists, is of animal kingdom origin being manufactured from the "ink bag" of the cuttlefish. Sepia is not a true pigment, but it is valued as a transparent color. The earth colors in the brown group were known and used by nations of great antiquity. The name umber came from the word Umbria, a province of Italy.

Raw Umber. There are a number of grades of raw umber, since earth colors under that name are found in various places, such as England, France, Germany, and America, and they vary greatly in quality. The best umber is called Turkey umber because it is marketed through Constantinople. The color comes from the island of Cyprus, and is not actually mined in Turkey.

Raw umber somewhat resembles the siennas and ochers, except that it contains considerably more of the manganese oxides, such as MnO_2 and Mn_3O_4. The raw umbers sometimes contain as much as 20 per cent of manganese oxides; and, in such cases they have strong drying qualities for oils that are used as vehicles in paints. The use of large amounts of umber in oil paints may cause trouble because of the strong drying action of the manganese oxides contained in the umbers.

Raw umbers of good grade are fairly permanent or even almost entirely permanent in light. In opacity and staining power the umbers rank high.

Paints containing raw umber dry very quickly and become unusually hard. They also wear exceptionally well. In color, raw umbers have a range from a yellowish brown to a dark brown. The pigment works very smoothly and easily under a brush.

Burnt Umber. In the preparation of burnt umber, the ordinary raw umber is roasted over a slow fire. The color of burnt umber is derived from its high content of Ferric oxide (Fe_2O_3). The other most important constituent of a good grade of Turkey burnt umber is manganese dioxide (MnO_2), which varies in quality, but which is commonly found in the pigment in amounts of about twelve per cent. Burnt umber may be used in limited quantities, and is valuable in paints and varnishes; on account of its high manganese dioxide content, it adds drying qualities as well as color to the mixtures.

Burnt umbers are more transparent than raw umbers, usually, and they acquire a darker, warmer reddish-brown color that is useful and much appreciated by painters. This brown pigment is used extensively in oil stains, for graining, and as a glazing color.

Vandyke Brown. This color is named after a celebrated Flemish portrait painter who is said to have used the pigment, which we call Vandyke brown, very effectively. The Vandyke browns resemble the umbers somewhat in composition, but are supposed to derive their coloring properties from bituminous, ferruginous, or carbonaceous earths that are found in Germany and Ireland, and also in some other countries. The Vandyke browns which are obtained from different countries vary greatly in composition. In general, they contain a very large amount of organic matter, with small amounts of iron and alumina compounds, and also some lime.

When Vandyke brown is ground in oil it is reasonably permanent. Ground or dissolved in water, it is less permanent in bright light. It is a much more transparent pigment than umber. It is, however, a favorite color with some water-color artists. Glazers and grainers use it to a considerable extent. Vandyke-brown pigment, ground in oil and thinned with turpentine, is often used as an oil-stain to imitate or represent walnut.

Vandyke brown when ground in linseed oil is a very poor drying pigment, and it should not be used without adding some manganese japan drier to the mixture.

An imitation Vandyke brown that is very permanent is sometimes made from drop black, burnt umber, and Prussian blue. These pigments are not as transparent as Vandyke brown; consequently they make a mixture of less transparency than the genuine color.

Metallic Pigments. The demand for various metallic paints which are made from powders of bronze, aluminum, zinc, tin, copper, and gold, together with a proper varnish medium or some bronzing liquid as a vehicle has grown greatly during recent years. Metallic paints are highly decorative under proper conditions, and are valued on account of their anticorrosive qualities when they are used to cover metals such as radiators for steam and hot-water heating. Metallic paints are good conductors of heat.

The alloy for making an imitation gold bronze is made from copper and zinc. The reddish gold bronzes contain from 1 to 5.6 per cent of zinc, while the yellow or light gold bronzes may include from about 15 to 19 per cent of zinc in their composition. Bronze powder is made from thin sheets of the metal, which are ground into very fine particles. Various color effects can be obtained in the metallic powders by heat treatments, as by heating in a paraffin bath; or new hues are produced by mixing certain coal-tar dye-stuffs in the paints to secure the desired color. A painter can change the colors of bronzes by the addition of colors ground in japan. Colors ground in oil do not dry quickly nor mix well in lacquer.

White bronze is made of the metal, aluminum, by grinding it into fine powder.

About six pounds of bronzing powder to each gallon of bronzing liquid are generally used in gold bronze or common bronze powders. Much less aluminum powder can be used, because it is very light and more bulky. It is usual to mix only about 1½ to 2 pounds of the dry aluminum powder to the gallon of bronzing liquid. Sometimes bronze powders are measured instead of weighed for mixing. A tablespoonful of bronze powder to each pint of lacquer makes a bronze paint that covers satisfactorily.

The bronzing liquid may be a very heavy-bodied boiled linseed oil. Rapid drying bronzing liquids are sometimes made from mixtures of heat-treated linseed oil and tung oil, together with japan driers and benzine as a thinner.

For inside bronzing, decorators often thin a good grade of rubbing varnish with turpentine, and add bronze powders until a paint of the proper brushing consistency is prepared. Spar varnish may be substituted for rubbing varnish whenever the bronze paint is to be used outdoors.

A quick drying bronze paint can be prepared by using banana oil, or preferably a good nitrocellulose lacquer, or even a mixture of brushing lacquer and banana oil, as a vehicle for holding the bronze powder in suspension in the paint and making it possible to spread it with a brush.

Characteristics of Paint Ingredients. Earlier in this Chapter it was pointed out that a paint consists of pigments, vehicles, driers, and thinners. It should be remembered in mixing paints that a thinner such as turpentine adds penetrating properties, and makes the paint flow more easily over the surface. One part of turpentine will thin about twice as much paint paste as one part of linseed oil. It follows that, if turpentine be substituted in part for linseed oil, there will be relatively more pigment in a paint film. Turpentine, however, gives a flat effect to a paint if it is added in any considerable amount.

Pigment Pastes. Paint pigments, such as the basic white

COURTESY W. P. FULLER AND COMPANY

18—1. This dough mixer blends dry pigments, extenders, and vehicles into a suitable paste for further grinding operations.

lead carbonate and titanium dioxide, can be obtained in dry powder form, but they are very difficult materials to incorporate into a paint mixture unless they have previously been ground in oil with proper machinery. For this reason paint factories prepare them in paste form. A mixture of lead pigment with oil in the form of a paste is called keg lead (Fig. 18-1).

18—2. The paint grinding process is completed here by a battery of overhead ball and pebble mills. The heavy paint is next drained off in floor level mixing tanks for tinting and thinning.

A white lead paste, or keg lead, as it comes from the manufacturer is composed of eight pounds of pure raw linseed oil to each 100 pounds of basic white lead carbonate. This amount of materials will make a bulk of about 2.75 to 2.85 gallons after mixing, and each gallon will weigh about 36 pounds. One

COURTESY W. P. FULLER AND COMPANY

18—3. This five-roll vertical roller mill is primarily used for grinding enamels and other pigmented finishes requiring high gloss properties.

should not confuse paint pigment pastes with mixed paint because, in ready-to-use paints, pastes are thinned and driers are often added. In each 100 pounds of properly prepared white lead paint, ready for use, there should be about 35 pounds of liquids to 65 pounds of pigment. For priming coats and some other purposes thin paints which contain relatively less pigment are used.

18—4. Paint cans are often filled and closed by special automatic machines.

Modern paint manufacturing plants not only have elaborate machinery for the preparation of paints (Figs. 18-2 and 3), pages 334 and 335, but also machines which automatically fill and label paint cans (Figs. 18-4 and 5).

Paint Mixing. Practical men have learned through experience that there is a best procedure or method of putting the ingredients together when mixing paints. A brief statement of the approved steps in preparing a ready-to-use paint mixture may be of value to inexperienced users of paint. The usual procedure is as follows:

1. Select a drum or other container about twice as large as the bulk of the final mixture, and wet the inside with a small amount of linseed oil.

2. Place the entire amount of one kind of pigment in the container. (Mix different pigments, such as white lead and zinc white, with the drying oil in separate containers.)

336

18—5. Proper labels are placed on each can by the automatic labeler. Notice the conveyer system above.

3. Pour linseed oil into the paste of lead or other pigment, adding only about one half of a pint at a time.

4. Stir the paste with each new quantity of oil that is added, until the mixture is free from lumps or thick portions of paste. A wooden paddle of convenient size is commonly used for the stirring or mixing process. Add only enough oil to break up the paste thoroughly at this time.

5. If other pigments, such as colors ground in oil, are to be added, they should be mixed into the pigment and oil mixture until the proper hue is secured. Color should be added slowly and cautiously, and test samples should be made.

6. The amount of drier indicated by the formula should next be stirred into the paint mixture. If boiled oil is substituted for raw oil, no drier is needed; and if used it will harm the paint.

7. Pour the remainder of linseed oil into the paint mixture

a little at a time, carefully stirring and mixing the pigments with the oil. (The amount of oil in paint formulas varies greatly.)

8. The thinner, such as turpentine or mineral spirits, should next be stirred into the paint. Turpentine tends to "flat" paints, and should not be used in excess.

9. In order to remove coarse particles, it is wise to strain the paint through a fine screen wire. If the paint is to be used inside of a building, or if a very smooth surface is wanted, a final straining of the thoroughly mixed paint through a double cheese cloth screen is advisable.

Formula for Mixing Paints.

First Coat. (For use when three coats are required.)

Formula No. 1

A thin priming white paint for outside use on new wood.
Pigment—Hydrated lead carbonate (white lead), 100 pounds
Vehicle—Raw linseed oil, 4 gallons
Thinner—Turpentine (gum turpentine preferred), 1 to 2 gallons
Drier—Japan drier, or preferably oil drier, 1 pint.

In bulk this mixture measures about 9 to 9⅛ gallons, if two gallons of turpentine are used.

Very sappy or resinous woods require a large amount of turpentine. Woods which easily absorb linseed oil, such as yellow poplar, basswood, pine, and old weathered unpainted surfaces, require a priming paint with much oil in it; while less absorbent woods, especially yellow pine, spruce, hemlock, bald cypress, and most hard woods, require less oil.

Too much drier in paint is harmful. The maximum amount of drier that should be used is 1 part of drier to 20 parts of raw linseed oil. If boiled oil is substituted for raw oil in paint, no drier should usually be added. An oil drier reduced with turpentine or benzine is considered superior to japan drier by many experts. Oil driers are very powerful and contain no rosin; and, in this respect, they are preferable to most japans which contain varnish gums, and often rosin which is cheap.

Second Coat. (When three coats are required.)

Formula No. 2

For an outside white paint for use on new wood.
Pigment—Hydrated lead carbonate (white lead), 100 pounds
Vehicle—Raw linseed oil, 1½ to 2 gallons
Thinner—Turpentine, 1½ to 2 gallons
Drier—Japan drier, 1 pint.

If 1½ gallons each of turpentine and raw linseed oil are used, the bulk of the mixture should be about 6⅛ gallons. The covering capacity of the 6⅛ gallons of paint should be about 3500 to 3600 square feet if it is properly spread with a brush.

For repainting outside on wood this formula is suitable for the first coat if 2 gallons each of raw linseed oil and turpentine are used to give fluidity.

Third Coat. (When three coats are required.)

Formula No. 3

For an outside white paint for use on new wood.
Pigment—Hydrated lead carbonate (white lead), 100 pounds
Vehicle—Raw linseed oil, 4 gallons
Thinner—Turpentine, 1 pint
Drier—Japan drier, 1 pint.

The third coat for outside painting should contain a large amount of drying oil, and very little turpentine, because the oil adds gloss to the paint, and increases the binder which holds the paint particles together.

This formula may also be used for the last coat in a two coat repainting job. When the paint is to be applied as a second coat for repainting, a heavier mixture containing only 3½ gallons of linseed oil instead of 4 gallons is preferable.

Special Titanium and White Lead Paint.

Formula No. 4

For a last coat for outside use.
Pigments, 65% by weight:

Hydrated lead carbonate, white lead,	71 per cent
Titanium oxide,	21
Magnesium silicate (asbestine),	8
Total pigments,	100 per cent

Liquids, 35% by weight:

Vehicle—Raw linseed oil,	91.0 per cent
Thinner—Turpentine or mineral spirits,	4.5
Drier—Japan drier,	4.5
Total liquids,	100.0 per cent

Manufacturers of mixed paints recommend titanium white to the extent of 10 to 25 per cent of the total pigments of an outside paint that is to be used for a finishing coat. The titanium white is added to prevent excessive weathering or powdering of the white lead, and to make a harder surface. In rainy regions or near the sea many painters substitute about 15 per cent of titanium white for white lead in a white-lead paint formula.

Asbestine is recommended, in small amounts because it is fibrous, acts as a binder, and helps to keep the paint in solution while in the can because of its light fluffy nature.

Interior White Paint for Plastered Walls.

Formula No. 5

For inside use for priming coat.
Pigment—Hydrated Lead Carbonate (White Lead), 25 pounds
Vehicle—Boiled linseed oil, 1¾ gallons
Thinner—Turpentine (Gum turpentine preferred), 1 quart.

The alkali in newly plastered walls should be reduced or neutralized by the use of a zinc sulphate solution before priming.

Flat Interior White Paint for Plastered Walls.

Formula No. 6

For second and third coats.
Pigment—Hydrated Lead Carbonate (White Lead), 25 pounds
Vehicle—Flatting oil, 2 to 3 quarts.

Formula No. 7

Another second coat of flat paint. (An alternative for Formula No. 6.)
Pigment—Hydrated Lead Carbonate (White Lead), 25 pounds
Vehicle—Raw linseed oil, 1 pint
Thinner—Turpentine, 2 quarts
Drier—Pale japan drier, ¼ pint.

Formula No. 8

Another third coat flat wall paint. (An alternative for Formula No. 6.)
Pigment—Hydrated Lead Carbonate (White Lead), 25 pounds
Vehicle—Pale enamel varnish, ¼ pint
Thinner—Turpentine, 2 quarts
Drier—Pale japan drier, ⅛ pint.

Interior Flat White Paint for Wood.

Formula No. 9

For first coat.
Pigment—Hydrated Lead Carbonate (White Lead), 25 pounds
Vehicle—Raw linseed oil, 3 quarts
Vehicle and thinner combined—Flatting oil, 3 quarts
Drier—Pale japan drier, ¼ pint.

Formula No. 10

Flat white paint for second and third coats.
Pigment—Hydrated Lead Carbonate (White Lead), 25 pounds
Vehicle and thinner combined—Flatting oil, 2 to 3 quarts.

Flat Enamel Undercoat Paint. (For inside use on wood especially.)

Formula No. 11

A second coat paint.
Pigments, 65% by weight:

Lithopone,	91 per cent
Titanium oxide,	9
	___
Total pigments,	100 per cent

Liquids, 35% by weight:

Vehicle—Linseed oil,	10	
Pale enamel varnish,	35	45 per cent
Thinner—Turpentine or mineral spirits,		55
		___
Total liquids,		100 per cent

This undercoat paint may be used for a priming coat by the addition of the following to each gallon of paint:
Thinner—Turpentine, 1 pint
Vehicle—Raw Linseed Oil, 1 pint.

Red Lead Paints for Metal.

Formula No. 12

For first or priming coat. (Red lead paints next to metal should contain no other pigment.)
Pigment—Dry red lead powder, 25 pounds
Vehicle—Raw linseed oil, 4¾
       Boiled linseed oil, 2⅜ 7⅛ pints
Thinner—Turpentine, up to ¼ pint per gallon, if required
Drier—Red lead is a drier; consequently no other drier is necessary.

Alternative Formula with Red Lead Paste.

Formula No. 13

Pigment—Red lead paste (Red lead and oil), 25 pounds
Vehicle—Raw linseed oil, 3⅓
       Boiled linseed oil, 1⅔ 5 pints
Thinner—Turpentine, up to ¼ pint per gallon of paint
Drier—None.

Brown Metal Paint for Second and Third Coats.

Formula No. 14

Pigment—Dry lead powder, 25 pounds
Vehicle—Linseed oil, approximately ⅓ boiled and ⅔ raw; total, 4¾ quarts.
Coloring pigment—Paste lampblack, 12 ounces to 6¾ pounds of the mixture.
Thinner—Turpentine, small amount as required.
Drier—None.

Priming paints for woods that are hard and nonabsorbent should be thicker and contain less linseed oil and turpentine than for porous soft woods. Woods which contain much resin, such as yellow pine, should be washed with turpentine. All knots and resinous places should be coated with shellac to prevent the exudation of gum, and then primed with a thin paint. Some experienced painters recommend the addition of a small amount of benzol to priming paints which are to be used on resinous woods. For cypress especially, the priming coat is more satisfactory if about ½ pint of benzol or toluol is added to each gallon of mixed paint. These solvents are very powerful, and seem to aid the priming coat in penetrating more deeply into the cells of coniferous woods that are somewhat resinous.

Various colored white lead paints can be used over red lead priming coats.

Red lead paints can be changed in color by the addition of paste pigments. Green paint is sometimes made by the addition of medium chrome green and Chinese blue in paste form until the proper color is obtained. Whenever colors are added, more linseed oil must also be added, or the paint will be too heavy to spread well.

Mixing or Blending Colors. It is very difficult to give dependable suggestions for mixing colors, because the pigments sold on the market vary somewhat in hue and color strength, even though they are sold under familiar names. The following suggestions may prove helpful in mixing colors:

Black (Purplish). Lampblack, 5 to 7 parts; tint with rose pink, about one part; and a touch of purple or violet.

Blue black. Ivory black, 13 parts; Prussian blue, about 1 part.

Blue (Light or Delft). White lead and cobalt blue, with a slight quantity of black.

Blue (Sky). Tint with cobalt blue, or equal parts of cobalt blue and Prussian blue. Ultramarine blue should not be used with white lead, but it may be used safely with zinc oxide.

Brass (Yellowish). White lead, 20 parts; chrome yellow (light), 6 parts; and equal parts of raw and burnt umber, 1 part.

Bronze. White lead, 9 to 11 parts; lemon chrome yellow, 4 parts; and raw umber, 4 to 5 parts.

Bronze (Green). White lead, dark chrome green, and lampblack; or white lead, medium chrome green, ivory black, and a small amount of raw umber.

Brown (Golden). White lead, 10 pounds; French yellow ocher or raw sienna, about 24 ounces; and burnt sienna, 8 ounces.

Brown (Warm). White lead, 2 to 3 parts; Venetian red, 3 parts; yellow ocher, 3½ to 4 parts; and ivory black (with a touch of blue), 1 part.

Brown. Indian red, 3 parts; yellow ocher, 1 part; and oil lampblack, 2 parts. Various browns can be obtained by changing the proportions. Venetian red may be substituted for Indian red, and burnt umber for the yellow ocher and lampblack.

Brown (Reddish). Vandyke brown, 2 to 8 parts; and burnt sienna, about 1 part.

Brown. Black and various reds, such as Venetian red, Indian red, burnt sienna, and vermilion.

Buff. White lead, tinted with yellow ocher or raw sienna. For a warmer tone, a little middle chrome yellow may be added.

Citron or *Citrine*. Orange, 4 parts; and chrome green, 1 part. Or lemon chrome yellow, about 5 parts, with raw umber, about 2 parts. Citron is a tertiary color containing yellow chiefly with smaller portions of red and blue.

Cream. Tint white lead with yellow ocher and a touch of Venetian red; or white lead, yellow ocher, and a little vermilion.

Drab. Various proportions of white lead, burnt and raw umber, and yellow ocher.

Drab. White lead, 25 pounds; raw umber, about 1 pound; and, if necessary, French yellow ocher until the brown tone is grayed.

Gold. Mix into white lead a gold made from a red such as vermilion, 1 part; and a golden ocher (or a mixture of yellows, including chrome yellow, yellow ocher, and raw sienna), about 5 parts.

Green. Mix various yellows and blues.

Green (Yellowish). Chrome yellow or lemon chrome yellow, 4 to 8 parts; Prussian blue, 1 part.

Green (Bluish). Use equal parts of Prussian blue with a mixture of chrome yellows, such as lemon and middle chrome.

Gray. Use the three primary colors red, yellow, and blue to neutralize each other. White lead and black make a dead or dull gray. Various grays can be made warmer by the addition of a little red or yellow. Cool grays may be obtained by the use of blue in the gray mixture.

Gray (Yellowish). White lead, 25 pounds; French yellow ocher, 1 to 1½ pounds; Venetian red, ½ ounce; and lampblack, from ½ to ¾ ounce. Raw Turkey umber may be substituted for the Venetian red, and ivory black for the lampblack. For a warmer gray, a little burnt sienna or yellow ocher, or both, may be added.

Ivory. White lead, 25 pounds; French yellow ocher, 1 pound; and Venetian red, up to ½ a pound.

Lavender. White lead, 25 pounds; cobalt blue, about 12 ounces; and a red such as madder lake, 4 ounces. Ultramarine blue is apt to darken with white lead. Prussian blue may be used instead of cobalt, but a less attractive color is produced.

Mahogany. White lead, about 1 or 2 parts; orange chrome, 10 parts; and a red, such as burnt sienna, about 3 parts, depending upon the strength of red desired in the mahogany.

Olive. Mix 4 parts of chrome green with 1 part of violet.

Orange. White lead and chrome orange. The various chrome yellows, or yellow ocher, can be mixed with a red pigment in order to make an orange color.

Pink. White lead with various reds, such as Indian red-rose madder, carmine lake, vermilion, and Venetian red, are ordinarily used in producing pink tones.

Purple. Equal parts of white lead, Indian red, and Prussian blue. Black may be added to darken the shade. Other reds, such as carmine or crimson lake, may be substituted for Indian red.

Rose. White lead with a little rose lake. Other reds such as vermilion, or even Turkey red, or crimson madder, are sometimes used.

Russet. Mix 4 parts of orange with 1 part of violet, and tint the white pigment.

Slate. The same as olive; or, mix white pigments with ivory black and Prussian blue in the proportion of about 3 to 1. Ultramarine blue is preferable to Prussian blue, except when white lead is used.

Stone. Tint white pigments with yellows and browns, such as yellow ocher and raw umber. Burnt umber and Venetian red are also added sometimes in small quantities.

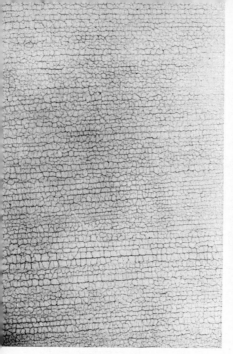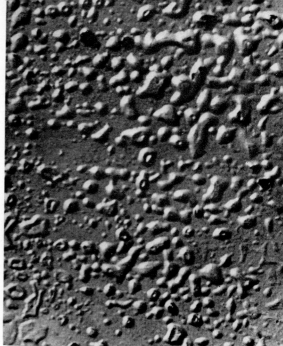

18—6. Checking is usually caused by applying a hard-drying finishing coat over too soft an undercoat. 18—7. Blistering and peeling indicate moisture behind the paint film. A surface should be thoroughly dry before paint is applied.

Tan. White pigments may be tinted with brownish yellow, such as raw sienna. Touches of burnt umber, or vermilion and chrome yellow, are sometimes added.

Violet. Use 4 or 5 parts of ultramarine blue to one of red, such as crimson lake or carmine. For white lead paints, substitute Prussian blue for ultramarine blue.

Walnut. Mix about 5 parts of burnt umber with 1 part of raw sienna; or substitute yellow ocher for the raw sienna, and add more brown.

Application of Paint. A few suggestions about the use of paint may prove of value to the inexperienced painter.

Paint should not be applied during very wet or cold weather. In fact, wooden surfaces especially will not absorb the oils of paint properly if the pores and cell walls of the material are even partly water-soaked. All painting should be done on dry material, or trouble of various kinds may follow.

Careful investigation by independent paint laboratories has established the fact that more than 90% of all paint failures

345

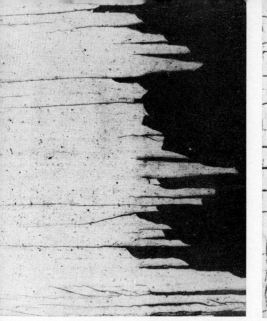
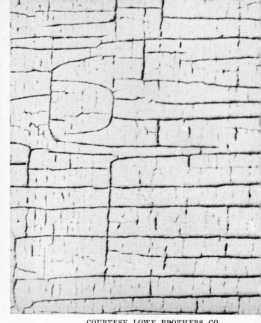

18—8. Alligatoring and flaking, somewhat similar to checking but more pronounced, are also caused by applying a hard-drying finishing coat over too soft an undercoat. 18—9. Cracking and scaling are caused by lack of elasticity of the paint, or temperature or moisture changes.

is due to: moisture back of the paint film, improper surface preparation before painting, and faulty application of the paint. The following six causes of paint failures are most frequently encountered:[2]

Checking. This is usually caused when a hard-drying finishing coat is applied over too soft an undercoat. It may have been that this undercoat was of a slow-drying type or was not given sufficient time to dry thoroughly (Fig. 18-6), page 345. Checking of the surface breaks the paint film, making it easy for moisture to reach the surface of the wood beneath.

Blistering and Peeling. When blisters appear, it indicates moisture behind the paint film (Fig. 18-7), page 345. As moisture collects behind the paint, the sun draws it to the surface; next the paint stretches, and finally breaks.

To correct blistering and peeling, get at the source of the moisture trouble.

Flaking and Alligatoring. This type of paint failure is somewhat similar to checking but more pronounced (Fig. 18-8).

---

[2] The Lowe Brothers Company, "The How's and Why's of Painting and Decorating," page 29.

346

The trouble starts when a hard-drying paint is applied over a soft-drying paint. Also the repeated application of new coats of paint over old ones without proper surface preparation may cause this type of paint failure.

Cracking and Scaling are caused by the lack of elasticity of the paint, or temperature and moisture changes (Fig. 18-9). When breaks in the paint film extend down to the wood, they are called cracks. When loose paint particles fall away from the edges of these cracks, the condition is referred to as scaling. Before repainting, remove all loose paint, and sand down.

Mildew. This is a frequent cause of paint discoloration. Mildew can be observed through a magnifying glass in the form of tiny spores (Fig. 18-10). Consult your paint dealer for the proper treatment of this type of paint failure. Quite often mildew can be avoided by using a fast-drying, light-colored paint. Apply the paint on a dry, sunny day.

Erosion. When this occurs, the paint film wears away too rapidly as a result of excessive chalking of the paint coating (Fig. 18-11). To avoid erosion, be sure that the paint you use is a well-balanced, normal chalking paint.

18—10. Mildew is a frequent cause of discoloration of paint. To avoid mildew, use a fast-drying, light-colored paint and apply when the day is dry and sunny. 18—11. Erosion is the too-rapid wearing away of the paint. To avoid erosion, use a well-balanced, normal chalking paint.

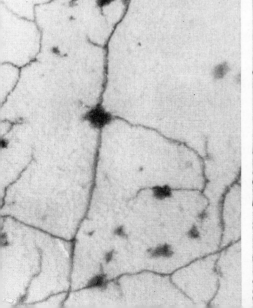
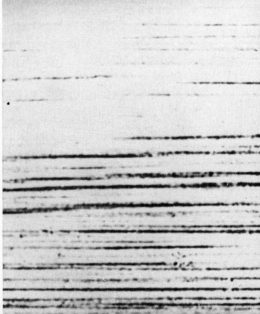

Surfaces to be painted should be free from dust, dirt, plaster, and mortar. The surface should be smooth, but not necessarily hand planed, scraped, and sanded, after the fashion of articles that are to receive a varnish or lacquer finish.

Knots in all resinous woods should be given a coat or two of shellac to prevent resin from exuding through the paint during hot weather (Fig. 18-12).

Old painted surfaces generally require cleaning with a stiff steel wire brush and a scraping-knife. It is often advisable to wash old surfaces with strong soapy water, or a solution of washing soda, made from about one-half pound of soda to each gallon of water. If the old paint is chipped off in spots, or is rough, the painter should use sandpaper of about the No. 1 size to smooth the defective spots. Sanding and brushing with a steel brush help in making a more level foundation for the new coats of paint.

Number of Coats of Paint. It is necessary to apply three coats of paint in order to secure a properly covered, attractive surface that will endure outdoor weather conditions for a reasonable length of time. The first coat is usually called the priming coat, the second the body coat, and the third the finishing coat. While three coats of paint are required on new work, repainting can usually be done satisfactorily with two coats. In repainting, the priming coat is usually omitted, unless the old paint is practically all gone, and the wood or other material is weathered.

Pre-priming of Wood Surfaces. It has become popular practice to give wood surfaces an application of wood preservative. These preservatives not only serve as a semi-primer, but act primarily as a check against excessive water absorption, fungus growth, termites, lyctus (powder post) beetles, and carpenter ants.

For best application, complete emersion is recommended. If this is impractical, the preservative can be liberally applied by brush. Such items as windows, doors, screens, storm sash, sills, siding, hardwood and softwood floors are treated. The wearing of protective clothing such as rubber gloves and aprons is recommended. Although no reaction may be expected from inhaling fumes, many of these preservatives are highly toxic upon external application.

The active bases of most wood preservatives are: penta-chlorophenol, tetrachlorophenol, and petroleum solvents or esters.

Priming. The composition of the first coat of paint is important because it is the priming material which enters into the pores of wood or other substances and forms anchorages. It is the priming coat that fills up the open cells in wood, and makes a foundation to which later films of paint will adhere. Priming paints which are to be used on cypress and yellow pine will penetrate these woods more satisfactorily if benzol, a powerful solvent for gums and oils, is used as part of the liquid. Cypress contains an oil, and yellow pine contains a resin, both of which are substances that prevent a satisfactory penetration of ordinary thin oil paints. Benzol in paint reacts on the oils and resins of coniferous wood, and permits the paint to enter the cells and adhere to the wood. About two-thirds of a pint of benzol to each gallon of priming paint produces a good penetrating paint for use on cypress and yellow pine.

When benzol is added to first-coat paints in appreciable amounts, the linseed oil and turpentine are reduced in about

18—12. Knots and sticky, resinous areas are given a coat of shellac. Shellac acts as a sealer, and prevents "bleeding." 18—13. Tip the bristles about 1½ inches into the paint. Next tap the brush lightly against the inside of the can rim so that any excess paint drops back into the can.

COURTESY LOWE BROTHERS CO.

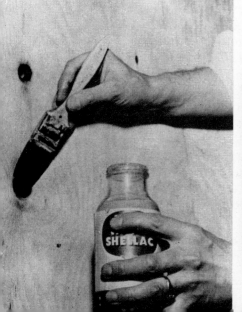

equal quantities; otherwise the paint would be too thin for most purposes. The benzol entirely evaporates in a short time, leaving a residue in the paint film composed of pigments, drying oil, and drier. The turpentine evaporates also, leaving only a slight residue of a varnishlike nature. Paints containing benzol should not be used for anything except priming, as this solvent may soften an undercoat if used in a second or third coat of paint.

Priming coats are somewhat similar in composition and color to paints used for later coats, but they should be thinner. Formerly, priming coats contained large amounts of yellow ocher, which is a cheap pigment. Ochers may, however, be used in moderate amounts for tinting lead paints. Yellow ocher easily absorbs moisture, and may cause paint to scale off. It may be used for tinting white lead, but it should not be employed in full strength as a body pigment.

It is very important that the priming coat of paint be well brushed into the cells of wood. Paint should not be flowed on after the manner of applying lacquer or a final coat of varnish, but it should be worked well into the pores of wood, or small openings of other materials, with a brush in order to seal up the surface and make a foundation that will hold the pigments and oils of the body coat on the surface. In painting, the brush should not be overloaded, because in this case paint may drop from the brush and do damage or make troublesome spots (Fig. 18-13), page 349.

In applying paint, the experienced painter usually begins at the upper left-hand corner of vertical surfaces. If the wall of a house is being painted, a portion of the upper left-hand corner is painted, applying the paint with the grain. The workman covers as much of the wall as he can reach, then moves down, and paints another area below the first one. This operation is repeated until the left-hand edge is painted. The painter then goes to the top, and paints another area crosswise at the top, joining the second area to the first before the paint sets. Lower portions are then painted.

Inside walls of plaster, especially, are painted with up-and-down strokes of the brush, starting at the top and left, and painting an area about three feet wide by two feet in height. Another similar area below the first one is then painted.

After an area about three feet wide has been covered from top to bottom, a new start at the top is made, and another section is painted with up-and-down strokes.

On account of the alkaline nature of newly plastered walls, it is advisable to apply a zinc sulphate solution to the plaster before painting. This prepriming solution is made from about three or four pounds of zinc sulphate to a gallon of water. After this neutralizing coating has dried thoroughly, an ordinary priming paint may be applied. There will be little danger of having the paint peel off if the alkali of the plaster is properly neutralized by zinc sulphate.

Putty and Puttying. After the priming coat of paint is dry, the next process is puttying or filling nail holes, grub or worm holes, all cracks, and other defects of any kind that damage the appearance of the surface.

Prepared putty in natural and dark colors can be obtained. One of the best kinds of putty for exterior use can be made by mixing whiting with white lead in oil paste in equal parts, and softening the mass, if necessary, with the proper amount of boiled or raw linseed oil. Dry colors can also be mixed with the pigments whenever a putty of a special color is desired.

Some commercial grades of oil putty are made from ordinary whiting and raw linseed oil, 5½ pounds of whiting to one pound of oil being used. A putty made from whiting and linseed oil, and containing no white lead, does not dry as hard as one containing more or less of the expensive lead pigment as an ingredient, but it is preferred for setting glass and for some other purposes. The poorest grades of commercial putty often contain more or less marble dust, and have little cohesion after they become dry.

Puttying should always be done after the priming coat has become dry. If puttying is attempted before painting, the wood about the opening which contains the putty will absorb most of the oil which should oxidize in the putty itself and remain as a binder. Unless the oil remains in the putty, the particles of pigment have little cohesion, and the mass becomes friable and crumbles away.

Many painters use a good grade caulking compound, which hardens chemically and gives the best service.

Painters often use the thumb, or sometimes the fingers, for

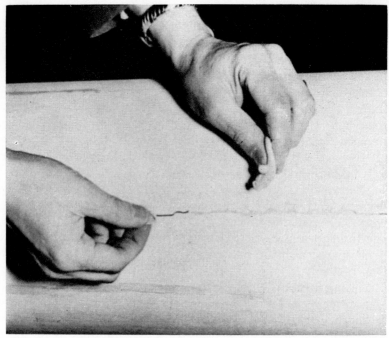

18—14. After the priming coat is dry, fill all nail holes and cracks with a
good caulking compound or putty.

pressing putty into small openings, such as nail holes (Fig.
18-14). For large holes, a putty knife is preferable. It is advisable to fill holes slightly more than full with putty, as there
is some contraction during the drying out of the oil.

The Body Coat, or Second Coat. Additional coats of paint
should never be applied until the undercoats are thoroughly
dry. The weather and the composition of the paint are variable
factors; consequently, it is impossible to give a definite time.
The time of drying usually varies from two or three days to
a week.

The second or body coat should be of the same color as
the finishing coat, and somewhat thicker than the priming
coat. More turpentine and less oil are characteristics of body
coats as compared with priming coats. A paint prepared in
this way will adhere well to the priming coat, and leave a flat
surface that will receive a final coat of gloss paint if desired.

Brushing the paint on the surface as evenly as possible should be the aim in applying the body coat.

The Third or Finishing Coat. A painter always aims to give the required color and good wearing qualities to the finishing coat. For outside service this means that the final coat should be a gloss paint. In order to secure gloss, turpentine is reduced to a minimum in the formula. Linseed oil replaces the turpentine, and adds its binding qualities to the final surface of paint.

The third coat of paint should be applied as smoothly as possible, using the brush by the method already described for spreading the priming coat.

House painters usually apply the trimming coat in connection with the finishing coat. Two containers and two brushes at least are required in this case. The trimming paint must be applied very carefully to avoid the possibility of having the two colors run into each other.

The painter should stir his paint frequently, and strain it if necessary to get rid of any chunks and coarse material which are apt to settle to the bottom, and which, if left in the paint, may get into the brush, and be carried to the surface.

Paints for floors and the inside trim of houses often contain a small amount of varnish which makes a harder surface. For outside use a good spar varnish may be mixed with the paint.

Hints and Precautions for Painters. White lead paints are poisonous if taken into the stomach. Dust from lead paints, if inhaled, may get into the throat, and finally into the stomach. There is very little danger, however, if the painter washes his hands before eating, and avoids the use of tobacco while painting. Tobacco which is handled with hands partly smeared with paint is dangerous. There is such a thing as lead poisoning, but it is entirely preventable, and is a very rare disease.

Paints containing turpentine and benzine should not be placed near an open fire, as these solvents are very inflammable.

Ultramarine blue contains sulphur, and should not be mixed with white lead or any other lead pigment.

Turpentine is not recommended for use on the hands in removing paint. Linseed oil will remove paint more easily, and then the hands can be washed with soap and water.

Benzine or kerosene are not good thinners, and should not be substituted for turpentine in paints.

Colored pigments should be added to the paste pigment and oil while the paint is being mixed, rather than to the paint after it has been completely thinned.

Paints are more homogeneous if they are mixed about 24 hours before using. According to some authorities, it is best to mix the drier into paint just before use.

Paints that are not kept in sealed containers become fatty; they will not work smoothly under a brush, and are practically worthless after a short time.

Unless you are an expert paint-manufacturer, you should not use any other drying oil than linseed oil in paints.

Care of Paint Brushes. In order to keep the bristles of a paint brush straight and in good condition, the brush must receive proper care. Paint brushes that are not to be used for some time should be cleaned thoroughly in kerosene. Benzine, gasoline, and turpentine may be used; but, in general, kerosene is the cheapest and most satisfactory cleaner. A brush which has been cleaned in kerosene should be allowed to dry out, or should be placed in turpentine before being used in paint again. If a brush is to be dried out and put away, it is advisable to wash it with hot water and soap, after it has been cleaned in turpentine or kerosene.

Brushes that are to be used in paint again in a few hours may be kept suspended in linseed oil in such a position that the bristles will not curl from the weight of the brush.

Paint and varnish removers, and sometimes amyl or butyl acetate, are good solvents for cleaning brushes that have become partly hardened with paint. These strong solvents will often save a paint brush that at first sight seems to be about ruined. A final cleaning in turpentine or kerosene will leave a brush in a suitable condition for use at a later time.

Care of Painters' Rags. The most important warning that should be given to a young painter is: *take care of the paint-saturated rags.* Many serious fires have occurred because a thoughtless painter forgot to take rags that were partly wet with paint out of the building or to burn them in a furnace.

Paints contain linseed oil or some other drying oil. Heat

is generated by all drying oils during the oxidation process, and oil-soaked cloth will become hot enough to ignite whenever oily rags are thrown into a pile. During the day rags and waste containing even a small amount of linseed oil should be thrown into a special fireproof wastecan. Every particle of waste or rags that painters have used in wiping off paint, or any wood finishing material containing linseed oil or any other drying oil, should be burned or taken outdoors. There is little danger from linseed oil or paint on a piece of cloth or canvas which is stretched so that the air can keep the surface cool. If, however, the same piece of cloth which is full of wet paint be rolled up into a tight wad, there will be slow generation of heat, and fire is apt to appear in time. The careful painter watches for oil-soaked rags, and oil-soaked clothes, and has no trouble from fires caused by spontaneous combustion.

Latex Paints and Their Application.[3] Probably the most outstanding development in paints during the last few years has been latex paints. Their growth and acceptance by the general public have been spectacular.

Just what is a latex paint? It is one made with a vehicle of which the principal ingredient is latex. A latex is the suspension of very small resin particles in water. Thus, latex paints are a type of water-thinned paints. The fact that water is used as the volatile portion of the vehicle is no indication that such paints are cheap and of low quality. In many respects water is ideal because it is odorless, non-toxic, inexpensive, colorless and has an evaporation rate generally suited for brush and roller application.

Because latex paints are alkaline, the range of obtainable colors is somewhat limited as compared to that of oil-based paints. But although such colors as iron blues and chrome greens cannot be used, most colors can be obtained by careful blending and tinting.

The popularity of these paints is probably due to their ease of application, and the fact that no brush line is left. A wall may be touched up after the paint is set without discoloration. The brush, roller, or spray method can be used. The roller technique is an easy way to apply latex paints, and with

---

[3] Fisher, E. M., *What You Should Know About Paints*, Ch. 7, pp. 101-113.

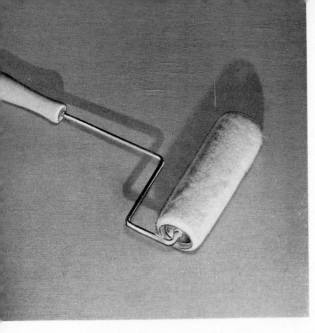

COURTESY
DEVOE AND REYNOLDS CO., INC.
18—15. For roller application of latex paint, select a roller of good quality, preferably one made of lamb's wool.

the use of the double roller some interesting designs can be secured. This roller consists of one fabric-covered roller which picks up the paint from the tray and distributes it over a second plastic roller which carries the design and distributes it on the wall.

18—16. Some helpful accessories for successful roller painting.

PHOTO BY ROBERT C. SMITHERAM, JR.

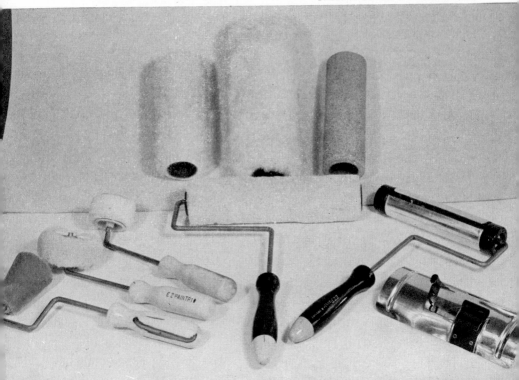

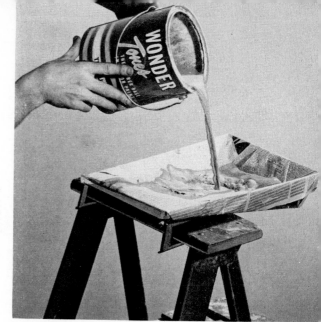

18—17. After lining the tray and fastening it to the stepladder, fill the tray to a point halfway up its slanted surface.

When a single roller is used, the following procedure is suggested:

1. Prepare all surfaces to be painted. Walls should be free of grease, dust or other foreign matter. Wash kitchen and bathroom walls before painting.
2. Have the necessary equipment on hand, such as roller with extension handle, tray, stepladder and brush. The roller should be of good quality, preferably lamb's wool (Fig. 18-15 and 16).

18—18. Load the roller by rolling it into the "shore line" of the paint. Next roll it back and forth on the dry part of the tray until the roller is evenly coated with paint.

357

COURTESY
DEVOE AND REYNOLDS CO., INC.
18—19. Paint walls by making the first stroke upward. Next move down without lifting roller.

3. Line the tray with aluminum foil or waxed paper to facilitate quick changes of colors.
4. Hook the legs of the tray on the stepladder and fill the paint tray to a point halfway up its slanted surface (Fig. 18-17), page 357.
5. With a brush or special corner roller, trim along the edges of the ceiling, walls, floor, and woodwork. Do not trim the edges of more than one wall at a time. By the time you

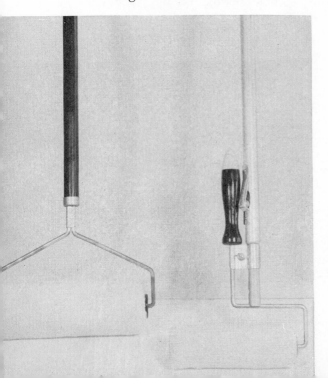

COURTESY
DEVOE AND REYNOLDS CO., INC.
18—20. To make painting of ceilings and floors less tiresome, fasten an extension handle to the roller.

358

18—21. To clean a roller that has been used in oil paint, place it in a closed jar, partly filled with turpentine or paint thinner. Shake well, remove from jar and allow to dry.

reach some of this edge work, it will be so dry that some "shading" will show.

6. Load the roller by rolling it into the "shore line" of the paint in the tray. Move the roller back and forth on the dry part of the tray until it is evenly coated with paint (Fig. 18-18), page 357.

7. Roll the paint on the ceiling with a light back-and-forth motion in any direction. Paint across the narrowest dimension of ceilings in strips not more than two feet wide. For easier application use a long extension handle.

8. Paint walls by making the first stroke upward (Fig. 18-19). Next move down without lifting the roller at the end of the stroke.

9. Paint floors like ceilings. Use an extension handle on the roller to make the work less tiresome (Fig. 18-20).

10. When all painting is completed, clean tray, brushes, and roller thoroughly in water and soap.

    (After using oil paint, first squeeze the excess paint from the roller. Next place the roller in a jar, partly filled with turpentine or paint thinner (Fig. 18-21). Shake well until clean.)

11. When the roller is thoroughly dry, store it in a plastic container to keep it fresh and clean.

Advantages and Disadvantages of Latex Paints. Like all

PHOTO BY ROBERT C. SMITHERAM, JR.

18—22. Before starting your paint job, examine the various brushes at your local paint store.

products, latex water emulsion paints have certain functional advantages and some disadvantages. Some of the *advantages* are:

1. They are practically odorless. A room painted in the morning can be occupied that same evening.
2. They are easy to apply, with brush, roller, or spray gun. The amateur painter can do a professional looking job.
3. They dry fast. Within an hour a surface is dry enough to touch without leaving marks.
4. They are washable after proper curing.
5. Tools are readily cleaned in lukewarm water.
6. In general, they produce a good appearance in one coat, although two coats are usually recommended.
7. Without the use of a primer, they can be directly applied on new dry-wall construction.

Some *disadvantages:*

1. They have poor adhesion to smooth surfaces such as a semi-gloss or gloss paint already on walls.

360

2. They may cause white streaks and mottled effects because of dampness. The emulsifying agents, preservatives, and alkali salts of the paint may come to the surface of damp walls, showing up in the form of streaks. However, the same conditions would ruin oil paint!

3. The presence of casein or soya protein in *some* latex paints may cause a breakdown of the paint film, especially under damp conditions.

4. They are likely to change viscosity in the can during storage, unless they are properly stabilized.

5. Because of the alkali in latex paints, the range of colors is limited to the use of those pigments which are resistant to alkali.

6. They tend to foam badly under excessive agitation, even though they contain anti-foaming agents.

7. The cost of latex paints is still somewhat higher than that of oleoresinous paints.

8. They are made with water as the principal solvent and will freeze at low temperatures.

9. The alkaline content and general composition of latex paints are such that they should not be directly applied to metal. All metal surfaces should first be given a high quality metal primer.

10. Latex sours after being thinned, if left in any container for longer than a few days.

Some Simple Hints for More Successful Painting. For the amateur, painting can be an interesting and satisfying experience. But as in many other occupations, success often depends upon following some of the basic rules of the trade. For example, the proper cleaning of surfaces to be painted is often neglected. Then, when the completed paint job does not stand up, the blame is often placed upon the manufacturer's product when actually the improper surface preparation is at fault.

Selecting Proper Colors. Whether it is an inside or an outside paint job the painter should have the colors clearly in mind. Paint dealers can be most helpful in this respect. Take advantage of their experience. Also look at the color schemes found in some of your friends' homes, model homes, home magazines, and model rooms in furniture stores. In your selection of colors keep in mind the following points:

1. Since the colors of rugs, carpets, or linoleum are fixed, have all other colors harmonize with them.
2. If the room is light and sunny, it will stand more color variations than a room with shady exposure.
3. Blue and blue-green colors make rooms seem larger; yellow colors give a sunlit feeling; pinks are warm and cheerful; greens are restful and relaxing; blues are more formal and dignified, and whites are clean and sanitary.

Painting the Wooden Exterior of Your Home. For the painting of the exterior of your home, have the following materials and equipment on hand:

> Primer and pure, prepared paint.
> Turpentine or paint thinner.
> One large (4″) and one small (2″) brush (Fig. 18-22), page 360.
> One dusting brush. This can be an old but clean paintbrush.
> Sandpaper, No. 1/2.
> Wire brush or scraper.
> Putty knife.
> Cleaning rags.
> Drop cloth or canvas.
> Two sturdy ladders—one long, one short—except for "ranch"-type, low-roofed structures.
> Two-gallon bucket and hook.
> Paint roller and tray.

18—23. Mix your paint properly. First pour off the liquid from the top of the can into a clean container. Mix the remaining heavy portion thoroughly with a wide paddle. Gradually pour the oil back in, stirring all the time. Your dealer can shake the paint for you *only if it is fresh.*
18—24. In painting clapboard or siding, coat the underside or edge of the board first.

COURTESY LOWE BROTHERS CO.

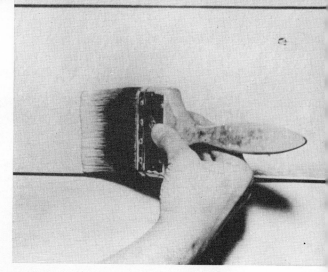

18—25. Paint the broad side of the board next and finish in smooth, horizontal strokes.

Depending upon the condition of your house, proceed as follows:

1. Remove all loose paint with scraper or wire brush. Sand.
2. Dust all surfaces before applying paint.
3. Remove all window screens and paint them separately.
4. Cover shrubbery close to the walls with a canvas or drop cloth.
5. Select a moderately cool, dry day to paint, and work in the shade as much as possible.
6. Mix the prepared primer paint thoroughly (Fig. 18-23).
7. On siding, apply the paint on the underside or edge of the board first (Fig. 18-24). Paint the broad side of the board next (Fig. 18-25).
8. Hang the paint can on a hook; fasten the tray on a convenient rung of the ladder so both hands are free.
9. Start to work at the top, working down (Fig. 18-26), page 364.
10. Allow the primer coat to dry for two or three days.
11. Fill cracks and nail holes with putty or caulking compound; smooth with sandpaper. Clean the surface.
12. Apply the second coat of paint, avoiding sags and runs.
13. Clean the brushes at the end of the day; burn oily paint rags.

Painting Your Stucco Home. Stucco homes are successfully painted with latex exterior paints. Unless the texture of the wall is too rough, roller application is suggested. It is very important for all surfaces to be clean and firm. A firm surface is one which will stand the weight of additional paint without

COURTESY LOWE BROTHERS CO.

18—26. Start painting at the top and work down. You may find it convenient to do the trim on gables at the same time as you do the siding.

flaking and peeling. Have on hand the following materials and equipment:

Exterior crack filler.
Exterior latex (water-base) paint.
Roller coater with extra covers; also tray.
One four-inch nylon brush.
Stiff wire brush and scraper.
Paint cloths.
Drop cloths for shrubbery.
Ladders (2).
Piece of coarse sanding paper to be placed in the bottom of the tray for easier turning of the roller.

Proceed as follows:

1. Wash the walls with a garden hose. Scrub any dirty spots

with a stiff brush and wash next with the hose (Fig. 18-27).

2. Wherever the surface flakes, peels, or powders, it must be removed by wire brushing. If this is a big job, it may pay you to rent a power tool with an attachable wire brush.
3. Surfaces previously painted with calcimine or bonding cement must be thoroughly cleaned by wire brushing before painting with latex paint.
4. Fill all cracks and holes with exterior crack filler; allow them time to dry before painting.
5. Plan your work so that you can finish one wall at a session.
6. Protect shrubs by covering them with a drop cloth.
   NOTE: It is highly recommended to apply a coat of sealer on old, cleaned walls. Ask your paint dealer what type of sealer to use. Apply this coat between steps 6 and 7.
7. Dampen the wall with the garden hose just before painting. *If two coats of paint are applied, do not dampen between coats.*
8. Start from the top and work down. The underside of eaves may be painted with latex, using the four-inch brush.
9. Look back over your work and see whether any spots have been missed. Touch up these spots.
10. Clean all tools with soap and water. Rinse with clear water.

Painting Window Sash and Trim. After the walls have been painted, you are now ready to start with windows, doors, and trim. This painting has to be done carefully, so allow yourself sufficient time. In addition to the tools previously used, secure some high-grade sash brushes. (A piece of stiff cardboard or

COURTESY LOWE BROTHERS CO.

18—27. Before painting brick, remove all loose mortar and wire-brush thoroughly to get rid of dust and dirt.

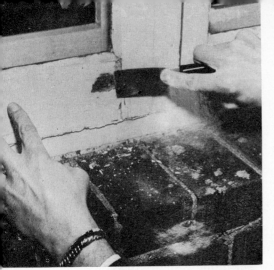

18—28. Remove heavy, cracked layers of paint with a putty knife. On large areas use an electric paint remover or blowtorch. 18—29. Remove all loose putty with a putty knife.

metal guide will keep paint off the walls.)

Proceed as follows when painting sash and trim:

1. Dust all surfaces to be painted. Remove dirt and grease with soapy water or a commercial cleaner.
2. Remove cracked layers of paint and any loose putty from the sash (Fig. 18-28 and 29). Before replacing the putty, apply a little priming paint (Fig. 18-30). This will prevent the bare wood from absorbing the oil in the putty. Putty that dries without sufficient oil turns into a chalky powder and falls out in a short time.
3. Remove rust scales from metal sash with a wire brush or sandpaper.
4. Carefully re-putty all sash (Fig. 18-31).
5. When painting a window sash with cross-pieces, start in the center and paint the top, sides, and the bottom in that order.
6. Use a piece of cardboard or metal guide to keep paint from the walls.
7. Clean all tools at the close of a work session, using turpentine or paint thinner.

Painting Roofs, Gutters, and Drain Spouts. Depending upon the size and shape of the roof, this job may better be done by a professional painter. He has the necessary equip-

366

ment to do the work safely. To paint the roofs of smaller homes and garages, you will probably need the following:

Shingle finish for shingled roofs.
Roofing cement to repair leaks.
Roof coating for tarred roofs.
Red lead for metal priming.

You should, of course, have on hand most of the other items, such as a putty knife, sandpaper, paint thinner, and sturdy ladders.

When doing this type of work, you may profit by the following points:

1. Start work when the roof is thoroughly dry and the forecast is for continued dry weather.
2. Clean the roof thoroughly. Use an ordinary kitchen broom.
3. Clean out gutters and drain spouts. Remove rust with a wire brush and sandpaper (Fig. 18-32), page 368.
4. Apply shingle finish with an inexpensive 6 or 7 inch calcimine brush, working from the top of the roof on down.
5. Metal drains and gutters that are in poor condition should be given a coat of red lead, to be followed by a coat of pure prepared paint (Fig. 18-33), page 368.
6. On composition and tarred roofs apply a recommended roof coating.

18—30. Never put new putty on bare wood. Apply a coat of priming paint first. If this is not done, the wood will absorb the oil in the putty, leaving the putty as a chalky, powdery substance. 18—31. When the priming paint is dry, apply the new putty before proceeding with the finish coat.

COURTESY LOWE BROTHERS CO.

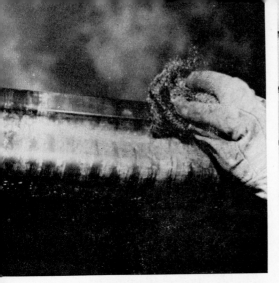

18—32. Before painting metal surfaces, remove all rust and scale with steel wool and wire brush. 18—33. If new galvanized metal must be painted at once, wash thoroughly with vinegar before painting. For best results, let galvanized surfaces weather for at least six months.

7. Use roofing cement to repair breaks in the roof, leaks around skylights, and in valleys. Next seal with roof-coating.

Painting the Interior of Your Home. Before any actual interior painting is done, you should have decided, of course, on the color combinations to be used in the various rooms. If you are in doubt as to what colors are most suitable, consult an interior decorator. Although this service may cost something, it probably will prove money well spent. Many furniture stores have interior decorators on their staff for free consultation.

Painting the interior of your home is best done by painting each room in the following order:

1. Paint the ceiling.
2. Paint the walls.
3. Paint the woodwork and
4. Finish the floors.

When painting ceilings, follow this procedure:

1. Move all the furniture out of the room. If it cannot be moved, cover all pieces carefully (Fig. 18-34).

368

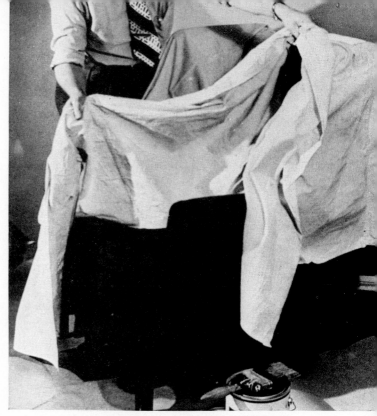

18—34. Protect heavy pieces of furniture by covering them with drop cloths or paper covers.

2. Remove all curtains, drapes, and Venetian blinds.
3. Cover the entire floor with drop cloths or newspapers.
4. Give the ceiling a thorough dusting.
5. With a scraper, remove any loose paint and blisters.
6. Fill all cracks with crack filler (Fig. 18-35).

18—35. Carefully fill all holes and cracks with crack filler. Build up beyond the surface of the ceiling and sand flush when dry.

369

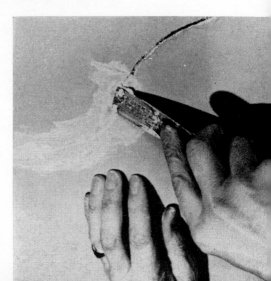

COURTESY LOWE BROTHERS CO.

18—36. To reach ceilings and upper wall surfaces, stretch a 2″ plank
between a stepladder and a low stool.

PHOTO BY ROBERT C. SMITHERAM, JR.

18—37. For ceilings, walls and floors select the proper brushes.

7. If the ceiling was previously painted with a latex paint, you can paint right over it. An old coat of calcimine can be washed off with warm water.
8. Do your painting in such a way that a good-sized area can be covered without continually moving the equipment around. Working from a 2″ x 10″ plank, supported by a saw-horse and ladder of proper height, will prove less fatiguing than by working from just a stepladder (Fig. 18-36). If the ceiling is smooth, you can paint it directly from the floor with the use of a long-handled roller. Select the proper brushes for a brush job (Fig. 18-37).
9. Clean your tools.

Painting walls also requires such preliminaries as dusting, washing off grease and dirt, removing loose paint, and filling cracks (Fig. 18-38). Also remove switch plates, registers, and ventilating grills (Fig. 18-39). Start painting in an upper left-hand corner of the wall. Work in horizontal stretches two or three feet wide from ceiling to floor. When using a roller, first

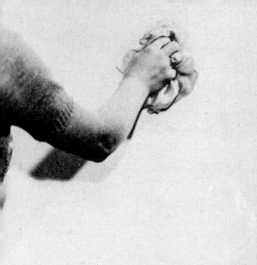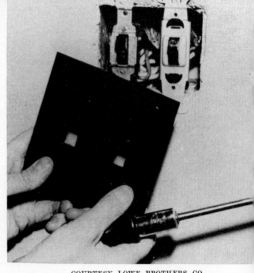

18—38. Dust all walls with a lint-free cloth moistened with mineral spirits. Remove grease spots with soap and water. 18—39. Remove switch plates for easier and neater painting. Also remove registers and ventilating grills.

paint a narrow band with a brush next to the ceiling and flow the paint into this band with the roller. If the walls were previously painted with calcimine, wash them down with water. Remove any flakes, scales, and loose parts by careful brushing and scraping.

When painting the bathroom and kitchen, select paints or enamels that stand up well under washing. Kitchen walls and ceilings collect dirt more readily than any other walls and ceilings in the house. By using the proper paint or enamel they can be washed down to make them look like new.

Complete the following preliminaries before painting your kitchen and bathroom:

1. Take down curtains, pictures, knicknacks and anything else on the walls.
2. Cover the range, refrigerator, and all other fixed appliances with drop cloths. Also cover the floor completely with drop cloths or old newspapers.
3. Remove cabinet and drawer handles for easier painting.
4. Remove all drawers and paint them separately.

5. Wash walls, ceiling, and woodwork thoroughly. This may well prove to be the hardest part of your paint job.
6. Fill any cracks with crack filler. Sand lightly when dry.

With walls, ceilings, and woodwork completed, the one remaining job is to finish the floors. New hardwood maple floors can be finished in a number of way such as:

1. Sand and wax.
2. Sand, shellac, and wax.
3. Sand, shellac, varnish, and wax.

Since oak is an open-grained wood, oak floors must be filled with paste filler. Filling may be done immediately after the floors are sanded or after a first coat of shellac has been applied. Old hardwood floors first should be thoroughly cleaned. The use of a commercially prepared floor cleaner is recommended. Some sanding out of stubborn spots may be necessary. If the floor was previously stained, light spots may be made to match with stain of the right color. Before applying the first coat of shellac, thin it down to proper brushing consistency with de-natured alcohol. When the floor is thoroughly dry, wax it with either a paste or liquid wax. Polish to a high luster with a mechanical polisher.

The procedure for painting floors is much like painting woodwork. A good grade of floor enamel is recommended.

Floors covered with linoleum should first be cleaned and next waxed. One or two coats of a high-grade floor varnish may be applied for a more durable finish.

Cement floors can be attractively painted with porch or deck paints. These paints can be applied by either brush or roller.

In closing this discussion on hints for more successful paint-ing, let us restate the three points which are the most im-portant:

1. Clean all surfaces properly. No paint will stick to grease or dirt.
2. Consult your dealer when buying paints. Follow his advice as well as the directions on the label.
3. Carefully clean all tools after each work session. A good painter is known by the way he keeps his tools.

SELECTED REFERENCES, CHAPTER XVIII

Paints and Painting

Architectural Record, "New Paint Products for Interior and Exterior Walls," 111, page 268, May, 1952.

Burr, W. W. and Matvey, P. R., "Latex, the Latest Development in Emulsion Paints," *Paint, Oil and Chemical Review,* 113, pp. 8-10, April 27, 1950.

Consumer Research Bulletin, "Caring for Paint Brushes," Volume 25, page 17, May, 1950.

Fisher, E. M., *What You Should Know about Paint.* National Painters Magazine, New York City, N.Y., 1952; 184 pages.

Larson, L. P. and Calbeck, J. H., "Comparison of Pre- and Post-war White Outside House Paint," *Paint, Oil and Chemical Review,* 112, pp. 25-26, June 9, 1949.

Lowe Brothers Company, *The How's and Why's of Painting and Decorating,* 38 pp.; Dayton, Ohio, 1954.

Mattiello, Joseph J., *Protective and Decorative Coatings,* "Drying Oils," Chapter I, Volume I, pp. 57-73, 1941.

Ibid., "Rubber Condensation Derivatives in Paint," Chapter XVIII-A, pp. 447-458.

Ibid., "Paint Driers," Chapter XXII, pp. 499-536.

Ibid., "Terpene Solvents," Chapter XXIII, pp. 537-573.

Ibid., "Petroleum Thinners of Ordinary Types," Chapter XXIV, pp. 573-595.

Ibid., "High-Solvency Naphthas," Chapter XXV, pp. 596-624.

Mechanical Engineering, "Rubberized Paint," 73, page 509, June, 1951.

McGee, R. A., and Brown, A. G., *Instruction Units in Woodfinishing,* "To Apply Outside Paint," Chapter VIII, pp. 56-62, 1950.

"Mildew Prevention, New Studies on Cause and Cure of Fungi," *National Painters Magazine,* 15, pp. 16-17, Aug. 1948.

National Lead Company, *Handbook on Painting,* 1946.

Snell, C. T., "Formulation of Paint Removers," Chemical Industries, 64, page 414, March, 1949.

Soderberg, G. A., *Finishing Materials and Methods,* Chapters V, VI, VII, VIII, and IX, pp. 42-81.

Chapter XIX

Lacquers—History, Uses, and Composition

Brief History of Lacquers. Few persons comprehend just what lacquer is, because the term has been used for at least three finishing materials of quite different composition. Sometimes the word is used in referring to certain varnishlike materials used in the celebrated and much admired lustrous finishes that for many years have been used by the workmen of Japan and China, and to lesser extent of Ceylon, India, and Burma.

During many centuries, at least as far back as 500 to 600 B.C. according to some authorities, Chinese and Japanese workmen have probably used these remarkable and beautiful finishes which unquestionably were superior to anything else of their kind in any part of the world. These oriental peoples discovered that a liquid exudation could be taken in spring and summer from a certain lac tree (*Rhus vernicifera*) by making cuts or scarifications, and that this fluid became thick and creamy, and later on changed, becoming darker in color. Several millions of pounds of this raw material usually pass annually through the Chinese city of Hankow, the greater part being shipped to Japan where it is known as "*Ki-urushi.*" At first when the sappy exudation comes from the trees it is of a gray-brown color and is somewhat viscous and sticky, or mucilaginous in consistency; but finally, after exposure to the air, it turns practically black, being coated over with a rather tough and thick covering.

Oriental lacquers dry by oxidation, like oil varnishes, being entirely dissimilar from nitrocellulose lacquers, which dry by evaporation. Tung oil or perilla oil is sometimes mixed with the natural lacquers from the trees, but these drying oils are not necessary and are regarded as adulterants. More body is added to the Chinese lacquers, according to one writer, by the addition of 30 grams of Roman vitriol and 40 grams of pig's gall to each kilogram of lacquer. Sabin, in his interesting and detailed description of Chinese and Japanese lacquers, also mentions the use of Roman vitriol and hog's gall in compounding Chinese lacquers.

The Japanese make their lacquer from the same gum or resinous material that is used by the Chinese. In Japan the lacquer is thinned with camphor which is thought to be the only proper thinner for making it more fluid. Some authorities think that the Japanese lacquer films or coatings are more durable than finishes made from any of our best resins. Their durability is undoubtedly greater because they are nearly always applied over a wood of exceptional hardness, called *teak*, which shrinks and warps very little, and does not often check or crack. The lacquering fluid originally is nearly clear, but films after being spread and exposed to the air at first turn to a reddish color and finally change to a rich black. The hardness of such films increases with time. Finishes made from them have a brilliant and permanent luster which is unchangeable with weather conditions. The oriental lacquers are also said to be impervious to varnish removers and other solvents.

An interesting peculiarity of Japanese lacquer made from the Rhus tree is that it hardens properly only in a moist atmosphere. If exposed to heat and sunlight, it remains in a tacky condition instead of drying properly. Oxidation takes place during the drying of a film, and sometimes as much as 5¾ per cent of weight may be added during the drying process at ordinary temperature.

The black lacquer or *"thitsi"* of Burma is made in a manner somewhat similar to that used in compounding the famous Japanese lacquer; but in this case the gumlike material comes from a different tree, the *Melanorrhea usitata*. The black lacquer of Burma is slower in drying than the Japanese lacquer.

The lacquer commonly used in Europe and the United States before World War I was simply a spirit varnish. It was often largely shellac, which takes its name from lac or "lakh." In the dictionaries or textbooks written years ago, lacquer was said to be a shellac or spirit varnish. These so-called lacquers were made in large quantities in both clear and colored solutions and were used sometimes on wood, but much more often on metals, such as brass especially, to prevent tarnishing and to give a soft pleasing luster.

Other spirit soluble gums, such as sandarac and elemi, were often added to the mixture of shellac and alcohol in compounding the lacquer. Spirit soluble vegetable dyes were formerly used in these spirit varnish lacquers, but coal-tar dyes gradually replaced them as dyestuffs in colored lacquers. Lacquers of this type were very thin, and had little body; consequently, a very large number of applications was necessary. These early lacquers were quite satisfactory and durable, and could be made to adhere more firmly to metalwork when baked on at temperatures under 115° C., which is the melting point of shellac. Lower temperatures than the melting point will soften and fuse the shellac gum very firmly to the metal.

The oriental lacquers as well as the spirit varnish or shellac lacquers, just described, are really varnishes, and not lacquers, in the sense that the word is now used in the United States. The metal trades for a number of years have been trying a new type of lacquer for a very tough, hard finish. This finishing material was manufactured in the form of clear lacquer, and also in pigmented compounds, sometimes called lacquer enamels. It was necessary to make this material very thin in order to apply it at all, which resulted in very thin films and many coats. It was not satisfactory in the early forms for finishing wood, because it did not adhere properly and soon peeled or scaled off.

The body material or solid content of these early metal lacquers consisted largely of pyroxylin, or high-viscosity nitrocellulose of a nonexplosive form. When large amounts of nitrocellulose were contained in the lacquer it became viscous and heavy and could not be spread evenly over a surface; consequently much reducer or thinner was added, and the film was so thin that it was often necessary to apply as many as 15 to 20 coats.

Chemists have since discovered that various varnish resins can be dissolved in solvents and incorporated in low viscosity nitrocellulose mixtures, and this discovery brought to the market a new type of finishing material for automobiles and furniture, especially, which we now call lacquer. Varnish resins add greatly to the body or thickness of the film. At the present time in the United States the term lacquer finish, when used in connection with automobiles and furniture, usually refers to this new type of finish made from nitrocellulose and varnish gums with various other substances in a highly complex mixture. These new nitrocellulose lacquers which include resins in their composition are somewhat similar to varnish in the thickness of the films that can be obtained from them. Relatively few coats of our latest nitrocellulose-resin type of lacquer are required, on account of the large amount of solid material contained in the mixture and the thickness of each layer or film after it has dried on a surface.

Another type of quick-drying finish called "varnish lacquer" has been produced. This lacquer dries more slowly than nitrocellulose compounds, but contains a specially treated varnish containing vegetable oils which act as ultra-violet-ray filters for sunlight, and add a plasticity similar to that of oil varnishes.

The term *lacquer* has gradually come to refer to a very quick-drying varnishlike finish which dries to great hardness. The term itself does not positively indicate any special composition.

Uses for Lacquers. Almost all of the large paint and varnish manufacturers in the United States are now making lacquers, which in some cases are being unwisely advertised as suitable for nearly all purposes. In the hands of a skilled finisher they produce satisfactory effects; but when a novice attempts to spread them with a brush over newly varnished surfaces, there is sure to be trouble because the solvents in the lacquer are similar to those contained in some of the paint and varnish removers, and the newly applied coating reacts with the old, resulting in a spoiled finish. If a varnished or enameled surface is old, hard, and well preserved, a lacquer finish may adhere satisfactorily soon after it is applied; but, later on, checking is apt to occur. Lacquer finishes have certain limitations, and cannot be used over other finishes indiscriminately with assurance of success.

Lacquer finishes are rapidly growing in popularity, and when used properly by one who understands them and their limitations they are attractive and durable and possess many good qualities. Lacquers of various kinds are used extensively on metalwork, particularly building hardware, electric-light fixtures, metal spinning and stamping objects, and often for toys, artwork, and even jewelry. Lacquers are also satisfactorily used on high-grade furniture. Pigmented lacquers are used on electric-light fixtures, novelties, and machinery, and also almost universally on automobiles.

Composition of Nitrocellulose Lacquers. Clear or transparent lacquers contain five types of ingredients, while pigmented lacquers, which are often called lacquer enamels, contain six types, the names of which are as follows: (1) nitrocellulose or pyroxylin, (2) compatible varnish resins and alkyd types, (3) solvents, (4) plasticizers and softeners, and (5) diluents or thinners. Lacquer enamels must give obscuration or hiding power, and to give this opacity various kinds of pigments and coloring matter are added to the lacquer. Pigments and coloring matter may therefore be considered as the sixth type of ingredient found in lacquers.

Nitrocellulose, Soluble Cotton, or Pyroxylin. The distinctive ingredient in a modern lacquer that makes it quite different in behavior from other varnishlike materials, is given various names, such as nitrocellulose, cellulose nitrate, soluble cotton, and pyroxylin. The words nitrocellulose and nitrocotton mean that the substance is made of cellulose or cotton that has been nitrated. Cotton is one of the purest forms of cellulose fibers, and is the chief source of raw material from which nitrocellulose is manufactured. Long-fibered cotton which is valuable for making cotton cloth is usually too expensive for nitrating; therefore the short-fibered material, called "cotton linters," is generally used.

In the factories the cotton gin removes the long-fibered cotton from the linters, hull fibers, dirt, and other impurities. The linters are separated from the waste material by boiling, chemical treatment, bleaching, washing, and drying, and are then nitrated through treatment with a mixture of nitric and sulphuric acids. The particular function of the sulphuric acid is to remove the moisture from the cotton fibers during the nitrating process.

The amount of nitrogen given to the cotton is very carefully controlled, and depends upon the use for which the nitrocellulose is intended. The nitrogen content of nitrocellulose used in lacquer varies from 11.5 to 12.4 per cent, with a viscosity of a half-second up to about 80 seconds. Nitrocellulose having between 12.5 to 13.5 per cent of nitrogen is called gun cotton, being used in the manufacture of smokeless powder and various explosives.

Nitrocellulose for use in making lacquer is made wet with denatured alcohol, in order to remove traces of water, and then dried out to a 30 per cent alcohol content mixture, which is not explosive though inflammable. The gun cotton type of nitrocellulose, having between 12.5 to 13.5 per cent by weight of nitrogen, is very explosive when dry, and is soluble only in acetone, while the nitrocelluloses which contain a lower amount of nitrogen are easily soluble in a mixture of anhydrous ethyl alcohol, anhydrous ethyl acetate, and other well-known solvents.

The viscosity of the early types of nitrocellulose used in making lacquers for metal was relatively high, and the amount of solvents and thinners were great in proportion, the result being a very thin film when the mixture was applied. The lacquers of the present day usually contain a nitrocellulose of rather low viscosity ($\frac{1}{2}$ second), and certain resins which, when combined, produce a film that is much like a varnish in body or solid matter.

Varnish Resins Used in Lacquers. The presence of resins in the mixture is the distinctive and probably the most important feature of modern lacquers, especially those made for wood. The latter type usually contains a higher proportion of resins to nitrocellulose than is ordinarily found in lacquers for automobiles. Wood lacquers are, consequently, more like varnishes on account of their greater solid content and the thicker films that can be spread with them. Lacquer finishes containing resins can be rubbed like coats of oil varnish, because they have gums in their composition. Resins are valuable in a lacquer for another reason besides increasing the solid content, namely, because they increase the power of the film to adhere to the surfaces to which they have been applied. The resins selected for lacquers are generally cheaper than nitrocellulose, and this is also an important factor, because it reduces the cost of the mixture per gallon.

Some of the resins, such as mastic and sandarac, have very

poor adhesive powers, and produce soft films when used in a nitrocellulose lacquer mixture; therefore, they are unsatisfactory. Other well known varnish resins seem to give increased adhesive properties. Resins that increase adhesive qualities of lacquer are: shellac, rosin, thus, elemi, pontianak, congo, and zanzibar. The selection of resins for a lacquer mixture depends upon other properties, among them being solubility in the same solvents that have been found best for dissolving the nitrocellulose itself.

Anhydrous ethyl or grain alcohol will dissolve many kinds of varnish resins, and the solutions will blend well with nitrocellulose solutions of the same solvent. Another good solvent for nitrocellulose, called anhydrous ethyl acetate, is a good solvent also for such gums as rosin, thus ester gums, and cumar. If anhydrous ethyl alcohol, in quantities varying from 5 to 30 per cent, is added to the solution of anhydrous ethyl acetate, the mixture will dissolve such gums as elemi, dammar, and shellac. Other resins such as sandarac, kauri, pontianak, and manila gum, are soluble in part; while such hard copals as congo and zanzibar are not soluble in the mixture of the two solvents, but are at least partly soluble in the anhydrous ethyl alcohol alone.

The resins now commonly used in lacquers are synthetic or chemically prepared ester gum (a chemical combination of rosin with glycerine), a resin from the rosin group, dammar, and shellac. A certain amount of waxy residue must be removed from alcoholic solutions of dammar and shellac before these resins in their solvents can be blended into the lacquer mixture. Sometimes a lacquer of heavy body is desired, and such gums as dammar, kauri, shellac, and synthetic ester gums are used in amounts which nearly equal the quantity of nitrocellulose itself. Automobile lacquers, however, often contain only one half the quantity by weight of resin compared with nitrocellulose.

The density and strength of lacquer films vary to some extent with the resins or resin incorporated in the lacquer mixture. Such varnish resins as kauri and congo are considered to be excellent for supplying the desirable qualities of hardness and toughness to the film. Both of these gums are, however, less easily soluble in the solvents which are used with nitrocellulose. Unfortunately the best grades of kauri resins are usually high priced. Dammar and other medium soft resins give toughness to lacquer films which remain rather soft. Hardness and brittleness, the latter being an undesirable quality, are imparted by soft resins and especially by rosin.

With these characteristics in mind, many manufacturers use a combination of several resins. The nonsynthetic gums often used in combination are generally selected from the following list: dammar, shellac, kauri, spirit-soluble manila, and congo. Dammar is the nonsynthetic gum most commonly used at present, although for outside service it is seldom incorporated in large amounts in high-grade lacquers. Bleached shellac, although high priced, is sometimes employed as a lacquer-resin because it is said to add hardness and adhesion and produces a fine gloss. Several synthetic gums are manufactured for lacquer making, especially cumar, amberol, beckesite, and ester gum.

From information available, it seems evident that ester gum is employed extensively in manufacturing lacquers. It should be noted, however, that ester gum when used alone produces a chalky lacquer that is somewhat spongy. It is usual, therefore, to add a small amount at least of dammar solution which has been dewaxed, because such a mixture of gums produces a more satisfactory film. Some other resin may be substituted for the dammar, however.

Alkyd Resin.[1] Alkyd resin, a composite of phthalic anhydride and glycerin, is a synthetic resin which is rapidly becoming the most widely used resin in lacquer. Alkyd resins can be modified to classify as drying (oxidizing) and nondrying (nonoxidizing) resins. The drying alkyds are modified with drying oil, such as soybean, linseed, oiticica, and tung oil. Cottonseed oil, coconut oil, stearic acid, rosin, and other resins are used in the modification of a nondrying type. Alkyd resins, when used with nitrocellulose in lacquer, greatly improve the outdoor durability, for it is the most durable resin obtainable for outside exposure.

Solvents for Nitrocellulose and Resins. The best solvents

---

[1] Soderberg, George A., *Finishing Materials and Methods,* Chapter III, pp. 28 and 29.

for lacquers consist of mixtures of various liquids because of the fact that no single fluid is known which is capable of dissolving compounds of nitrocellulose and varnish gums and holding them in proper condition while they are being applied as films or coatings. The selection of proper solvents for use in manufacturing lacquer is of fundamental importance, for the reason that success or failure depends more on the solvents than on the selection of any particular varnish resin or other detail of composition. From the user's standpoint it is very desirable that no objectionable odor such as that given off by fusel oil shall come from the solvents chosen. On account of the fundamental differences in the methods of drying of lacquer and varnish—lacquer drying by evaporation, and varnish by both evaporation and oxidation—the solvent, or rather the mixture of solvents with plasticizers and softeners, must dry slowly enough to enable the lacquer to be applied successfully.

Keeping qualities and stability of chemical composition while the lacquer is in cans in the liquid state are also necessary; therefore the solvents must not slowly decompose. The price of lacquers would be practically prohibitive were it not for the fact that solvents are selected that can be used in the same mixture with cheap hydrocarbon diluents, such as benzene, toluene, and xylene, which serve the double purpose of improving the flowing or leveling qualities of lacquer during its application, and reducing its cost per gallon when used as thinners.

An understandable and simple classification of lacquer solvents seems to be difficult to make. Various methods have been suggested. A physical classification resulting from grouping the different solvents and diluents or thinners according to their boiling points has recently been suggested, and seems to be more comprehensible than any chemical classification which has yet been offered. Hydrocarbons, such as benzene, toluene, and xylene, are often listed among lacquer solvents because they are solvents for many resins, especially those used in lacquers. These hydrocarbons are not solvents of nitrocellulose, and cannot be used in large amounts without a tendency to gel or coagulate the clear solution of nitrocellulose, thus producing a cloudy mixture.

The term solvent in the lacquer industry is now often used

in a rather restricted and special sense. Liquids that have the power within themselves to dissolve nitrocotton or nitrocellulose are frequently called solvents or active solvents. Among the most used of the active lacquer solvents are certain organic esters, such as amyl acetate, butyl acetate, ethyl acetate, and butyl propionate. From the various alcohols, such as methyl, ethyl, amyl, butyl, and propyl, a number of valuable esters are now manufactured, some in large quantities and at a very moderate price, particularly butyl acetate. All of the acetates are said to be nitrocellulose solvents. The acetates furnish several excellent solvents, while others are usually found among the formates, propionates, lactates, carbonates, oxalates, and ketones, the last named furnishing acetone, methyl ethyl ketone.

In the lacquer industry the term nonsolvents is usually given to those liquids used as a solvent for varnish resins, and that become solvents for nitrocellulose by the addition of some other liquid. These so-called nonsolvents or inactive solvents, such as amyl alcohol, butyl alcohol, ethyl alcohol, and even methyl alcohol to a rather limited extent, can usually be made into active solvents for nitrocellulose in various degrees of strength by the addition of an active solvent. The chief function of lacquer nonsolvent liquids is to dissolve the varnish gums or resins which are used in various proportions to give adherence, body, and luster to the lacquer films. Nonsolvents are cheaper, in general, than true nitrocellulose solvents; consequently they help in reducing the cost of the materials used.

Some writers classify the active nitrocellulose solvents and nonsolvents or gum solvents in one group, calling all of them solvents; while other authorities place the inactive nonsolvent liquids in a group with the hydrocarbon diluents, which have somewhat similar functions and tend to blend the various mixtures and reduce the cost of the liquids.

Some of the best solvents for lacquers are combinations of solvents, such as ethyl ether and ethyl alcohol. Another excellent mixture for solvents is a combination of ethyl alcohol and ethyl acetate. Various important binary combinations may be used as lacquer solvents, as follows: ester alcohol, ether alcohol, ketone alcohol, ketone ester, ketone ether, and ester ether.

The physical classification of solvents, inactive or nonsolvents, and diluents depending upon boiling points can be outlined as follows:

1. *Low boilers*—distillates which boil and vaporize at temperatures below about 100°.

	Boiling Point in Degrees Centigrade		
Ethyl alcohol (anhydrous)	78.3 to		78.4
Ethyl acetate (anhydrous)	77		
Isopropyl acetate, 95%	85	to	90
Methyl acetate	56	to	57
Ethyl propionate	98	to	102
Isopropyl alcohol	82		
Acetone	57		
Methyl ethyl ketone	77	to	81
Benzene or Benzol	80		
(a hydrocarbon diluent)			

2. *Medium boilers*—distillates which boil and vaporize at about from 108 to 135°.

	Boiling Point in Degrees Centigrade	
Methyl Cellosolve	124	
Diethyl carbonate	125	to 126
Amyl acetate	138	to 142
Amyl alcohol	121	to 139
Butyl acetate	115	to 135
Butyl alcohol	117	
Methyl isobutyl carbinol	130	to 133
Methyl isobutyl ketone	111	to 117
Hydrocarbon diluents:		
Toluene or Toluol	111	
Gasoline or Benzine	93	to 107
Semi-aromatic hydrocarbon	104	to 140

3. *High boilers*—distillates which boil and vaporize at about from 140 to 200°.

	Boiling Point in Degrees Centigrade	
Ethyl butyl ketone	148	
Butyl cellosolve	163	to 172
Ethyl cellosolve	132	to 137
Ethyl lactate	152	to 155
Diacetone alcohol	164	
Hydrocarbon diluents:		
Xylene or Xylol	139	to 141
Semi-aromatic hydrocarbon	110	to 167
V. M. and P. Naphtha	125	to 170

A discussion of the various good and bad properties of these solvents would not be profitable in a book of this type, which is not intended as a guide to manufacturers of lacquer.

Some of the most common solvents, however, may be referred to briefly.

Anhydrous ethyl alcohol (C_2H_5 OH), which is a pure alcohol that does not contain water, is probably the best of all of the inactive lacquer solvents, because, when activated with a small per cent of ethyl acetate, it easily dissolves nitrocellulose and also many of the varnish gums that are likely to be selected for use in lacquers. Ethyl alcohol in the anhydrous form is a much better solvent for nitrocellulose and spirit-soluble resin gums than is the ordinary 95 per cent by volume ethyl or grain alcohol, and it also blends mixtures of the two substances, which are usually dissolved separately, much better than does the less pure alcohol.

Anhydrous alcohol has another advantage; because, when it is used, a larger amount of cheap hydrocarbon diluents such as benzene, toluene, or xylene, can be added to the lacquer. Ethyl alcohol, however, has great water-absorptive powers, and is apt to take moisture from the air and hold it in the film during the evaporation process. The lowering of the activity of the alcohol solvent permits the precipitation of some of the solid components of the lacquer, and this change in solubility causes a discoloration of a film which is known as "*blushing.*"

Ethyl alcohol, even when denatured with active solvents for varnish gums and nitrocellulose, should be used with caution and only in limited amounts. It is commonly used by manufacturers for wetting the nitrocellulose, thus making it safer for handling and shipping. The wood finisher should not thin lacquer with ethyl alcohol unless it is properly mixed with the necessary active solvents and diluents.

Ethyl alcohol is often called a nonsolvent because it will not dissolve nitrocellulose unless activated by having some other liquid introduced into it which has the needed solvent activity.

Anhydrous ethyl acetate ($CH_3COO_2H_5$), an organic ester, which is in a purer form than the 85 per cent ethyl acetate of commerce, is really an active solvent for nitrocellulose, while ethyl alcohol is not; but the former is not so efficient in dissolving varnish resins as is the latter substance. A mixture of the two solvents—anhydrous ethyl alcohol and anhydrous ethyl acetate—seems to produce an excellent fluid for dissolving the solid content or body materials that are required in lacquer. The two solvents just named are commonly used in lacquer, and are known by some as low boiling solvents.

Monoethyl ether of ethylene glycol, sometimes called *Cellosolve*, is a medium to high boiling solvent which boils at 132°-137° C. It has proved to be a superior solvent for nitrocellulose, dissolves gums such as shellac, kauri, sandarac, mastic, elemi, and rosin "E," and is excellent in a lacquer because it enables the mixture to stand a greater dilution with nonsolvent hydrocarbons, such as toluene, than is possible with most other solvents having similar boiling points. Lacquers containing this solvent possess good power for covering and hiding, and show less tendency to cut through the undercoats with a brush after several coats have been applied.

Monoethyl ether of ethylene glycol can also be diluted with gasoline or water. Its ability to absorb water is of advantage to a lacquer because it prevents "blushing" or cloudy effects in drying out. Blushing is the result of precipitation, either of gums or nitrocellulose, when the solvents do not keep them in a satisfactory liquid form. The glycol ethers do not have an unpleasant odor, and are useful in lacquers that are sprayed. This lack of a disagreeable odor is valuable in the finishing room, and especially in rooms in which the woodwork is being refinished, for they can be used again shortly as the lacquer usually dries practically hard within an hour.

The glycol ethers are valuable solvents for use in both spraying and brushing lacquers. One authority reports that it is possible to make brushing lacquers that will spread as well with a brush as paint enamel, if one of the glycol ethers, such as monoethyl ether of ethylene glycol, is used in proper amounts as a solvent.

Diethyl carbonate is an excellent medium-boiling nitrocellulose solvent which improves the flowing qualities of lacquer and has a pleasant odor. The odor of many of the other medium boilers sometimes used is very disagreeable, and their use in spraying lacquers practically necessitates the installation of ventilated hoods. Diethyl carbonate is a stable compound of synthetic production which is a good solvent for nitrocellulose, and also for many of the resins used in lacquers, such as mastic, rosin, ester gums, thus, and cumar. Some gums, including kauri, sandarac, manila and elemi, require the addition of at least 5 to 10 per cent of anhydrous ethyl alcohol to diethyl carbonate solutions before they will dissolve completely. As much as 40 per cent of the two solvents just mentioned must be alcohol in order to dissolve shellac gum.

Congo resins and other hard copals cannot be dissolved in these solvents. Dammar gum leaves a waxy portion which will not dissolve. Unless a small amount of alcohol is used in connection with diethyl carbonate the lacquer solution of gums and nitrocellulose is apt to be too viscous. Lacquers containing diethyl carbonate as one of the solvents cannot be diluted with as much of the cheap hydrocarbon diluents, such as benzene, toluene, or xylene, as they can if a certain amount of ethyl lactate (a commonly used high boiler) is also contained in the mixture of solvents. Diethyl carbonate is excellent, especially in lacquers that are to be used on brass, as it seems to possess superior nontarnishing qualities in connection with this metal.

Butyl alcohol (C_4H_9OH) is a medium boiling gum solvent, which is contained in fusel oil and is separated from it by distillation. It is often manufactured from fermenting corn by special treatment. The boiling point of butyl alcohol is 117°. Like other alcohols, it is an excellent solvent for many varnish resins, but it does not dissolve nitrocellulose, the hard copals, or ester gum. While its solvent action is less than that of the low-boiling anhydrous ethyl alcohol, it helps in forming good solvent mixtures with aromatic hydrocarbons used as diluents and with some of the esters which are often used to dissolve nitrocellulose.

The chief objection to the use of butyl alcohol as a lacquer solvent is its mild but disagreeable, choking odor, which is not as seriously objectionable as formerly because of better methods of manufacture. On account of its cheapness and availability, it is found in many lacquers, usually in a mixture with butyl acetate, an active solvent for nitrocellulose that seems to activate butyl alcohol and make it also an active solvent for nitrocellulose. Butyl alcohol is very valuable, however, because it has a low rate of evaporation, which helps it to flow better and to make a smoother and tougher film.

Butyl acetate, which also has a medium boiling point, is one of the cheapest and most common lacquer solvents that can be obtained. It is a good solvent for nitrocellulose, and will dissolve some of the varnish resins, such as dammar, mastic, elemi, rosin "E," and ester gums. Some of the resins used in lacquers are insoluble in butyl acetate, among which are shellac, sandarac, and zanzibar, which are practically insoluble; and kauri and other copals, which are only slightly soluble when butyl acetate is used alone unmixed with other solvents.

Butyl acetate will stand more dilution in nitrocellulose mixtures with hydrocarbons than will diethyl carbonate, but it is inferior to monoethyl ether of ethylene glycol and ethyl lactate, which have dilution ratios about twice as high when toluene is used as a thinner. Butyl acetate is, however, greatly superior to ethyl acetate and ethyl alcohol in slowness of evaporation. The most serious defects of butyl acetate as a lacquer solvent are its choking, disagreeable odor, its lack of absorptive power for water, and its inability to blend solutions containing resins with those containing nitrocellulose.

Amyl acetate ($CH_3COOC_5H_{11}$), an ester which helped in starting the lacquer industry, is another medium boiling solvent which is made as a small by-product resulting from the manufacture of ethyl alcohol. Amyl acetate is the most important constituent of fusel oil, which is an intermediate product coming from crude ethyl alcohol and is found only in small quantities in this substance; consequently, the supply of amyl acetate is somewhat limited. It is an excellent solvent for nitrocellulose and many of the varnish resins, but it dissolves shellac gum only slightly. It has a very disagreeable and choking odor which tends to limit its use in lacquers. It gives good flowing qualities to lacquer, and allows of even greater dilution with hydrocarbon thinners than will butyl acetate which is frequently used in its place.

Ethyl lactate, a high boiling active solvent, possesses certain of the qualities of an alcohol as well as some of an ester, and for this reason, probably, it has unusual solvent power for nitrocellulose. Its characteristics, similar to those of the alcohols, explain why it will dissolve very completely such gums as shellac, rosin, pontianak, ester gum, and kauri. Although superior to other commonly used ester solvents in its dissolving power for most of the varnish gums, its reaction on congo and dammar resins is slight. It has excellent properties as a blending agent for the two types of solutions, one containing nitrocellulose and the other containing varnish gums.

In addition to these good qualities, ethyl lactate, when contained in a nitrocellulose lacquer, will permit the solution to be thinned with more toluene or other hydrocarbon solvents than is possible with most of the other similar dissolving agents. Its use in a lacquer is also favored because it imparts a high gloss to the film. These good qualities together with its pleasant odor indicate that ethyl lactate will be much used as a high boiling solvent in nitrocellulose lacquers.

Plasticizers and Softeners. Lacquers made from resins and nitrocellulose dissolved in the solvents that are ordinarily used are apt to be much too brittle, lack good adhesion, and will not flow well or become smooth on surfaces after being applied. It is to correct these defects, common to lacquers, and to impart a certain amount of plasticity which will permit a slight expansion and contraction of the film, that plasticizers and softeners are used.

Without plasticizers, lacquers set so rapidly that it is practically impossible to apply them smoothly and evenly, especially with a brush. Very rapid drying or too much moisture in the air is apt to bring about another trouble known as *"blushing,"* a cloudy condition of the film produced by moisture, and the lowering of the temperature because of the rapid evaporation of the volatile solvents. If too much moisture condenses on a film, the nitrocellulose in the lacquer becomes no longer soluble and is precipitated from the solution. "Blushing" is not liable to occur, except when lacquer is applied during very rainy weather, unless the mixture lacks proper plasticizers.

The plasticizers and softeners should be solvents for both nitrocellulose and resins, and they must blend well in lacquer mixtures. This blending of the solution of resins in their solvents, with the mixture of nitrocellulose in its solvents, helps to form a lasting union of the two solutions, and is one of the important functions of plasticizers.

Both plasticizers and softeners differ from solvents in one respect, in that they remain permanently in the varnish-like film after it is spread, while solvents evaporate, leaving little or no residue. The plasticizers have a high boiling point, usually above 300° C.; and, except for the residue left in the film, their characteristics are somewhat similar to those of the high boiling solvents.

The purpose of the softeners in lacquer is to increase the adhesiveness and permanence of the film, and to cause it to be more tough, flexible, and elastic, thus allowing greater freedom for expansion and contraction.

The softeners that have found most favor in the lacquer industry in the past are castor oil, rapeseed oil, and camphor. The two oils, especially castor oil, have been most successful in pyroxylin or nitrocellulose mixtures for use on artificial leathers. While castor oil does soften and improve the flexibility of films made from such compounds, it has poor keeping qualities, and is liable to become rancid after a time. Another objection to the use of these oils in nitrocellulose lacquers is that they are not solvents for the varnish resins which are generally used, nor for the nitrocellulose itself. Castor oil is, however, soluble in alcohol, which is an ingredient of most lacquers.

The ideal softener should possess good stability or aging qualities, and should be a solvent for nitrocellulose and varnish gums; therefore such oils are not entirely satisfactory because they fail to meet these conditions. Camphor, although the standard softener for many pyroxylin compounds, is not entirely satisfactory for use in lacquers on accoount of its great volatility and rather disagreeable odor. When castor oil is contained in lacquers it is found in small quantities only, varying in amount from about one half of one per cent to five or even seven per cent. The amount of camphor used as a softener also varies greatly, but rarely exceeds 25 per cent of the weight of the nitrocellulose in the lacquer. Treated China wood oil, in amounts up to about seven per cent, has also been recommended as a softening agent which will give a lacquer film greater elasticity.

Chemists employed in the lacquer industry have investigated a large number of substances that have been proposed as plasticizers and softeners. At the present time, esters having high boiling points and coming from phosphoric or some of the organic acids are favored, and take the place of both plasticizers and softeners, which are terms often used without any very clear distinction or differentiation in meaning. The important advantages of these high boiling esters over castor oil and camphor are found in greater stability, and in solvent power for nitrocellulose.

The most commonly used esters which are made from phosphoric acid are triphenyl phosphate and tricresyl phosphate. Esters of the organic-acid type, such as those derived from phthalic (thăl'ic) acid, are now widely used as plasticizers and are highly favored by experts. Diamyl phthalate, dibutyl phthalate, and diethyl phthalate are among the best of the present-day plasticizers, and have largely been substituted for castor oil and camphor in the newer types of lacquers. The phthalates seem to be superior to the phosphates, and that diamyl phthalate showed up better in tests than any of the other plasticizers.

The phthalates are derivatives of phthalic acid, a white crystalline compound $(C_8H_6O_4)$ which is produced by the oxidation of naphthalene, a well-known coal-tar product. When synthetic esters, such as the phthalates, are selected as the plasticizers in a lacquer mixture they are often included in amounts up to 50 or 60 per cent and occasionally to 100 per cent by weight of the nitrocellulose content.

The elasticity of varnish films comes from the slowly oxidizing oils which they contain. Old films always check after the oils have become largely oxidized or burned up. Such films are very brittle, for they lack the plastic element which they originally contained. It should be remembered that nitrocellulose lacquers usually contain no oils except those which sometimes function as softeners, and these are not much used at the present time. Nitrocellulose is not used in varnishes, but is an important ingredient in lacquers. Unfortunately, while making a film tough and strong, it does not add a plastic element, such as that given to varnish by linseed oil or China wood oil.

Plasticizers and softeners, then, have important functions in lacquers. Without these substances to add elasticity, lacquers would be unfit for many uses. Even with the best lacquers, there is evidence to indicate that the films are not elastic enough to withstand changes of temperature and great variations in humidity. Especially is this true when they are spread on wood which expands and contracts to a measurable extent, particularly when placed outdoors where it is exposed to the sunlight and weather.

Experience indicates that the best plasticizers and softeners are not entirely effective in eliminating temperature checks which come crosswise of the grain on wood, because the lacquer film varies in size with changes in temperature, while the wood lengthwise of the grain does not change appreciably in dimensions with either changes of temperature or humidity. Lacquer films are also liable to crack *with* the grain of wood, on account of changes of humidity in the atmosphere, and in the wood itself, which shrinks and swells across the grain or in width and thickness, thereby opening up longitudinal checks which do not entirely close after the coating is once ruptured. In their tendency to check, lacquers resemble "short-oil" varnishes, which are also deficient in plastic elements.

Diluents or Thinners. When a thin lacquer having greater fluidity and less body or solid covering material is required, a diluent must be used. A thin lacquer spreads more easily and smoothly under a brush, and is much more satisfactory for ordinary use with a spray gun, than is a thick or viscous lacquer. The reducers or diluents commonly kept in the finishing room for thinning paints, shellac, varnish, and wood filler should not be used. Paints may be diluted with linseed oil and turpentine, shellac with alcohol, varnish with turpentine, and wood filler with turpentine, naphtha, or benzine; but lacquer is a carefully compounded material containing various less well-known solvents which hold the nitrocellulose and varnish gums in solution, and only a few of the cheaper hydrocarbon thinners can be introduced into such a mixture without great damage to the lacquer itself.

It is true that a certain amount of ethyl alcohol varying from 10 to 25 per cent is very frequently used as a solvent in compounding lacquer mixtures; but any further increase in the amount of alcohol is liable to cause trouble, because alcohol is not an active solvent for nitrated lacquer cotton and very readily absorbs moisture from the air. Such an addition of water to a nitrocellulose film is a common cause of "blushing," or the precipitation of a gray or white substance, which ruins the transparency of a clear lacquer, and may change the color of a lacquer enamel. Petroleum naphtha and benzine must not be freely mixed into lacquers because, in excessive amount, they precipitate the nitrocellulose itself and ruin the lacquer completely. Linseed oil seems to prevent proper drying qualities of lacquer films, which remain tacky or sticky for a long time.

The proper thinners for use in lacquers are coal-tar derivatives, including such hydrocarbons as toluene, benzene, and xylene. (Benzene and benzine are different substances chemically, the latter being a petroleum distillate that must not be confused with benzene, which is derived from coal tar.) Such thinners as toluene, benzene, and xylene are cheaper than the solvents which are used for dissolving nitrocellulose and varnish resins, and are solvents for most of the gums commonly incorporated into lacquers.

It has been stated that a mixture of such resins as dammar, shellac, kauri, manila, and congo is very often used in compounding lacquers. Of these resins, dammar is entirely soluble in benzol; shellac gum is almost insoluble in this hydrocarbon solvent; kauri is about 67 per cent soluble; and manila and congo are 60 per cent soluble. Of the other varnish resins sometimes selected for incorporating into lacquers, elemi and mastic are entirely soluble in benzol, while thus, cumar, and ester gums are largely soluble. (Benzol is a mixture of benzene, toluene, and xylene, which often contains 70 per cent of benzene, and from 24 to 27 per cent of toluene, the balance being xylene.)

The amount of benzene, toluene, and xylene that can be added to lacquer mixtures is limited because these hydrocarbons are not solvents for nitrocellulose. These diluents, however, act as blending agents for the two mixtures; one of which is made of solutions of varnish resins in their selected solvents, and the other nitrocellulose in its solvents.

When added in limited quantities, suitable diluents help in keeping the mixed lacquer clear by removal of cloudiness. The user of lacquer should be warned that large quantities of benzene, toluene, or xylene must not be used to thin the mixture, because these hydrocarbons tend to jelly or coagulate the nitrocellulose solution, and may even cause a precipitation of this substance. Benzene, a low boiler having a boiling point of 80° C., can be added to lacquer in larger quantities than can toluene, a medium boiler with a boiling point of 111° C., or xylene, a high boiler which boils at about 143° C. It should be noted, however, that the high boiler, xylene, tends to make a lacquer film dry more slowly because of slower evaporation than that which takes place when toluene is used, and that the latter substance causes slower drying and evaporation than when benzene is the diluent used.

Toluene is considered by many manufacturers the most satisfactory of all of the lacquer diluents. Recently, its use has increased and, according to one writer, toluene is now incorporated into lacquers in amount about equal to that of all other thinners and solvent ingredients combined.

Without diluents lacquers would be so expensive that their use would be very limited. The solvents that are necessary for dissolving nitrocellulose and varnish gums, and for producing solutions that will blend, cost more than those used in an equal amount of enamel, varnish, or shellac; consequently, lacquers cost more than these other finishes. Even though a limited amount of diluents, often varying from 35 to 45 per cent of the total weight of the lacquer, is used in manufacturing these quick-drying finishes, they are more expensive, in general, than varnishes and enamels.

Diluents have no permanent function in lacquer films after the latter are spread, because they soon evaporate, leaving practically no residue in the finish itself.

General Formula for Lacquer. The general formula for nitrocellulose lacquer, Table VII, page 396, gives much information about the ingredients found in lacquers, their special functions, and the amount of each that is used.

Pigments properly prepared are often added to make lacquer enamels. The amount of pigment added varies greatly. A white lacquer enamel might be prepared by adding 32 ounces of zinc oxide to the above mixture. A black lacquer might be made by mixing $3\frac{1}{4}$ to 4 ounces of Super Spectra Black with an equal amount of castor oil and adding to the gallon of lacquer. Even Carbon Black is sometimes used. Colored pigments in amounts varying from 12 to 18 ounces mixed with oil plasticizers may be used in making lacquer enamels. The manufacturers have special equipment for grinding colors for use with lacquers in order to secure fineness and perfect mixture.

While it may be true that a formula for clear lacquers may

seem to be easy to prepare, there are many details of manufacture that are complex, and expensive equipment is needed; consequently the work should be done under the direction of trained and experienced chemists. The preparation of colors for use in lacquer enamels is also a technical process that should be left to factory experts.

TABLE VII.

General Formula for Lacquer

Class of Ingredients	Name of Ingredients	Chemical and General Information	Amount Used	Special Function in Lacquers
	1. *Nitrocellulose.* Two types: S., soluble in alcohol slightly activated. R. S., soluble in esters, especially acetates.[1]	Made from Cotton linters, ½ second viscosity. Regular Soluble. Nitrated with treatment of nitric and sulphuric acid to 11.9% to 12.1%.	Varies from 6 oz. to 32 oz. Usually 8 oz. to 16 oz. per gallon of liquid.	To form a film that is colorless, tough, hard, viscous, and varnishlike, but brittle. To act as a tough, hard binder for the gums. It has functions similar to those of drying oils in oil varnishes.
Solids which remain in the film. (20% to 30% by weight not including pigments.)	2. *Varnish-resins,* or gums—ester gum and dammar, usually; sometimes shellac and rosin, kauri and shellac; occasionally manila gum or pontianak.	Gums used are largely alcohol soluble. Ester gum is a synthetic product. Mixture of two gums, usually, preferred because cheap ester gum makes a chalky film.	Varies from 50% to 200% of weight of nitrocellulose. Many lacquers have weight of gums about equal to weight of nitrocellulose. Spraying-lacquers have less gum.	To increase "body" or solid content, to add adhesiveness, to reduce cost, to produce more gloss, to make rubbing possible.
	3. *Plasticizers.*	High-boiling esters—dibutyl phthalate most common. Other phthalates, tricresyl phosphate, castor oil, and other oils sometimes used.	Varies from 16% to 100% of weight of nitrocellulose. Lacquers with high gum and pigment content have more plasticizer.	Produce films that are more plastic, softer, less brittle. They increase flow, remain in the film, retard time of setting, prevent blushing and cracking.
	Ethyl acetate.	Low boiler, 77° C. Small amounts or none used in brushing lacquers.	Varies from 2% to 25% when used.	To dissolve nitrocellulose. Produce quick drying. Reduce cost. To help in spreading.
SOLVENTS FOR NITROCELLULOSE	Butyl acetate generally used. Butyl propionate, diethyl carbonate, and amyl acetate. Sometimes used.	Medium boiler, 125° C. Usually are esters such as acetates. Most important nitrocellulose solvents. Most commonly used solvents for both spraying and brushing lacquers.	Varies from 15% to 40% and is found in many formulas.	To produce smooth flow. To reduce brittleness and blushing. To retard setting.
Evaporate	Ethyl lactate.	High boiler, 152° C. Evaporates slowly, and is sometimes used in brushing lacquers.	Varies from 2% to 4% of total liquid when used at all.	To retard setting and drying of the films. To improve flowing and brushing qualities. To prevent blushing.

[1] S. S.—Special Solubility.   R. S.—Regular Solubility.

TABLE VII.—Continued

GENERAL FORMULA FOR LACQUER

Class of Ingredients	Name of Ingredients	Chemical and General Information	Amount Used	Special Function in Lacquers
GUM SOLVENTS	Anhydrous ethyl alcohol.	Low boiler, 78° C. All nitrocellulose is shipped wet with alcohol—70 lbs. of nitrocellulose and 30 lbs. of alcohol.	Varies from 3% to 63% of the liquids. Large amount may cause blushing.	To dissolve varnish gums. Solvent for S. S. nitrocellulose when activated with an ester such as butyl acetate.
GUM SOLVENTS Often called non solvents for nitrocellulose.	Butyl alcohol, also called Butanol.	Medium boiler, 177° C. Often used in lacquers and becomes an active solvent for nitrocellulose when activated with butyl acetate.	Varies from 5% to 25%, with 10% most common.	Solvent for varnish resins and gives flow to lacquers. To help prevent blushing. To add good brushing qualities.
Evaporate	Amyl alcohol, also called Pentasol.	Medium boiler, 126° to 132° C. Good solvent for nitrocellulose when activated with amyl acetate.	Varies usually from 4.5% to 10% of liquids.	To impart flow to Lacquers. Solvent for gums.
DILUENTS Solvents for gums; also thinners. Evaporate.	Toluol or Toluene.	Distils at 111° C. It is the most generally used hydrocarbon thinner or diluent.	Usually between 30% and 55% of liquids when xylol is not used.	To act as a thinner and gum solvent. To cheapen the lacquer. To blend the other mixtures.
	Xylol or Xylene.	Distils at 143° C. Often used with toluol in a mixture.	Generally between 30% and 60% of liquids when toluol is not mixed with it; 40% is commonly used.	To act as a thinner and gum solvent. To retard the drying of the film and cheapen the lacquer. To blend the gum and nitrocellulose mixtures.

Clear Brushing Lacquer for Wood. The following formula gives an idea of the composition of an unpigmented brushing lacquer:

Solids:
Nitrocellulose, ½ second R.S. (Regular Soluble) nitrocotton, 8 oz.
Gums: Dammar (high grade), 5 oz.
      Ester gum, 3 oz.
Plasticizer, Dibutyl Phthalate, 3 oz.
Liquids; total, 1 gallon:
Solvent for Nitrocellulose: Butyl propionate, 15%
                    Butyl acetate, 15%
Nonsolvent, Butyl alcohol, 20%
Diluents: Toluol, 20%
      Xylol, 30%

To improve the flexibility of this lacquer, all or part of the above gums may be substituted to include the use of non-oxidizing, oil-modified alkyd resin.

Spraying lacquers are not so much like varnishes as are brushing lacquers, and contain a smaller per cent of gums relatively to the amount of nitrocellulose.

Formula for High-Grade Spraying Lacquer.

Solids:
Nitrocellulose: R.S. (Regular Soluble), ½ second viscosity, Cotton, 20 oz.
Gums: Dammar, high grade (Grade A Batavia or Singapore), 5 oz.
      Ester gum, 5 oz.
Plasticizer: Dibutyl Phthalate, 8 oz.
Liquids; total, 1 gallon:
Solvent for Nitrocellulose: Butyl acetate, 30%
Nonsolvents: Butanol (Butyl alcohol), 10%
          Ethyl alcohol (Anhydrous), 10%
Diluents: Toluol (Toluene), 40%
      Xylol (Xylene), 10%

Here again it is advisable to include the use of alkyd resins to upgrade the quality of the lacquer for specific uses, such as alcohol resistance, light stability, and flexibility.

Automobile lacquers for spraying usually have more nitrocellulose relatively to the resins than is the case of wood lacquers, which contain a higher percentage of resins. Wood lacquers are therefore more like varnishes, and the films have more body and gloss than automobile lacquers.

Clear or Transparent Lacquers. Wood finishers sometimes wonder why manufacturers do not recommend lacquer in its clear or transparent form for outdoor use, while their lacquer enamels are especially advertised as being superior for such use. Nitrocellulose, when included to the extent of about 50 per cent of the solid material in lacquer, easily and rapidly changes or decomposes in direct sunlight, or on being exposed to outside weather conditions.

On the inside of buildings, where the ultra-violet rays of sunlight have been removed by filtering through window glass, clear lacquers do not break down chemically or physically, and can be used with satisfaction.

Lacquer Enamels and Colored Lacquers. Pigments in white, black, and various colors are often added to clear or transparent lacquers, if obscuration and a change in hue or tone are desired with a quick-drying finish. The addition of pigments gives lacquer a resistance to the actinic rays of sunlight, and has made lacquer enamels successful for outdoor use. It is well known, however, that clear lacquer will not give service under such conditions.

Pigmented lacquers can be purchased in most of the hues, including a great variety of tints and shades. If the three primary colors—red, yellow, and blue—in addition to black and white, are kept on hand, a colorist can mix almost any color which he desires, just as is done with paints or enamels. This statement means that the lacquer enamels can be mixed together to produce other colors. It does not mean that painters' colors which are ground in oil can be added to clear or transparent lacquer or to white lacquer enamel. This should not be done, because the oil vehicle in which the pigments are ground does not mix properly with nitrocellulose mixtures. If one wishes to add new coloring pigments he can obtain the best results by securing colors ground in japan rather than those ground in oil.

House painters and wood finishers usually obtain the various hues desired from oil-ground colors, while sign-painters and automobile painters commonly select colors ground in japan for their work. Grinding japan is a very quick-drying varnish, which is made from some resin such as shellac or rosin, a linseed-oil vehicle, and a solvent, together with metallic oxides, which are known as driers. Such japans are thinned when necessary with a very quick-drying liquid, turpentine being the most satisfactory.

A lacquer which contains a white pigment that will produce obscuration of the surface can be colored by the use of various coal-tar dyes soluble in alcohol. While spirit-soluble dyes which are liable to fade in sunlight are sometimes incorporated into a transparent lacquer, pigment colors ground in japan are the materials most satisfactory for a practical finisher to add to lacquer enamels. Good results can undoubtedly be secured by adding japan-ground colors to a lacquer thinner, and then incorporating this pigmented mixture into a clear lacquer. This method is suggested by one manufacturer, but the novice is more apt to secure good results by purchasing ready-prepared pigmented lacquers and mixing together colors of the same brand only.

Pigments may be incorporated into lacquers during the manufacturing process by several quite different processes. If castor oil or some other specially prepared oil is used as a plasticizer, the oil and the colors may be ground together and added to the lacquer mixture. Sometimes the pigments are rolled into a heavy plastic mass of nitrocellulose containing a portion of its solvents. More of the solvents are added to the colored or pigmented nitrocellulose mixture after the heavy steel rollers have thoroughly amalgamated the pigments and nitrocellulose into a very homogeneous mass. The other lacquer ingredients, such as the resins in solutions, plasticizers, and diluents, are thus compounded with the pigmented nitrocotton mixture.

Other methods are also used by manufacturers, some of whom grind the pigments with certain amounts of completely compounded clear lacquer, the grinding being done in pebble mills. Another plan is to grind the pigments with some of the lacquer reducers, and add this mixture to heavy clear lacquer. In general, it is wise to let the factory expert mix the pigments into lacquers, because he has the proper skill, knowledge, and equipment for such work. The danger from the use of colors ground in japan comes from linseed oil which is ordinarily found in most japans. Linseed oil does not usually react well in lacquers, though it is sometimes used in small quantities.

Pigments are of great value in lacquers in addition to their coloring function; and, because of their presence in lacquer enamels, these finishes can be used outdoors successfully. Clear or transparent lacquers, however, do not wear well when exposed to bright sunlight. The pigments in lacquer enamels seem to absorb the ultra-violet rays, and prevent their destructive action, which seems to be a decomposition of the nitrocellulose component of the film.

While it is true that pigmented lacquers gradually are affected with old-age checks when used on automobiles, they have proved to be long-lived compared with enamel and varnish finishes, except where enamel is baked on. Most of the large automobile factories have adopted some type of lacquer enamel, or pyroxylin, as a durable and satisfactory motor-car finish.

Colored lacquers differ from lacquer enamels in much the same way that water stains are different from pigmented oil stains. In the case of water stains, a transparent dye is used for coloring matter, while an opaque pigment, possessing more or less obscuration for any surface on which it is placed, is the color-giving material in pigmented oil stains. Colored lacquers are manufactured by adding spirit-soluble coal-tar dyes to clear lacquers. Electric-light bulbs and other articles of glass, besides ornamental metalwork, are often colored with an attractive translucent effect which is produced by dyed lacquers.

SELECTED REFERENCES, CHAPTER XIX

Lacquers—History, Uses, and Composition

Adams, R. C., "Varnish versus Lacquer for Furniture Finishing," *Industrial Finishing*, 22, page 76, March, 1946.

Bede, J. A., "Hot Lacquer Spraying Problems Solved," *Automotive Industry*, 104, page 48, plus, Jan. 15, 1951.

Blackmore, P. O., "Plastic Resins as Protective Coatings," *Organic Finishing*, 8, pp. 39-40, May, 1947.

Buller, R. F., "Lacquer Solvents in the U.S.A.," *The Chemical Age*, 61, pp. 703-704, Nov. 19, 1949.

Gibbia, S. W., *Woodfinishing and Refinishing*, "Lacquer," Chapter VII, pp. 101-122; 1954.

Long, J. S., "History of Lacquers," *Paint Oil and Chemical Review*, 110, pp. 12-14, Nov. 27, 1947.

Mattiello, Joseph J., *Protective and Decorative Coatings*, volume 1, "Ethylcellulose," Chapter XXIX, pp. 759-804; 1941.

Ibid., "Lacquer Solvents and Formulation of Solvent Mixtures," Chapter XXVII, pp. 641-738.

Ibid., Volume 3, "Lacquers," Chapters XVIII, XIX, and XX, pp. 497-610.

Moore, G. A., "Functional Use of Lacquer," *Paint Oil and Chemical Review*, 110, pp. 110-112, Nov. 11, 1948.

Soderberg, G. A., *Finishing Materials and Methods*, "Cellulose Lacquer Varnishes and Enamels," Chapter III, pp. 25-32; 1952.

Chapter XX

Lacquer Finishes and Lacquer Technique

Advantages of Lacquers Over Varnishes and Enamels. Many advantages of lacquers and lacquer enamels over varnishes and varnish enamels have been advanced. The advantages that seem to be conspicuous to users and manufacturers are listed as follows:

1. Lacquers set quickly and dry hard sooner than varnishes; consequently, production can be speeded up, and less floor space for drying is needed.
2. They dry to a very stable, almost unchangeable hardness through evaporation.
3. Their rapid drying avoids dust specks which are so troublesome with varnish.
4. They do not oxidize and crumble away after a time as oil varnishes always do. In other words, chemical action ceases in lacquer films after they harden.
5. When used with intelligence, lacquer coatings are very durable and long lived, comparing favorably with the best of the varnishes and enamels.
6. Lacquer finishes wear well under exposure or use, and are not easily affected by soap, dilute alcohol, or weak acids, oils, road tar, water or ice, by reasonable changes in temperature, or by the reduced actinic action of indoor sunlight.
7. Pigmented lacquers wear well, and are not easily checked by exposure to the ultra-violet rays of outdoor sunlight.
8. Films of lacquer do not change in tone or shade while drying.
9. Lacquer finishes dry with a soft satinlike luster or low gloss.
10. Coatings of lacquer are about as moistureproof as similar films of spar varnish.

11. The best lacquer finishes resist rather high temperature without becoming soft or tacky; consequently, they are not usually seriously affected by hot dishes or even by boiling water. Repeated abuse through heat, however, may cause temperature checks which will always show, as the edges of the cracks do not reunite later on.

Disadvantages of Lacquer Finishes. The user of nitrocellulose lacquer should be informed about the difficulties of applying it, and about some of the shortcomings of the material as a finishing medium. The chemical composition of lacquers prohibits their use under certain conditions.

The novice can use paint, shellac, and varnish by placing coats of any of them over or under, and no serious chemical reactions are ordinarily produced; but with lacquer one must carefully consider what is to go under or over it, or serious trouble may follow.

The chief disadvantages of lacquer finishes, in the opinion of experienced finishers, may be listed as follows:

1. Lacquers are very difficult to apply with brushes, because all such finishes set and dry too quickly.
2. Clear lacquers show a tendency to shrink in drying because of absorption by the undercoats, or on account of evaporation of the high boiling solvents, which are the last of the volatile elements to leave the film. This shrinking makes the problem of the filling up of the large cell openings of very porous woods exceedingly difficult.
3. Undercoats of varnish, enamel, oil, wax, or paint cannot be used directly under lacquer coatings, because some of the solvents in the lacquer are the same as, or similar to, the liquids in paint and varnish removers; consequently they will soften and destroy such finishes. Covering the undercoats with shellac of standard strength, or even with a considerably thinned mixture, usually, will protect them from the destructive action of lacquer solvents.
4. Lacquers should not be applied directly over surfaces that have been finished with linseed oil stains or ordinary wood fillers, because of bleeding and streaking into the upper coats through the action of the solvents upon the linseed oil in the undercoats. Under lacquer finishes, water stains

and special wood fillers containing the minimum of linseed oil should be used. A coating of shellac over a surface filled with ordinary wood filler will, to a large extent, protect it from damage by the lacquer solvents.

5. Spirit-soluble stains cannot be used satisfactorily directly under clear lacquer finishes without danger of muddy effects.

6. Lacquer finishes must be rather thin when applied; consequently, they have a reduced body or depth, and a greater number of coats is required.

7. A high gloss similar to that obtained from rubbing and polishing varnishes cannot be obtained from lacquers. The highest gloss can be secured by giving a final coat of clear lacquer; but, unfortunately, such a transparent film cannot be applied over pigmented lacquers for outdoor use because of the destructive action of the ultra-violet rays of summer sunlight, which causes serious checking of the non-colored finishing coat.

8. Lacquer-films over wood sometimes check crosswise on account of temperature changes; or more often, they crack parallel with the grain because of shrinking and swelling of the wood. These changes in size, of course, are caused by variations in humidity.

Undercoats for Lacquers. The complex nature of lacquers, which include several powerful solvents as necessary ingredients, makes it imperative that only such undercoats be used as are not easily softened, dissolved, or changed chemically by the application of films of lacquer. Experienced finishers have discovered, however, that sometimes lacquers can be sprayed over certain undercoats with less likelihood of trouble than when brushes are used for spreading it.

If one knows that such ingredients as ethyl alcohol, butyl alcohol, and other alcohols, ethyl acetate, butyl acetate, amyl acetate, and the various ethers of ethylene and propylene glycol, besides other substances of great dissolving possibilities, are used commonly as solvents for the nitrocellulose and resins which give body to a lacquer, he will realize that these complex finishes are very apt to have the softening action of paint and varnish removers, and that they cannot be applied directly over new finishes—particularly paints, oleoresinous varnishes, wood fillers, and oil finishes.

Linseed oil in films oxidizes very gradually, and finishes containing it dry slowly and do not become hard for a long period of time. The oxidation of the oil changes it chemically into varnishlike materials which are quite different from the original organic compound. Linseed oil in its liquid form is easily soluble in most of the lacquer solvents. The oil in newly made films of finishes, though apparently dry after a few days, is really only partially oxidized, and is still soluble in most of the solvents in nitrocellulose lacquers.

For these reasons, lacquers cannot be used directly over any finish which contains linseed oil until months have passed, and the oil has oxidized so completely that it has lost its solubility to a great extent, and is not easily softened by solvents. Paints, oil varnishes, oil finishes, ordinary wood fillers, and varnish enamels, to a limited extent, all contain linseed oil in varying amounts. While they are new, films made from any of these finishes cannot be covered with nitrocellulose lacquers without some intervening coat to separate the solvents in the lacquer from the undercoats, thus preventing destructive action on the linseed oil.

Special wood fillers are now prepared for use immediately under clear lacquers on porous woods when natural finishes are desired. These fillers are similar to other wood fillers, but should contain minimum amounts of linseed oil and drier. Ordinary paste wood fillers are satisfactory, however, if coated with shellac before applying lacquer.

On automobiles, special oil primers and surfacers should be used under the lacquer finishes. Primers of proper composition should be used between the final lacquer coats and the undercoats which contain a certain amount of oil.

Several manufacturers furnish specially prepared undercoating finishes which are intended to be placed between lacquer films and the previously applied wood fillers. Spirit-varnish gums, such as shellac, which do not readily dissolve in the lacquer solvents, are selected as the proper resins for these special surfacers.

Shellac, in liquid form which is sometimes called shellac varnish, is an effective and convenient surfacer to place over wood filler or other oil-containing undercoats, thus protecting them from the final coat or coats of lacquer. Shellac varnish is made from 190° proof denatured alcohol and shellac gum. Ethyl alcohol does not dissolve linseed oil; therefore, it is a good solvent for a surfacer which is used to cover any of the undercoats containing this oil.

When the function of a coating of shellac varnish over stains and wood filler is chiefly that of a sizing to protect the undercoats from lacquer, it is often advisable to dilute the factory made four pound cut liquid shellac to one half strength, though thinner or thicker mixtures may be used. The stronger mixtures tend to give more body to the finish and, in some cases, are preferred because the lacquer films are in general much thinner than coats of rubbing varnish.

Films of shellac varnish are not readily dissolved by coatings of the standard lacquers of today, because shellac resin or gum, as it is frequently called, is not easily soluble in many of the lacquer solvents. Shellac gum is only slightly soluble in ether, amyl acetate, most of the glycols, and some of the other lacquer solvents, or in benzol which is a combination of the diluents, benzene, toluene, and xylene.

These hydrocarbon thinners are generally used in quantities that amount to about 35 to 50 per cent of the entire weight of a lacquer mixture. While shellac gum is soluble in strong ethyl alcohol, butyl alcohol, ethyl acetate, and some other solvents frequently incorporated into nitrocellulose lacquer compounds, it must be remembered that these ingredients which will dissolve shellac gum are very volatile, and evaporate quickly from a thin coating such as a film of lacquer. It has already been stated that ethyl alcohol and ethyl acetate belong to the low boiling, quick evaporating group of solvents. Butyl alcohol is a medium boiler, and is used because it is cheap and available, but its odor is disagreeable, and its use in lacquers may decrease with the discovery of better solvents.

Though it is known that in a liquid state shellac and lacquers usually mix together satisfactorily, it has been found by experiment that lacquer can be spread over thoroughly dry coatings of shellac varnish without appreciably affecting the shellac film itself. While the hardened coat of shellac may be softened somewhat, it will not be dissolved and worked into the lacquer film if the latter is applied quickly with a brush or is sprayed over the surface. The relative amount of solvents in most lacquers that will dissolve shellac gum is not great, and these liquids leave the surface with exceptional rapidity on account of their volatility.

New coats of oil varnish cannot be used successfully under lacquers, because the solvents contained in these nitrocellulose finishes may dissolve any unoxidized linseed oil contained in a varnish undercoat. Undercoats of varnish containing tung oil are apt to become wrinkled or blistered by applying lacquer over them. The strong lacquer solvents may even soften and roughen the resins in the undercoats, some of which are like kauri gum in that they are soluble, or at least partly dissolvable, in both the solvents and diluents that are used in making the lacquer.

If a coat of varnish or enamel has dried hard, or is several years old and the drying oils have changed through oxidation, lacquers can usually be applied without difficulty.

The proper stains for use on wood under clear lacquers are the various kinds of water soluble dyes. Acid water soluble coal-tar dyes are satisfactory, easily obtainable, and are generally used for staining wood, because such colors are among the most permanent known. Another reason for the use of water stains is that lacquers and other finishes can be coated over them without an uneven muddy effect, which would happen in case the lacquer solvents dissolved any of the stain in the undercoating.

Mahogany stains are not recommended for use under lacquer, because many of them will "bleed" through a shellac sizing, or even through a heavy film, into a lacquer finishing coat and spoil it. Oil and spirit coal-tar dyes are not recommended for staining under lacquer; but they can sometimes be used, if thoroughly protected by coats of shellac before any lacquer is applied. Water stains are most satisfactory for general use, and are recommended by some authorities as the only proper stains to use under lacquer.

Non-grain-raising stains can also be successfully used. These stains have been perfected to the point where they have retained the advantages of various types of stains without their disadvantages.

Lacquer Sealers as Undercoats. Another first-coater available to finishers is lacquer sealer. Lacquer sealers are extensively used as priming coats over stained and filled surfaces. They consist of nitrocellulose, resins, and plasticizers dispersed in a suitable solvent. They contain such sanding agents as zinc and calcium stearates. The actual solid content ranges from 12 to 21 per cent. This means that 100 lbs. of sealer contain from 12 to 21 lbs. of solid matter.

Various so-called sanding sealers have been developed designed to promote easier sanding. They are specially formulated to shorten drying time, sand readily, increase adhesion, and provide a coat that binds well to succeeding lacquer coats.

Lacquer sealers are generally sprayed full body at 40 to 50 lbs. of air pressure. When the film thickness is kept to a minimum, they usually air-dry in from 30 minutes to 2 hours. When the sealer has dried hard, sand either by hand or with a portable finishing sander, using 5/0 to 7/0 finishing paper. Carefully remove the fine dust formed by sanding before applying the first coat of lacquer.

In some instances, particularly on cheap, close-grained woods, a combination sealer-stain is used. This material is a sealer containing dyes or pigments. It gives both color and finish to a wood surface in a single operation. Sanding of stained sealer coats requires particular care, since it is easy to cut through the stain into the whitewood, leaving an uneven stained effect. So-called "transparent toners" are also used to produce a uniform color background. When containing 10 to 21 per cent solids and sanding agents, toners may be used as colored sealers.[1]

Application of Lacquers. The self confident person who thinks that he can do almost anything is very apt to have some of the conceit taken out of him the first time he attempts to apply lacquer with a brush over a large surface. It is true that there are some brands of lacquer on the market which are slower in setting than others, but there is room for improvement in the brushing qualities of practically all nitrocellulose finishes. Lacquers are attractive in their effects, but they are the most difficult of all wood finishes to apply with a brush.

---

[1] Deniston, G. L., The Science of Modern Woodfinishing, pp. 140-142.

Although not easy to spread by hand, they can be sprayed very successfully with an air gun. Spraying is the method used almost exclusively for covering large surfaces.

A surface over which lacquer is to be coated must be prepared properly; it must be clean, dry, and smooth. Water stains are liable to expand wood, because they add humidity. After staining with water stains, articles made of wood should be allowed to dry at least 24 hours in a warm, dry room in order to allow all excess of moisture to evaporate.

Metal surfaces which are to be lacquered must be carefully cleansed and brightened. Small areas may be prepared with sandpaper, but large surfaces are usually treated with a sand blast.

If it is desired to refinish old surfaces with lacquers, it is necessary that they be properly cleansed, preferably with turpentine, in order to remove any grease, oil, wax, or polish which may be left on the old finish. In general, sand old varnish, shellac, enamel, or other hard finishes to perfect smoothness. This treatment, in which No. 00 to No. 0000 sandpaper is used, also removes the gloss from the old finish, and helps new coats to adhere to the undercoats.

Surfaces which are checked, or are rough and contain spots partly peeled off, must be smoothed over with fine sandpaper or steel wool of fine grade.

Sometimes both clear lacquers and lacquer enamels have proved very unsatisfactory when applied over old varnish or enamel finishes. Lacquer finishes when applied over undercoats containing varnish are very apt to check badly or peel off after a few months, and sometimes trouble has appeared within several weeks. Experiments indicate that lacquer finishes are satisfactory when spread over proper undercoats, and that old varnish and enamel undercoats should not be used in important refinishing.

Nylon Brushes. Brushes, their use, characteristics and care, have been mentioned occasionally throughout this text. Nothing specifically has been said about nylon brushes. In nylon brushes the contact materials or bristles are synthetically produced whereas the bristles of other brushes come from such sources as Chinese hog, horse hair, Siberian mink, rice root and many others (Figs. 20-1a and 1b), pages 410-411.

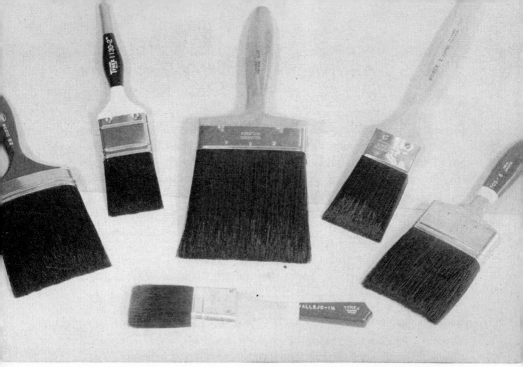

PHOTO BY ROBERT C. SMITHERAM, JR.

20—1a. Selected nylon brushes for varnishing, enameling and lacquering.

Soon after the start of World War II, the importation of bristles used in the manufacture of brushes came virtually to a stand still. After a great deal of research in the laboratory, scientists finally succeeded in producing, synthetically, a contact material which has many of the desirable characteristics of a high quality paint brush. In this new process many problems had to be overcome. Not only was it necessary to tip the bristles, but they also had to be sharpened, tapered, and the ends split. Continued experimentation and research finally produced a nylon brush which has proved equal if not superior to the best pre-war brushes.

The following are some of the good characteristics of nylon brushes:[2]

1. Nylon filaments will outwear hog bristles from three to five times.
2. The paint or enamel film laid down by a properly made, high quality nylon brush is smooth and uniform, leaving no brush marks.

---

[2] Soderberg, G. A., *Finishing Materials and Methods*, Chapter XII, page 159.

3. The paint carrying capacity of a high grade nylon brush increases with use.
4. Nylon bristles are resistant to paint solvents and water. This does not mean, however, that a dirty nylon brush can be stored in a container partly filled with water.
5. After proper cleaning, nylon brushes can be stored without danger of damage by mold, vermin or moths.

Continued research and improved manufacturing techniques may eliminate some or all of the following disadvantages:[3]

1. A nylon brush does not have the pickup capacity of a pure bristle brush.
2. Nylon is soluble in and seriously affected by such liquids as phenol, carbolic acid, paint and varnish remover and materials containing acetone, lacquer or lacquer thinner.
3. Denatured alcohol in shellac has a tendency to soften nylon bristles.

Regardless of these disadvantages, nylon brushes are being accepted by professional and amateur finishers as a part of their finishing tools.

Spreading Lacquer with a Brush. The happy selection of a brush is often helpful in the application of several of the types

[3] *Ibid.*, Chapter XII, page 159.

20—1b. Typical artist's brushes. Center brush is made of pure sable.

PHOTO BY ROBERT C. SMITHERAM, JR.

of finishes for wood. When lacquer is to be applied by hand, it is particularly important. The brush should not be too soft nor too stiff and coarse. A medium soft fitch brush of good quality, vulcanized in rubber and rubber bound, is well adapted for spreading lacquers.

Fitch brushes were originally made from the hair obtained from the tails of American skunks, but in order to secure more elasticity many manufacturers mix soft skunk hair with other stiffer hair or even with Chinese boar bristles. The medium soft grades of high quality brushes for shellac and varnish, made from the best bristles from China, are the most satisfactory. Camel's hair brushes, now generally made from the tail hair of Siberian squirrels, are too soft for use with brushing lacquers.

All things considered, the best brush for spreading lacquer is a large cement set or rubber set oval or flat varnish brush made from medium soft bristles of good quality.

The following suggestions may be helpful to persons without experience who wish to apply lacquer with a brush:

1. Proper undercoats are absolutely necessary. Shellac or special lacquer undercoats should generally be used over other finishes before lacquer is applied. On new, unfinished wood, shellac or sanding sealer makes a good sizing which will seal the pores of the wood and help to give "body" to a lacquer finish.
2. Brushing lacquer must be applied very rapidly and carefully, using a brush or brushes of the proper size. Each stroke of the brush should completely cover a certain area as the lacquer is flowed on the surface. Much brushing after the manner of applying wood filler must be avoided.
3. The brush must be kept wet or full of lacquer while in use, and should be wiped on the point only after refilling from the can or pail.
4. Open grained or porous woods must be filled properly, and surfaced with shellac or a specially prepared lacquer undercoat, in order to make level surfaces, because lacquer does not flow into the cell openings and fill them as other finishes do.
5. Brushing lacquer must be flowed over a surface with a wet

brush held at an oblique angle instead of perpendicularly to the surface. Lacquer is always flowed over a surface and cannot be "brushed out."

6. The finisher must stand in a position that will enable him to see well, because the surfaces must be covered properly and completely at the first application. Retouching improperly covered spots after the lacquer has set even for a few seconds will produce a rough finish wherever the brush touches the edges of the partly dried films surrounding the unfinished area.

7. All removable doors and all pieces of furniture, whenever possible, should be placed in such a position that lacquer can be applied on horizontal rather than on vertical surfaces. It is possible to apply thicker coats to horizontal than to vertical surfaces, and there is much less danger of runs and sags. This method results in superior smoothness and evenness. Lacquer sets so rapidly that the first side of an article will dry hard enough to handle in a few minutes, then another side can be placed in a horizontal position ready for lacquering under the most favorable conditions.

8. Whenever it becomes necessary to join a partly set lacquer film to a new wet coating, it is best to soften the edge that has begun to thicken by the use of another brush and lacquer reduced to one half strength with thinner. This procedure will usually prevent roughness where the lap of the newly lacquered film joins the partly set edge of the coating previously applied.

9. If lacquer does not spread freely under a brush, it is often advantageous to thin the mixture with a thinner, which can be secured from the lacquer manufacturer.

10. A small amount of thinner placed conveniently near is helpful when spots or drippings must be removed before covering a surface.

11. The brush should be cleaned with a properly prepared thinner as a solvent after a lacquering job has been completed. A cheaper brush cleaning liquid than lacquer thinner can be made from denatured alcohol and acetone mixed half and half.

12. No sandpapering between coats of lacquer is necessary unless the surface has become roughened and must be

leveled or smoothed. Under varnish, however, it is advisable to sand the last coat of lacquer, because varnish adheres better to a sanded surface than to one that has a high gloss.

13. Only one coat of some brands of lacquer can be applied smoothly over a surface when a brush is used. The solvents in lacquer are so powerful that they are apt to soften an undercoat of lacquer, and the friction of the brush is often sufficient to cause roughness and undesirable brush marks. If proper undercoats are used one coat of lacquer applied with a brush will usually make a good finish. Brushing lacquer has more "body" than spraying lacquer.

If more than one coat of lacquer must be applied, the finisher should allow the first coat at least one or two days to harden before the second coat is brushed on, or the later coats may be sprayed over the surfaces with an air gun after from 3 to 24 hours. Some manufacturers have suggested that lacquer should have one hour for drying between coats. Experience has shown, however, that a much longer period for hardening is preferable. Several coats of some brands of lacquers, especially those containing ethylene glycol solvents, can be applied successfully by flowing the new films over the surfaces quickly and carefully with soft lacquer brushes.

14. While lacquer sets very quickly, it should be given sufficient time for hardening between coats and before rubbing. The best results are obtained by allowing coats of lacquer to dry 48 hours before rubbing is attempted.

Lacquer and Paint Spraying Equipment. Almost all lacquer finishes, whether in factories, schools, or home workshops, are now applied with a spray gun.

The following equipment is desirable for a successful spraying job:

1. *A compressor,* which takes air from the atmosphere, compresses it, and supplies the pressure which is needed to operate the gun. Power to compress the air is supplied either by an electric motor or by a gasoline engine. Compressors range in size from small to large units. When only a limited

20—1c. The compressor supplies the air pressure needed to operate the spray gun for big jobs. A home "kit" may be powered by smaller units—such as a vacuum cleaner.

amount of spraying is done, the compressor can be small. Some home vacuum cleaners can satisfactorily supply the needed air pressure.

In industrial finishing and auto refinishing, compressors such as shown in Fig. 20-1c are used.

2. *An air transformer.* As the compressed air moves on its way to the gun, it first passes through a transformer. Here any dirt, rust, oil, or moisture that may be in the air is collected and drained off (Fig. 20-1c). The transformer also makes it possible to regulate the pressure needed to operate the gun successfully. Pressure for most spraying jobs ranges from 35 to 50 lbs.

3. *Air hose.* The air is carried from the transformer to the gun through a hose. It must be of the proper inside diameter and length to insure sufficient pressure at the gun. It should be carefully checked for leaks, since any leaks would lower the pressure at the gun appreciably. Hoses that carry material to the gun should be made with a solvent resistant lining to avoid swelling and disintegrating.

4. *A spray gun.* This instrument is the heart of any finishing system. It can be either pressure fed or suction fed. Selection depends upon the type of spraying to be done. The gun shown in Fig. 20-2 is pressure fed. The material is forced into it by means of a pressure tank as shown in Fig. 20-3.

In most pressure-feed guns, the air and lacquer (or paint) meet outside the gun, forming a so-called external mix. However, there are pressure-feed guns where the air and lacquer mix

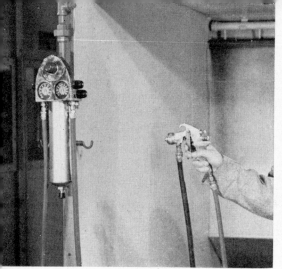
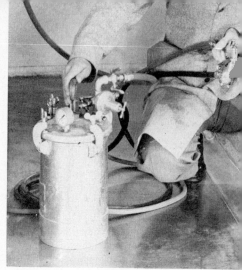

20—2. Pressure at the gun is regulated by a transformer, as shown to the left. It also removes dirt and moisture from the air. Note drain plug at bottom of unit. 20—3. For most production work, a pressure feed tank is used to provide material to the gun.

inside the gun (internal mix). This type of gun is highly useful for heavy materials of the slower drying types. A fast-drying material such as lacquer would clog the slot in the air cap too quickly on this gun. Because air passes through this gun at all times, this kind is often referred to as a bleeder-type gun.

In suction-feed guns the air and lacquer always mix outside the gun (Fig. 20-4). They differ from pressure-feed guns in that the material is drawn up into the gun without the need of supplying extra air pressure to the material.

The suction that draws the fluid into the gun is caused by the manner in which the air cap is designed in relation to the fluid tip. The fluid tip on the pressure-feed gun is flush or slightly

20—4. Typical suction-feed spray gun.

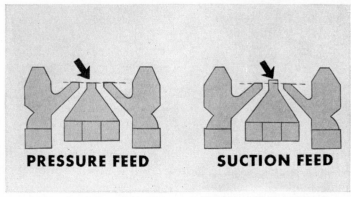

COURTESY THE DE VILBISS CO.

20—5. Arrows indicate position of fluid tip in relation to
air cap.

under the face of the air cap, whereas the suction-feed tip
protrudes slightly beyond the air cap (Fig. 20-5). This condition causes the air stream to create a vacuum in front of
the tip. This, in turn, pulls liquid material toward it, up
from the container, through the gun, and finally forces it
out (Fig. 20-6). This type of gun is often referred to as a
non-bleeder type, in which the trigger controls both air

20—6. In a suction-feed gun, a vacuum is created in front
of the tip. This vacuum pulls the paint or lacquer toward
it and forces it out. No such vacuum is formed in the
pressure-feed gun.

COURTESY THE DE VILBISS CO.

PRESSURE FEED   SUCTION FEED

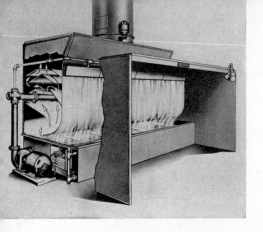

COURTESY
AMERICAN BRAKE SHOE CO.,
KELLOGG DIVISION
20—7. Cutaway view of an
air-washer type spray booth.

and fluid. Since the cup has a capacity of one quart only,
this gun is little used in industry but is ideally suited for the
small shop.

5. *A spray booth.* It is important to have a spray booth, especially when there is a great deal of spraying to do. Spray
booths are either of the dry or of the air-washer type. In
the dry booth, an exhaust fan removes the fumes. It may be
placed in the ceiling or in the back of the booth.

The water-wash booth is so designed as to remove 95 to 99
per cent of the spray particles from the air in the room. This
is accomplished by providing for a continuous waterfall
between the booth and the fan (Fig. 20-7).

In case no booth is available, have a protective device on hand
in the form of a respirator (Fig. 20-8). It should be used
especially when spraying in rooms or areas where there is
little or no ventilation.

Spray Gun Adjustments. In using any spray gun there are a
number of adjustments of extreme importance. These should
be studied carefully. Best results are dependent upon the

COURTESY THE DE VILBISS CO.
20—8. Respirators protect the health
of the operator when a booth is not
available. In big furniture plants, protective spray booths are used.

418

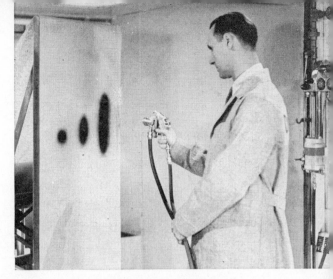

20—9. Before spraying an object, the gun is adjusted to form the correct pattern.

proper flow of material from the nozzle, correct proportioning of atomizing air pressure with flow of material, and proper spray width.

Most spray guns are fitted with an adjusting screw which affords control of the flow of material from the nozzle, but in practically all cases it is recommended that this control is left wide open and the fluid flow adjusted at the pressure feed tank.

A spreader control affords a means of changing the spray pattern from a round spray to various width fan sprays as may be required (Fig. 20-9). There is also an air adjusting valve which can be attached to the air inlet of guns to control atomizing air pressure.

In making adjustments of the spray gun, too high an atomization pressure is to be avoided since it will spread or thin out the center of the spray pattern. Insufficient air pressure on the other hand will not atomize the material sufficiently and will produce a coarse, spattered effect. This adjustment can be checked by studying the spray pattern produced by the gun.

Since flow of material from the gun nozzle determines the speed at which the gun must be moved across the surface, the speed of operation sometimes can be increased greatly by using a setting which permits faster flow of material. To prevent excessive deposit of paint, work out a sequence of motions which will give the minimum number of strokes to cover the surface efficiently without double coating any part of it. A comfortable rapid stroke should result in sufficient coverage without runs or sags.

When learning the use of a gun, an experimental period

419

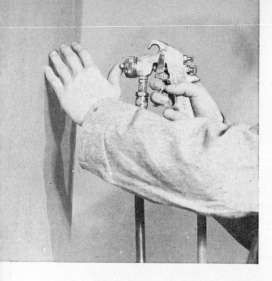

COURTESY THE DE VILBISS CO.
20—10. Proper distance of gun from surface may be measured as shown here. It should be from 6 to 8 inches.

using various settings of the adjustments will be found of value in determining the most efficient operation. The different results obtained by changing fluid pressure, atomizing air pressure and spreader adjustments, should be noted.

Spray Gun Technique. In finishing any particular assembly, the most efficient combination of spray gun movements to produce the desired coverage should be worked out carefully and not left to the individual operator's discretion. Someone familiar with motion study, working in close co-operation with a man in the finishing department who is thoroughly familiar with spray gun technique, will produce the best system for painting any particular object.

The elementary factor that should be understood thoroughly at the outset is the most efficient method of spraying a flat surface. An operator using a spray gun for the first time

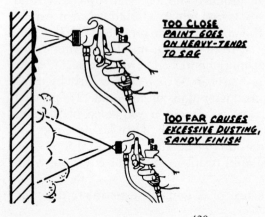

TOO CLOSE
PAINT GOES
ON HEAVY—TENDS
TO SAG

TOO FAR CAUSES
EXCESSIVE DUSTING,
SANDY FINISH

20—11. A gun held too close to a surface, causes sags; when held too far away, it causes spray dust.

would be wise to spray a few practice panels before undertaking actual work, in order to get the feel of the gun, and develop the proper stroke.

The spray gun stroke is made by moving the gun parallel to the work and at a right angle to the surface. The distance from the gun to the work should be from 6 to 8 inches. An easy way to measure this distance is shown in Fig. 20-10.

Work should be done with straight uniform strokes, moving backwards and forwards across the surface in such a way that the spray pattern overlaps the previous stroke by 50%. The closer the gun is held to the work, the more paint is deposited on the surface and the faster the gun must be moved to prevent sags, while holding the gun too far from the work causes dry spray and excessive spray dust (Fig. 20-11). The effect caused by dry spray is generally known as "orange peel" (Figs. 20-12 and 13).

This relation between the gun distance and the stroke speed is very quickly understood and the average sprayer will move the gun in or out as needed to permit a comfortable speed while depositing a full wet coating of material.

The obvious faults of arcing the stroke or tilting the gun as shown in Figs. 20-14, 15, and 16 should be noted. In certain types of work it is often necessary to tilt the gun but this should not be done on surfaces suited to the correct gun position, pages 422 and 423.

20—12. "Orange peel" is the result of not enough thinner reaching the surface to help the paint particles flow out. 20—13. Close-up view of "orange peel."

COURTESY THE DE VILBISS CO.

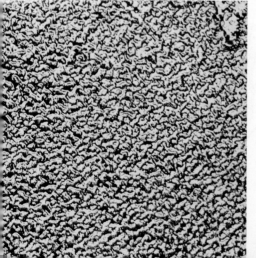

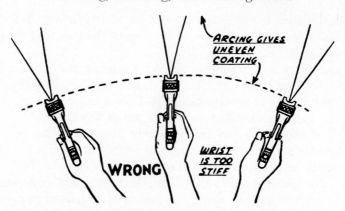

20—14. Arching of the gun results in an uneven surface.

Holding the Gun. Another important factor is to hold the gun at all times perpendicular to the surface being sprayed and Fig. 20-16 illustrates in solid lines the correct position in which the gun should be held. Dotted lines indicate the incorrect position.

The trigger controls the action of the gun and the operator should learn to use the trigger during each stroke. The further the trigger is drawn back, the greater will be the flow of material and to avoid building up the material at the ends of the stroke, the correct procedure is to begin the stroke, then pull

20—15. For even surface coating, move the gun in a straight line at a distance from 6-8 inches from the surface.

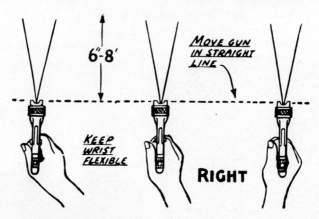

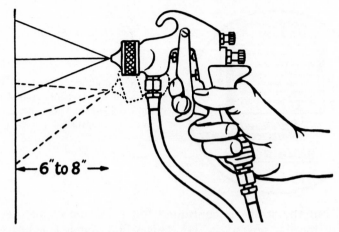

20—16. Spray gun should be held perpendicular to the surface as shown here by solid lines. Tilting the gun up or down gives an uneven spray pattern.

the trigger, releasing it again before the stroke is completed.

The technique of spraying a panel is shown in Fig. 20-17. Each stroke is "triggered." The stroke is started off the work and the trigger is pulled when the gun is opposite the edge of the panel. The trigger is released at the other edge of the

20—17. When spraying a panel use alternate right and left strokes, triggering the gun at the beginning and end of each stroke. The spray pattern should overlap one-half the previous stroke for smooth coverage without streaks.

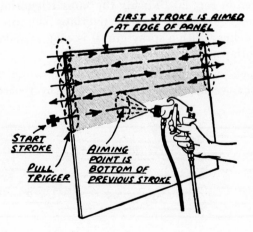

FIRST STROKE IS AIMED AT EDGE OF PANEL

START STROKE

PULL TRIGGER

AIMING POINT IS BOTTOM OF PREVIOUS STROKE

20—18. Banding — Vertical bands sprayed at the ends of a panel prevent over-spray from horizontal strokes.

panel but the stroke is continued for a few inches before reversing for the second stroke. This triggering is the heart of spray technique. The big point, of course, is to hit the exact edge of the work, maintaining full coverage without overspray.

In order to reduce overspray most operators use a "banding" technique as shown in Fig. 20-18. The single vertical stroke at each end of the panel assures complete coverage and eliminates the waste of paint which results from trying to spray right up to the vertical edge with the usual horizontal strokes. At the top and bottom of a panel the gun is aimed at the edge, see Fig. 20-17, and is automatically a banding stroke.

A long panel can be sprayed with vertical strokes, but most sprayers have better control with the more natural horizontal stroke. The panel is sprayed in separate sections 18″ to 36″ long as shown in Fig. 20-19 using the same triggering as with a smaller panel, but each section overlaps the previous one about four inches. With a spray gun it is easy to make perfectly invisible overlaps.

20—19. Long work is sprayed in sections of convenient length, each section overlapping the previous section by 4 inches.

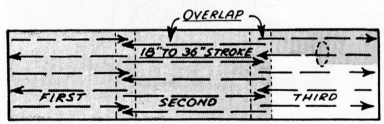

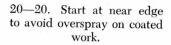

20—20. Start at near edge to avoid overspray on coated work.

When spraying a level surface always start on the near side and work to the far side as shown in Fig. 20-20. This is absolutely essential where cellulose lacquer is used since lacquer overspray landing on wet work will dry sandy. A certain amount of gun tilt is usually necessary for level surfaces, but where practical the work itself should be tilted up so that the spray gun can be held at as near a right angle to it as possible.

Where a spray gun with a suction feed cup attachment is used on a job that requires the gun to be tilted, care must be taken to ensure that the tilt is not excessive as otherwise the paint may clog the air vent in the cup lid and thus stop the flow of material.

When spraying at an upward angle for any length of time, the complete cup attachment should be rotated on the gun through 180 degrees so that the air vent lies in front of the fluid inlet and the fluid tube within the cup curves to where the material will lie when the gun is tilted.

20—21. Edges and corners are done first, spraying directly at the corner to catch both surfaces with one stroke of the gun. The center is sprayed like a plain panel.

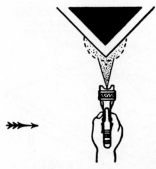

20—22. Spraying the outside corner of a box. Adjoining surfaces are banded with one stroke of the gun.

When a panel is to be sprayed on the edges as well as on the face a modified banding technique is used, Fig. 20-21. One stroke along each edge coats the edges and bands the face of the panel at the same time, page 425.

An outside corner of a box or cabinet is treated in a similar manner as shown in Figs. 20-22 and 23.

If an inside corner is sprayed square-on as shown in Fig. 20-24, the coating is not uniform but the technique is fast and practical. Where an even coating is necessary each face of the corner is sprayed separately as in Fig. 20-25. After making the vertical stroke at the corner, short horizontal strokes should be used to cover the area adjacent to the corner in order to avoid overspraying or double coating the adjoining surface.

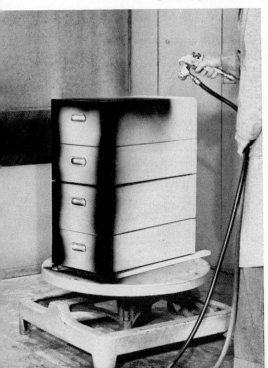

COURTESY THE DE VILBISS CO.

20—23. In spraying a project like this, all edges and corners are sprayed first. Notice convenient turn table.

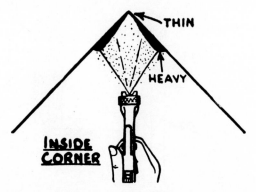

20—24. Spraying directly into the corner gives an uneven coating but is satisfactory for most work.

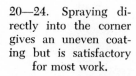

The rule here is to make the spray pattern fit the job. Do not use a wide horizontal pattern on a slender post. A smaller horizontal pattern or a large vertical fan spray gives complete coverage without excessive overspray. On the other hand do not try to work with too small a spray pattern (Fig. 20-26).

Iron grills, fences and similar work should be sprayed to get the most finishing material on the largest area at each stroke. A picket fence is sprayed with a single up-down angle stroke on each side. A wire fence or other intricate work should also be sprayed at an acute angle as shown in Fig. 20-27, and

20—25. Spraying each side of the corner separately gives an even coating. Use a vertical spray pattern.

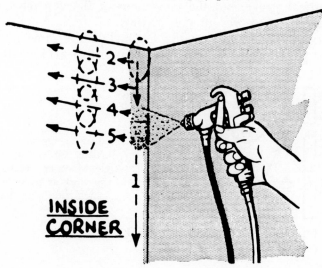

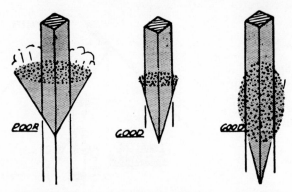

20—26. Avoid excessive overspray on slender work—adjust the spray pattern to fit the job. The center illustration shows the best method for most work.

it is helpful to use a shield behind the wire as paint deflected will help to coat the back of the work.

A flat round disc is sprayed like any other plane surface, banding the edge as described on page 424, and then spraying the center.

Small, cylindrical shapes such as table leg turnings are best sprayed with a round spray pattern, vertical stroke, using three or four lapping strokes to obtain full coverage (Fig. 20-28). A vertical fan pattern can be used in conjunction with the vertical stroke, but the movement of the gun must then be speeded up to prevent sags or runs.

Large cylinders are usually finished in the same manner as a flat panel except that the strokes are shorter, (Fig. 20-29).

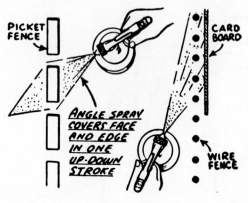

20—27. Open work is usually sprayed at an angle to cover as much of the work as possible with each spray gun stroke.

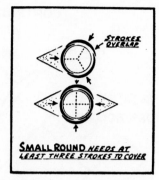

20—28. Use a round spray or vertical fan pattern for table leg turnings or similar small round surfaces.

A small diameter cylinder is more efficiently sprayed with lengthwise strokes as illustrated in Fig. 20-29.

An important element which has been found to increase greatly the efficiency of spraying operations is the principle of keeping a continuity of motion, from the time the gun is triggered when starting to paint an article until the gun is triggered off and the article is completely painted.

This does not necessarily mean that the entire article should be painted without shutting off the gun, but it does mean that this should be done wherever the shape of the article permits. It has been found that by mounting certain kinds of work on a turntable which can be revolved easily it is possible to finish

20—29. Round work should be treated to curve the strokes to conform with the surface. If available, use a revolving table.

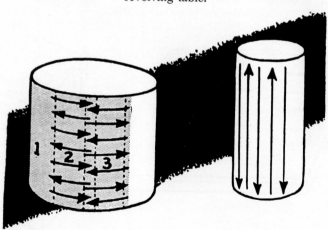

CONTINUOUS SPRAY MOTION

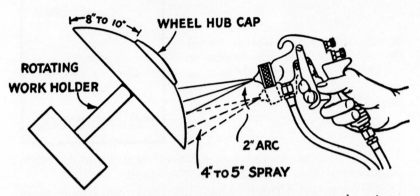

20—30. Finishing a wheel hub cap in one continuous stroke using a rotating work holder.

such objects with one or two simple motions without shutting off the spray gun more than once or twice.

Such continuous, or nearly continuous operation of the gun will assure maximum coverage per unit of time and so will produce a maximum output from the spraying operation.

In such work, it usually is necessary to provide a turntable to hold the object during painting so that it may be rapidly positioned from time to time for complete access to all portions. Then, by working out a suitable sequence of motions for the

20—31. Showing the path of a spray gun for most efficient spraying with the minimum of strokes.

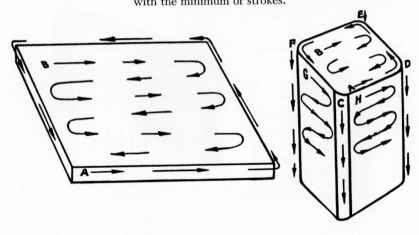

spray gun, complete coverage of the article can be obtained with a few rapid strokes and simultaneous or alternate movements of the fixture holding the work.

The illustrations are examples of the recommended practice in spray gun motion and show how an article can be efficiently covered by one or more continuous strokes of the gun.

Where the object to be painted is of such a shape that it can be sprayed while it is rotated, the gun can be held open from beginning to end of the stroke.

For example, Fig. 20-30 shows a method used in spraying metal hub caps of wheels. The work here is held and rotated by the turntable. For this job a 5-inch spray pattern is used. As the hub rotates, the operator simply pulls the trigger back and moves the gun in a 2-inch arc, finishing the cap in one continuous operation.

It is not necessary to zig-zag this stroke or move from top to bottom and back again. In the example shown the top half of the hub cap is finished on its turning through 360 degrees, and the second half on the second complete revolution by the slight movement of the spray gun. The width of the spray pattern must be adjusted to suit the area to be covered.

Fig. 20-31 shows how continuity of motion can be worked out for a flat surface such as a table top. Fig. 20-31 also shows a diagram of how continuity of motion may be planned for solid objects such as cabinets, metal covers, cases, etc. In both of these cases the spray gun is triggered to feather out the strokes.

In any motion study for spray guns it is desirable to determine the fewest number of strokes and least amount of motion necessary to obtain the desired coverage. To this end, the design and use of suitable fixtures will be found a great aid.

Of course, it is most essential to follow at all times the printed directions given with the spray gun regarding the best way to clean the gun and keep it in first-class operating condition if maximum painting efficiency is to be obtained.

Some General Gun Cleaning Precautions. The spray gun is a precision-built tool which should be handled with the same care as any other fine instrument. Proper lubrication assures smooth operation. If a gun is used almost constantly, the fluid needle packing should be oiled daily. Also put a drop of oil on the air valve stem and on the trigger bearing screw.

COURTESY THE DE VILBISS CO.

20—32. A spray gun must be thoroughly cleaned after completing a spray job. Drain any material from the gun by placing a cloth over the air cap, pulling the trigger at the same time. 20—33. After cleaning the material cup, fill it half full with thinner.

Never drop the gun into a container of thinner to clean it, because dirty solvent will clog the air passages of the gun. Thinner also removes any lubrication from the gun and dries out the air valve and fluid needle packings.

Procedure for Cleaning a Suction Feed Gun.

1. Loosen the air cap two or three turns and remove the ma-

20—34. Re-assemble the gun and spray thinner, cleaning out all passage-ways. 20—35. After soaking the air cap for a short time in thinner, brush and wipe dry.

COURTESY THE DE VILBISS CO.

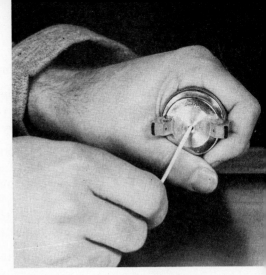

20—36. Clean clogged holes in air cap with a tooth pick or pointed match stick. Do not use wire, nails or other hard metal tools.

terial cup. Hold a cloth over the air cap, pull the trigger, and force whatever material remains in the gun back into the cup. Then empty the cup of material and clean it thoroughly (Fig. 20-32).

2. Fill the cup about half full of thinner (Fig. 20-33).
3. After it has been re-assembled properly, spray the thinner. This cleans out the passageways (Fig. 20-34).
4. Remove the air cap and, if dirty with dry lacquer or paint, let it soak in clean thinner. After it has had a thorough soaking, brush and wipe off the air cap (Fig. 20-35).
5. If the small holes in the air cap are clogged, clean them with a match stick or toothpick (Fig. 20-36). Do not try to clean the air cap holes with wire, nails, or other metal tools. Such practice is likely to damage the air holes and result in imperfect spray patterns.
6. After the gun has been thoroughly cleaned, store it with about one inch of thinner in the cup. Although this will evaporate in time, it will soften any remaining dirt in the passageways of the gun. As the gun is used again, this softened dirt is more likely to be carried away.[4]

Some Common Spraying Troubles.[5] Even though the preceding spraying techniques are followed, the inexperienced operator will meet with certain problems. Some of the more common spraying troubles are the following:

---

[4] The material and illustrations presented on pages 414-433 are used by special permission of the De Vilbiss Company, Toledo, Ohio.

[5] Soderberg, G. A., *Finishing Materials and Methods*, Chapter XXIII, pp. 179-181.

Orange peel. Here the finish has a pimplelike appearance, resembling the texture of an orange (See Figs. 20-12 and 13, p. 421. It may be caused by the following reasons:

1. There is insufficient or too cheap a thinner mixed with lacquer or paint.
2. The distance between the gun and the sprayed surface is too far.
3. The gun is held too close to the work, causing a ripple effect.
4. Air pressure is too low or too high.

Sags and runs. These may be caused by:

1. Applying the material too heavily.
2. Moving the gun too slowly.
3. Putting too much thinner in the paint or lacquer.
4. Arcing the gun.
5. Faulty triggering at the end of each stroke.
6. Incorrect position of the air cap.

Streaks. These may be caused by:

1. Dirty air cap or fluid tip.
2. The incorrect angle of the gun in relation to the sprayed surface.
3. Improper overlapping of the spray.

Blushing. This is the tendency of lacquer to appear cloudy in its film. This trouble often happens under humid conditions, when moisture in the atmosphere condenses within the lacquer film, causing it to appear flat and off-color.

Mist or fog. This may be caused by:

1. Too much atomization.
2. Keeping the gun too far from the sprayed surface.
3. Overspray falling on the sprayed surface.

Sputtering and fluttering. Sudden starting and stopping of the spray pattern causes a nonuniform film. The causes may be:

1. The material is too heavy for the gun used.
2. There is a loose or damaged fluid tube.
3. The air cap and the fluid tip are loose and not tightened to the spray gun.

4. The opening in the top of the fluid cup is clogged up.
5. The fluid cup is nearly empty and in need of refilling.

In addition to the troubles listed here, a gun may cause trouble for reasons not readily detected. If, after a careful attempt to correct the difficulties, a gun still does not perform satisfactorily, it is best to have it overhauled at the factory.

Drying of Lacquers. Films made from lacquer set very quickly—in a very few seconds—and dry rapidly by evaporation, and not by oxidation, as is the case of oil varnishes which dry partly by evaporation in losing their solvents and then by slow oxidation of the oils contained. Because many of the solvents that are constituents of lacquers are very volatile and the lacquers themselves contain no drying oils, usually, there is a very remarkable speed in the setting and drying of nitrocellulose finishes. The present-day lacquers have more body or solid content than some of the earlier mixtures, and form thicker films which must be given more time for proper drying than was required for the earlier compounds of this type.

Experienced users of lacquers prefer to allow about 24 hours between coats, especially with brushing lacquers or undiluted spraying lacquers. Undercoats of lacquer are very apt to soften and become rough when later coats of these mixtures with their powerful solvents are applied over them unless they are very hard as a result of thorough drying. Some lacquers are said to dry in an hour, others in about four hours, allowing three coats to be applied in a day. Lacquer finishes are smoother, however, if plenty of time is allowed for drying. Undercoats of brushing lacquer are liable to be damaged by brushing on a fresh coat before the previous one has entirely hardened throughout the entire thickness of the film.

In coatings sprayed on with an air gun, some parts are thicker than others, and these thick films must have sufficient time for proper hardening. The rate of drying of coats of lacquer can be speeded up somewhat by placing the freshly finished articles in a warm room, but the newly spread film should be thoroughly set at ordinary temperatures or pinholes may appear because of too rapid drying.

Whenever a rubbed finish is desired over several coats of lacquer, two or three days should be allowed for the drying of the last coat before the final rubbing and polishing. The length of time needed for the drying of films or coatings varies somewhat with the different brands of lacquer. The furniture factories which use lacquer often allow only five to twelve hours for drying in a heated room before rubbing is done.

The Hot Spray Process.[6] The hot spray process for application of finishing materials is a relatively new technique. A patent on the process was issued in 1939. It provides a method wherein a material both higher in solids and viscosity than could be normally sprayed is reduced to a sprayable viscosity by heating. By using heat as a viscosity reducing agent it is, in effect, substituting heat for thinners without reducing solid content.

When first introduced, the hot spray process did not prove too satisfactory because of a lack of trouble-free equipment which would allow continuous and rapid spraying. It had been evident for many years that numerous advantages existed for applying paints, lacquers, and similar type products at elevated temperatures if equipment could be designed which would be inexpensive, simple to operate, practical from a safety angle, and easy to maintain.

The failure of equipment to operate satisfactorily in the years prior to World War II caused many finishers and finish manufacturers to adopt a "hands off" attitude toward the hot spray process. Within the last several years, a number of heaters have been developed which have to a great extent eliminated the defects of the earlier equipment and the process is gradually gaining acceptance as a practical production technique.

As in the case of ordinary spray equipment, these heating units require a certain amount of attention to ensure efficient performance. The hot spray process being new to many should be introduced into a finishing department with a thorough demonstration of both materials and equipment.

What is Hot Lacquer? A hot lacquer is a perfectly normal lacquer. It is made from nitrocellulose, gums, resins, plasticizers, flattening agents or pigments, and thinners, much the

---

[6] The material on "The Hot Spray Process" is used here by permission of the Grand Rapids Varnish Corporation.

same as a regular lacquer. Hot spray lacquers, like regular lacquers, work best when formulated with a specific set of finishing room conditions in mind. The finish manufacturer must work closely with the finisher in assuring successful installation of hot lacquer into the normal finishing schedule. The greatest difference between regular lacquer and hot spray lacquer is in solid content and viscosity. The solids content of a regular lacquer normally is in a range from 21 to 27 per cent solids. A hot spray lacquer will run from 27 to 35 per cent solids. In the maximum case this would amount to an increase of 66% in solids. A regular lacquer will generally run 24 to 28 seconds viscosity in a No. 4 Ford cup.[7] A hot spray lacquer may run as high as 160 seconds in a No. 4 Ford cup. Experience shows that for production spraying, 65 to 90 seconds fits most production lines best, with a solids content in the range of 27 to 33 per cent. The question arises, what does this increase in solids mean in film thickness on the work? Normally with two coats of 21 per cent cold spray lacquer, we may expect to get a dry film thickness of 2 to 2.5 mils. It is quite easy to attain this same thickness with one coat of 33 per cent solids hot spray lacquer.

Recently regular cold spray lacquers in the range of 32 to 35 per cent solids have been introduced. This high solids content, in the same range as hot spray lacquer solids, may seem to simplify the problem of higher solid lacquers. However, this is not quite true. The high solids content in a lacquer which is low enough in viscosity to spray at room temperature is achieved usually by using extremely low viscosity type nitrocellulose which results in a film of very low strength. The opposite is true in hot spray lacquers. A nitrocellulose of higher viscosity can be used, resulting in a film which is even stronger than would be obtained in a regular lacquer based on the same formula.

The solids portion of both regular and hot spray lacquer are similar in composition. There is, however, a difference in the volatile or thinner portions. The thinner portion of a regular lacquer is made up of a blend of rapid evaporating thinners,

---

[7] The Ford cup is an instrument that measures the viscosity or flowing resistance of lacquer and other finishing materials.

medium evaporating thinners, and a small amount of relatively slow evaporating thinners. This yields a lacquer which is balanced for quick setting, nonblushing, good flow and leveling, and no trapped air or orange peel. This combination is not satisfactory or necessary for a hot spray lacquer. Due to the fact that heavier coats normally result from hot spray, the faster evaporating solvents are omitted to prevent air and vapor bubbles from being trapped in the film as a result of too rapid drying. The slower solvents are usually omitted or reduced because without the fast evaporating solvent, the heavier and warmer film will flow satisfactorily. Also the slower evaporating solvents may be harmful because in heavy coats they may be retained in the film longer than is desirable. Just as in regular lacquers, because of variables in plant conditions, the thinner portion of a hot spray lacquer should be tailored to fit local conditions.

Equipment needed for hot spraying. For the application of hot spray lacquers, normally only one additional piece of equipment must be added to the regular equipment in the finishing room. This is the heating and circulating unit. There are a number of types of heaters on the market today which have been tested and approved as satisfactory. These heaters are usable with any spray gun. One of them will heat lacquer from an initial temperature of 70° Fahrenheit to 160° Fahrenheit in 15 to 20 minutes, holding about a half gallon of lacquer in the heating unit and links. It will deliver up to 32 oz. of heated lacquer per minute with a temperature drop of only around 10° Fahrenheit between the heating unit and the spray gun, using a 10 ft. hose. The lacquer is circulated by an air-motor-driven pump, and heated lacquer is delivered for continuous spray with a bypass at the gun to assure properly heated lacquer at all times. Most heaters are of an electrical type which operate on either 110 or 220 volts. They may be operated in connection with a pressure tank or drum pump or will draw from the container with their own pump. The temperature to which the lacquer is heated is controlled by an adjustable thermostat. There is also a set of coils for heating the atomizing air if it is desired.

Unlike the heaters of the past, which often gave trouble when the factory closed for the day or for lunch, now most heaters can be turned off and started up later with only a 15 to 20 minute wait necessary to bring the lacquer up to temperature. For short periods, the heater and circulator may be left running. While there is still room for improvement in minor details, the heaters available today make the successful application of lacquer by the hot spray process thoroughly practical, and their use is increasing all the time.

Advantages of Hot Spraying. Some of the advantages and savings through the use of hot spray lacquer are the following:

1. The lacquer contains more solids and less thinner. Thinner is costly and is lost after the lacquer has been applied.
2. Because of the higher viscosity on the work, there is less sagging. Fewer pieces are rejected for this reason.
3. Greater film thickness is applied with fewer coats.
4. Fewer coats result in less handling, lower labor cost, and increased production.
5. Blushing is eliminated. When a regular lacquer strikes the work, it is at a temperature approximately 15° Fahrenheit lower than the room temperature, and unless the solvent blend is correctly balanced will condense moisture from the surrounding air. Hot spray lacquer has dropped to no lower than room temperature as it strikes the work, so there is much less chance of condensation and blushing.
6. Smoother films with less orange peel are obtained.
7. Surface imperfections are better covered.
8. Better cold check resistance can be obtained because viscosity is not quite such a limiting factor and higher viscosity nitrocellulose with greater strength can be used in the formulation.

Sanding, Rubbing, and Polishing Lacquer Films. Sanding between coats of lacquer is sometimes necessary if for any reason the surface is rough or has other defects that will interfere with the final smooth finish. Sanding can be done with a very fine grade of waterproof sandpaper, used wet, preferably No. 4/0 to No. 6/0. Curved surfaces can be smoothed with very fine steel wool. It is not important to sand between the various coats of lacquer in order to secure proper adhesion, because a new nitrocellulose film will stick tightly to an undercoat. If the finisher wishes to apply a coat of varnish over a

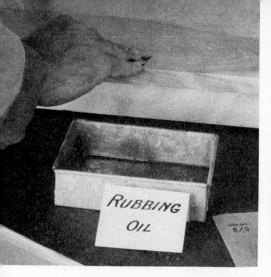
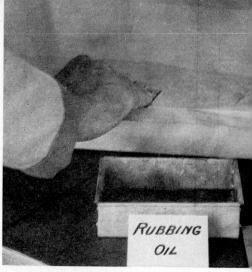

20—37. When thoroughly dry, the final lacquer coat is first rubbed with No. 8/0 waterproof sandpaper. Use either water or oil as a lubricant.
20—38. Next rub with No. 320 automobile paper or No. 370 crocus cloth. Use rubbing oil as a lubricant.

lacquer film, it is always wise to sand between coats, because varnish always adheres more satisfactorily to a sanded than to an unsanded surface. The sanding of lacquered surfaces is rather slow work, however, because a coating of this material is exceptionally hard. It is this unusual hardness that prevents the finish from being easily scratched or marred and is, on the whole, one of the good qualities of lacquer.

Rubbing and polishing improve the effect of a lacquered surface just about as much as these same operations soften and beautify a varnished surface. The procedure is very similar in the two cases. Lacquer films can be smoothed or leveled slightly with wet waterproof sandpaper of a very fine grade, such as No. 6/0 or No. 8/0, before the rubbing process with pumice stone is begun (Fig. 20-37). Special sandpaper, which should always be used wet, such as automobile abrasive paper Nos. 280, 320, and 400, are superior to other abrasives for smoothing lacquered surfaces (Fig. 20-38).

Lacquer coatings or films must be thoroughly solidified before any sanding or rubbing is attempted. Although the surface of a film of lacquer seems to be perfectly dry after a few hours, the coating seldom fully hardens so that it is in proper condition for rubbing under 24 hours, and it is usually wise to allow not less than two or three days for the evaporation of the solvents, in order that the lacquer may not have any soft spots where too thick a coating was applied. Some manufacturers recommend that at least four days be allowed for drying after the application of the last coat, especially on three-coat jobs where only one coat is applied each day. The drying time can be considerably shortened by the application of artificial heat in a heated drying room.

A finisher can do a lacquer rubbing job successfully with either the water or the oil process. Very fine pumice stone is preferable, especially for rubbing with water. Coarse pumice stone is liable to scratch a surface, and leave a grayish residue in the abrasions, left by the cutting material. The rubbing is done lengthwise of the grain, using a felt pad and proceeding as in rubbing a varnished article. A rubbed surface is always cleaned with a rag dampened with benzine or other similar liquid which is not a good solvent for lacquers.

Polishing a lacquered finish which has been rubbed produces a finer luster. Polishing can be done by a method similar to that used on varnish. Rottenstone and water are often rubbed over a lacquered surface, and a fine gloss is obtained with a mechanical buffer or a fine polishing pad. Commercially-prepared lacquer rubbing compounds are also available. These are prepared of such fineness that they remove the smallest scratches. Rubbing can be done with a felt-covered block or with a mechanical polisher (Fig. 20-39), page 442.

Flat Lacquers and Waxed Lacquer Finishes. Lacquers can be "flatted" or dulled in the manufacturing process by a method similar to that used in making flat varnishes. The addition of aluminum stearate to the lacquer in compounding it dulls the gloss of the film made from it, and gives it much the appearance of flat varnish finishes. In use, always apply flat lacquers over flat lacquers, because gloss lacquer undercoats are apt to show through in spots.

Very attractive wax finishes may be made over surfaces that have been covered with coats of ordinary gloss lacquer. The foundation or undercoats for wax may be a coat of shellac, sanded, and covered with one or two coats of lacquer. Before applying the wax, however, remember that oil rubbing with fine pumice stone will produce the best surface. Two undercoats of lacquer are greatly superior to two coats of shellac; because lacquer coatings do not scratch easily or deeply; be-

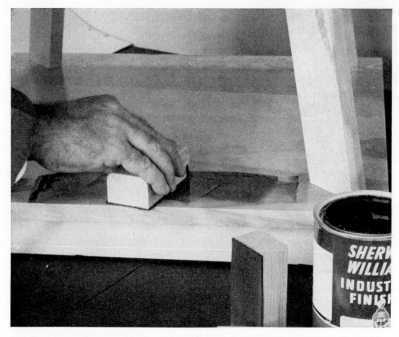

20—39. The final rubbing and polishing can be completed with rotten-stone and oil or with a commercially prepared lacquer-rubbing compound.

cause they are much more waterproof than shellac, which can be washed off in cleaning with an alkali soap in water; and because of the fact that lacquer films do not print or become sticky in hot weather and, in general, are very heat resisting.

Mixture of Shellac and Lacquer. An excellent waterproof shellac can be made by preparing a mixture of about one part of lacquer with three or four parts of shellac varnish. Various proportions and strengths of the two ingredients can be used. The best results are obtained by pouring the lacquer into the container first, and then slowly adding the shellac varnish, gradually blending the two by thorough stirring.

Waterproof shellac is an excellent finish for many purposes, and can be applied with a brush or with a spray gun. *Mixtures of shellac and lacquer do not keep well,* and are not often sold on the market for this reason. They will remain in good condition in a liquid mixture for several days, but must always be thoroughly stirred before use, because the two ingredients—lacquer and shellac—seem to separate.

A mixture of shellac and lacquer should be treated almost like shellac varnish in storing in glass in order to prevent its darkening. It can be applied with a brush about as easily as shellac, and produces a fine soft, lustrous finish which is very attractive and possesses many desirable qualities.

Waterproof shellac naturally is far more water resistant than ordinary shellac varnish. It can often be used to advantage under varnish or lacquer as a substitute for shellac, which is unsuitable as an undercoat for articles which are to be kept in damp places.

If a shellac varnish contains shellac wax, it may cause trouble because films made with lacquer and such a shellac varnish may not dry properly. It is usual, however, to remove most of the shellac wax from the shellac gum in the manufacturing process; consequently, the good brands of shellac varnish contain very little wax, and this small per cent can very largely be removed by filtering out all insoluble matter from the liquid shellac.

SELECTED REFERENCES, CHAPTER XX

Lacquer Finishes and Lacquer Technique

Deniston, G. L., *The Science of Modern Woodfinishing*, Chapters XII and XIII, pp. 179-229; 1949.

De Vilbiss Company, "Spray Gun Motion Study." Toledo, Ohio.

Ibid., "Making the Most of the Spray Painting Method."

Ibid., "A B C of Spray Painting Equipment."

Gibbia, S. W., *Wood Finishing and Refinishing*, "Lacquer," Chapter VII, pp. 106-122; 1954.

McGee, R. A. and Brown, A. G., *Instructional Units in Woodfinishing*, "To Apply a Lacquer Finish," Unit 5, pp. 36-39; 1950.

Qualatone Products, "The Finish of Your Lacquer Problems." 21 Gay Street, New York City, N.Y.

Soderberg, G. A., *Finishing Materials and Methods*, "Spraying," Chapter XXIII, pp. 179-181; 1952.

Von Fisher, W. and Bobalek, Edward G., *Organic and Protective Coatings*, "Hot Spray Lacquers," Chapter XII, pp. 260-280; 1953.

Wampler, Rollin H., *Modern Organic Finishes*, "Cellulose Lacquers, Spirit Varnishes, High Integrity and Special Finishes," Chapter II, pp. 15-34; 1946.

Ibid., "Spray Painting," Chapter IV, pp. 50-83; 1946.

Chapter XXI

Blond and Bleached Wood Finishes

Light-Toned Wood Finishes. Fad and fancy, always in search for something new, have stimulated a variety of light finishes produced by bleaching the natural tones of such woods as maple, walnut, and mahogany particularly. Such a finish may be for a light effect; or sometimes the wood is restained in attractive tones which give the appearance in color of new and interesting woods that may harmonize with some much-desired room color scheme. Pale woods, such as hard maple, may be bleached nearly white, leaving only a tint of a grayed cream color which finishes in an unusually light tone for wood. When bleached woods are not stained in finishing, some of the very light effects are produced, such as blond maple, which is often called platinum maple; or, if walnut is used, the bleached finish may be known as platinum walnut, or may have some trade name. Mahogany, when bleached and finished in a light effect, whitens and is transformed into a blond or platinum mahogany. All of these bleached woods are much lighter than the natural woods and give a brightness that is unusual in natural wood furniture.

Staining bleached woods is another method of obtaining new and different colors that are usually lighter in effect than the natural woods. Bleached walnut may be stained, and the finishes produced called "sun tan" or "gray onyx"; or bleached mahogany may be stained and filled with a brown filler, and lo! we have a "faded mahogany" finish that is different and attractive.

Bleaching, which means a whitening or loss of color, has been known in some of its forms for ages. Bleaches have been used to whiten various materials, particularly cloth fibers and paper pulp, oils of several kinds, and beeswax.

Very slow but effective means of bleaching textiles have been known for centuries. The historians do not record the procedures used in antiquity by the Phoenicians, Egyptians, Greeks, and Romans. After the Crusades, the Dutch became the bleachers of Europe and retained leadership in the art of bleaching until the latter part of the 18th century. Then, in England, a much more rapid process than the old one of alkaline lyes, washing, and sunning employed by the Dutch came into use through the substitution of dilute sulphuric acid. The new process brought greatly increased speed in bleaching. The use of chlorine came in England about 1787. It was introduced by Scheele after a suggestion by James Watt.

The modern methods of bleaching wood are similar to those used in whitening textiles. Different processes have been found best for the various fibres such as cotton, linen, wool, and silk. Some of the same bleaching materials are now used for bleaching wood.

Bleaching Agents Used on Wood. *Oxalic acid* was formerly the bleaching agent usually recommended for bleaching wood. A solution for bleaching may be prepared by use of about 10 to 16 ounces of the white crystalline powder to a gallon of quite hot water. *The bleaching solution is poisonous* and should be kept in glass or earthen jars. Its bleaching reaction on wood is rather weak, and the dust from sanding wood treated for bleaching is dangerous to breathe. The acid should be washed off and the bleached surfaces allowed to dry. Washing removes most of the danger from inhaling poisonous dust while sanding. For safety, if much sanding is to be done, about 3 or 4 ounces of borax should be dissolved in hot water and brushed on the wood to neutralize the poisonous acid. A dust mask or wet sponge may be worn over the nose if any large job of sanding is to be done after bleaching with oxalic acid.

Experience indicates that an oxalic solution is most effective if applied hot in two or three coats, and then a No. 2 solution of hyposulphite soda in a strength of 1 ounce of "hypo" to 12 ounces of hot water should be applied. These bleaching agents are usually spread with a rubber-set, flat wall brush. The borax solution mentioned above should be the third and final wash—given to neutralize the other chemicals.

Two-solution bleaches of another type which have alkaline

rather than acid reactions are quite generally used and are sometimes similar to some of the bleaching agents commonly used for wool. At present two-solution bleaching materials are the most powerful agents for removing color and, on the whole, the most effective, the cheapest, and the most practical.

Wood bleaching is very successfully accomplished by use of an application of a solution of potassium permanganate followed before the first coating dries by a solution of sodium bisulphite. The following formula indicates the best strength of chemicals for use:

Solution No. 1
> 1 ounce potassium permanganate (other amounts may be used)
> 1 gallon water (distilled preferred)

Solution No. 2
> 3 ounces sodium bisulphite (4 ounces for strong bleach)
> 1 gallon water (distilled preferred)
> Allow the mixture sufficient time for cooling before use.

The permanganate solution should be applied very freely with a brush. If the wood is allowed to dry, it will be of a slight purple tint, which will fade out with other bleaches. It is best, however, to apply Solution No. 2 before the first solution dries. The sodium bisulphite solution causes a bleaching out of all dark-colored pigments and produces a whitening or bleaching of almost any wood, though the final tone or color varies with different woods.

The combination of an application of permanganate of potassium solution followed by a wash or coating of sodium bisulphite has proved to be a very powerful bleaching agent for wood. After the desired color has been obtained, sponge the wood with clean water to remove any excess of bleaching chemicals.

Sometimes a solution of sodium hyposulphite in a strength of 2 to 4 ounces to the gallon of hot water is substituted for the No. 2 solution of sodium bisulphite. The bleaching results of both of these chemicals are similar when used in a second solution. The hyposulphite should not be used without a previous treatment with potassium permanganate solution because it is ineffective.

Other Bleaching Agents. It is possible to bleach wood with several other chemicals which are mostly alkaline, or used with an alkali, or following the application of one. The best known and most affective of these bleaches are peroxide of hydrogen (H_2O_2) and lime bleaching powders.

Hydrogen peroxide is effective but rather expensive, sometimes used for small jobs and for bleaching stains. Before application, a wash coat of ammonia or dilute sodium hydroxide is placed on the wood. Then the bleaching agent, hydrogen peroxide, may be brushed onto the wood several times in full strength, if necessary, in order to obtain whiteness. The wood seems to darken at first, then the dark-colored extract or pigment is bleached, by oxidation of products soluble in water. If the hydrogen peroxide is fresh and strong, a 30% solution with water is often enough. Wear rubber gloves and wash with water if hydrogen peroxide comes in contact with the skin.

Bleaching powders produce a whitening by a reaction of chlorine upon ordinary slaked lime when made into a thin paste with water. For walnut and some other woods, and especially for floors, this bleaching agent has been found to be quite satisfactory. The bleaching paste or solution must be mopped or brushed onto a floor promptly because the active chloride of lime is an unstable compound which decomposes rather quickly under ordinary conditions when it is moist or wet. After bleaching, the chemicals should be sponged or mopped off with clean water in order to prevent any future bleaching or any unwanted reaction with the finishes.

The ordinary bleaching powders of chloride of lime are wet with water, which brings about a chemical reaction that produces the active bleaching agent called calcium hypochlorite ($Ca(OCl)_2$) and also calcium chloride ($CaCl_2$). Sodium hypochlorite ($NaOCl$) in solution is still better, and leaves the surface of the wood in better condition for finishing than when calcium hypochlorite made from bleaching powder is used.

When chloride of lime paste is used for bleaching floors and other wood surfaces, it should be mixed into a thin paste prior to application and cleaned off before it becomes quite dry. If further bleaching is needed, a No. 2 solution of sodium carbonate (Na_2Co_3) should be applied before the wood has become completely dry. The No. 2 solution is made by placing a pound or a little more of the dry sodium carbonate salt into a gallon of hot water.

21—1. When bleaching wood, protect your hands with rubber gloves.

Dust from sanding of bleached floors and other large sur-faces is quite irritating if the finisher forgets to wear a dust mask or wet sponge over his nose.

Commercially Prepared Two-Solution Bleaching Agents. The demand for prepared, very strong bleaching agents for wood that really bleach, has become so great that there is at least one firm that has placed on the market a two-solution bleach which is sold under the name of Simpson's Bleaching Solutions No. 1 and No. 2. These bleaching agents may be sub-stituted for the potassium permanganate and sodium bisulphite bleaching solutions suggested for use in the "Instruction Sheet for Platinum or Blond Maple," which follows. Rubber gloves should be worn and rubber-bound brushes should be used in applying these strong bleaching agents (Fig. 21-1).

Procedure after Bleaching. Wood surfaces, in general, should be sponged off with clean water in order to remove any chemicals that have not been neutralized and which might have objectionable reaction to the wood, or to the finishes which are applied over the bleaches. The surfaces of wood which have been bleached or wet with water should be allowed to dry out thoroughly, after which they need careful sanding with No. 2/0, and then with fine sandpaper (No. 4/0).

Platinum and other very light bleached finishes are improved and kept whiter by the use of a thin coat of bleaching lacquer, which should be placed over the smooth bleached wood. Bleaching lacquer is a first-coat finishing material that should be applied to bare wood after bleaching. It is a lacquer that has had some rather weak bleaching agent added to it in order to produce a very pale finish. Bleaching lacquer whitens somewhat, and a lighter and paler finish is produced than by the use of thin, white shellac, which is sometimes substituted for it. In fact, bleaching lacquer when applied to smooth, bare wood produces an almost invisible covering. Bleaching lacquer may also be used as a mixing lacquer with shellac. The bleaching lacquer or white shellac coating over the bare wood should be very thin when used over porous woods, or the pores or cells of the wood will be filled to such an extent that paste filler will not find proper anchorage.

The procedure for finishing bleached woods after the coat of bleaching lacquer is similar to that usually followed for lacquered finishes, and is about as follows:

1. Fill carefully with white or natural paste filler.
2. Apply one coat of lacquer sanding sealer or pale white shellac.
3. Sand with No. 5/0 finishing paper.
4. Apply three or four coats of water white semigloss lacquer.
5. When thoroughly dry, rub with No. 8/0 waterproof paper, using paraffin oil as a lubricant.
6. Complete rubbing with prepared lacquer rubbing compound or pumice stone and oil.
7. Polish with wax.

Instruction Sheet for a Platinum-Maple or Blond-Maple Finish. This procedure may be followed for finishing various light-colored, close-grained woods, such as maple, beach, satinwood, and holly, or even pine.

Materials Necessary for a Lacquer Finish:

Bleaching materials: 1 ounce potassium permanganate and 3 or 4 ounces of sodium bisulphite, a sponge, sandpaper No. 2/0 and No. 4/0, bleaching lacquer, pure white shellac, water-white semigloss or dull lacquer, pumice stone and rubbing oil, and polishing wax.

Platinum-maple or blond-maple, and other very light finishes, are secured by bleaching and are left as white as possible—no stain being used after bleaching. Bleaching lacquer also assists in securing the very light or blond effect. Other names given to similar finishes are: Colonial, Early American, and Whitney Maple Finishes.

Procedure for Platinum or Blond Maple Finish:

1. Before bleaching, all wood surfaces should be made as smooth as possible with sharp tools, then sandpapered lengthwise of the grain with a medium grit sandpaper, and finished with a fine grade, such as 4/0. Use the sandpaper over a block of wood.

2. Apply a No. 1 bleaching solution prepared from potassium permanganate and water. A rubber-set brush of proper size should be used in applying the bleaching agent very freely and rubber gloves should be worn to protect the hands.

3. Before the solution No. 1 is quite dry, apply a No. 2 bleaching agent made of sodium bisulphite and water. Apply both bleaching solutions when cold.

4. After the sodium bisulphite coating has dried, all bleached surfaces should be sponged thoroughly with water in order to remove any excess of bleaching chemicals.

5. Resanding with 4/0 sandpaper is needed after bleaching and washing with water in order to remove the fuzz raised by these operations.

6. Apply with a spray gun a coat of full strength bleaching lacquer. Omit any sanding after this coat dries.

7. About two coats of white shellac of 3½- or 4-pound cut should be applied in full strength and sanded when dry to a smooth surface. Coats of sanding sealer may be substituted for the white shellac if the sanding sealer be pure white. Sanding sealer is made for application with a spray gun.

8. Over the shellac or sanding-sealer coatings spray on one or preferably two coats of water-white, dull lacquer in full strength.

9. Rub the lacquer coating when dry with rubbing oil and pumice stone until the surface is smooth.

10. Polish the rubbed lacquer surface with a furniture polishing wax. Some finishers prefer to omit the polishing with wax.

Platinum-Walnut and Platinum-Mahogany Finishes.

These woods and other open-pored woods that need a filler can be given platinum or bleached finishes by the same process that is suggested for maple. The one important difference is that walnut, mahogany, and similar woods having open pores need a paste filler. The wood filler should be applied after the coating of bleaching lacquer has dried. This means that an ordinary natural or white filler coating is given between steps Nos. 6 and 7 in the procedure.

Instruction Sheet for a Bleached and Stained-Walnut Finish. Porous woods, such as walnut and mahogany, which need a paste filler, are often bleached, then stained with a rather weak, light-toned water stain, to which about one fourth of the volume in denatured alcohol is added. For some effects a bleaching lacquer is applied over the stain and under the filler. For other finishes the filler is placed on the stained wood and bleaching lacquer is omitted.

Materials Needed for Bleached Walnut-Stained Finishes:

Bleaching materials: Use Simpson's Two-Solution Bleach, a sponge, sandpaper No. 2/0 and 4/0 preferably of the wet-or-dry type, bleaching lacquer sometimes wanted, water-white denatured alcohol shellac or sanding sealer, natural or light paste filler, white semigloss lacquer, rubbing oil and fine pumice stone, and furniture polishing wax. For a gray-onyx walnut finish obtain a gray-onyx walnut stain powder. For a sun-tan finish, secure a sun-tan, water-soluble stain powder. Other light-toned water stains may be used for different tone effects. Brushes for applying the bleach solutions and stain are also needed. The brushes used with the bleaches should be rubber bound, and rubber gloves should be worn. The bleaching agents should not be placed in metal containers and are best stored in a cool, dark place.

Procedure for a Sun-Tan Bleached-Walnut Finish:

1. Smooth with sharp tools, then sandpaper with No. 2/0, and finish always lengthwise of the grain with No. 4/0 sandpaper.

2. Apply a heavy coat of No. 1 bleaching solution. After the bleach has dried thoroughly, sand the surfaces smooth with No. 4/0 sandpaper.

3. Coat the surfaces freely with No. 2 bleaching solution, using a different rubber-bound brush and wearing rubber gloves.

4. After the bleaching solutions have dried, wash off the bleaches and, when dry again, sand the surfaces with a No. 4/0 sandpaper to remove the fuzz.

5. Apply very evenly a coat of sun-tan walnut stain, rubbing it out just before it dries.

(For a gray-onyx walnut finish substitute a gray-onyx stain for the sun-tan stain.)

6. Spray over the dried stain a coat of bleaching lacquer. This step is often omitted, but it is a valuable protection if light sanding is needed over the stain. Bleaching lacquer will slightly bleach the stain if used.

7. Fill with a light or slightly tinted paste wood filler.

8. After the filler is thoroughly dry, apply a coat of white shellac. Sandpaper the shellac coating smooth after 12 to 24 hours. Sanding sealer may be substituted for shellac.

9. Two coats of white semigloss lacquer should be sprayed over the shellac undercoats if a spray gun is available.

10. Rub the lacquer with pumice stone and rubbing oil for a smooth finish, or smooth with No. 3/0 steel wool and oil.

11. Polish the smoothed finish with furniture wax and much rubbing.

Pickled or Limed Effect Finish. This finish is used on open-grained woods only. Instead of bleaching the wood, secure the desired whiteness by filling the pores with either unslaked lime paint filler, or white stain blonding mix. When using unslaked lime, mix one pound into two quarts of water. This mixture is applied to the surfaces like any wood filler. When using a paint filler, mix five pounds of soft white-lead paste with two pounds of silex. Apply this mixture and remove it like any wood filler.

White stain blonding mix is made by mixing white titanium powder with a penetrating sealer to paste consistency. In this procedure, all surfaces are first given a coat of penetrating sealer. Before this dries, the blonding mix is rubbed in. After taking on a dull appearance, it is removed like other wood fillers. When a satisfactory light effect has been produced, a washcoat of shellac or lacquer sanding sealer can be applied, to be followed either by a number of coats of varnish or by lacquer.

SELECTED REFERENCES, CHAPTER XXI

Blond and Bleached Woodfinishes

Blackwell, R., "The Use and Abuse of Wood Bleaches," *Industrial Finishing*, 23, pp. 90-98, May, 1947.

Deniston, G. L., *The Science of Modern Woodfinishing*, "Novelty Finishes," Chapter XIV, pp. 230-244; 1949.

Gibbia, S. W., *Woodfinishing and Refinishing*, "Blond Finishes," Chapter XII, pp. 188-201; 1954.

Hogstrom, E., "Bleached Finishes," *Industrial Finishing*, 22, page 88, Feb., 1946.

Soderberg, G. A., *Finishing Materials and Methods*, "Bleaches," Chapter XVII, pp. 113-115; 1952.

Chapter XXII

Flock and Its Application

What Is Flock? Flocking, only a few years ago considered a novelty finish, is rapidly becoming standard for a great variety of articles.

Flock consists of small, carefully cut fibers, which at first glance look like dust or fuzz. It is principally produced from three fibers: viscose rayon, cotton, and hair.

Viscose rayon is manufactured from continuous filaments, known as tow. They are straight, untwisted and of controlled diameter (deniers).

Cotton flock is made from new, high-grade cotton. Although cotton rags can be used as a source material, they produce an inferior quality of flock.

Hair used in flock manufacture is primarily goat hair. After the skins and hides are inspected carefully, the hair is removed by a lime process. Following a careful washing, it is next dried at a temperature of 220° Fahrenheit.

In addition to these three sources, flock is also produced from synthetic fibers, such as nylon, orlon, and cellophane. Such vegetable fibers as sisal, jute, and hemp are used as well as animal fibers, silk and wool. Of these materials, rayon and cotton are the most widely used in the flock-coating industry.

Flock is ordinarily produced in three forms:

1. Precision ground flock
2. Random-cut flock and
3. Ground flock.

Precision and random-cut flock can be made from nylon, orlon, rayon, and animal hair. Ground flock is usually made from cotton, animal hair, sisal, and wool.

Through a process of dyeing, flock is available in any color of the spectrum.

22—1. Flock, applied to the inside of silverware boxes, is decorative and protective.

COURTESY CLAREMONT WASTE MANUFACTURING COMPANY

Uses of Flock. In general, flock can be applied to any surface which will hold adhesives. Its use is either decorative or functional. As a decorative means it is used for the linings of drawers, trays, cedar chests, silver chests, gift boxes, and other articles (Fig. 22-1). Toys, bookcovers, and greeting cards are made attractive by the use of flock (Fig. 22-2).

22—2. Toys are made more attractive with flock.

COURTESY CLAREMONT WASTE MFG. CO.

As a means of interior styling flock is used in the automobile, airplane and home industry. From a functional standpoint flock can be used successfully for the following:

1. Marproofing of index files, letter trays, statuettes, bookends, lamp bases, and smoking trays.
2. Snagproofing of baskets and hampers (Fig. 22-3).
3. Accoustical coverings for musical instruments, radio cabinets, and record players.

In industry, flock has its functional use in the soundproofing of aircraft, bus, and home interiors.

22—3. Flock can be used on a great variety of articles for decorative as well as functional purposes.

COURTESY CLAREMONT WASTE MFG. CO.

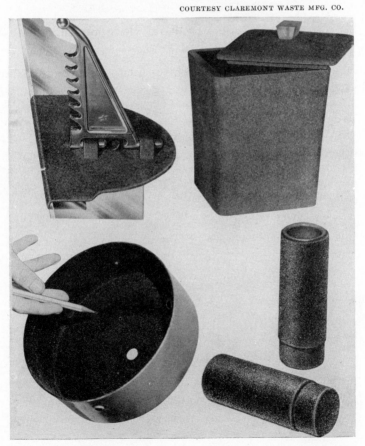

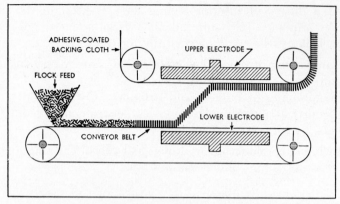

COURTESY CELLUSUEDE PRODUCTS

22—4. Electrostatic flocking machine.

Application of Flock. In general, there are three methods by which flock can be applied to a surface:

1. The Electrostatic Method. This is limited to overall coatings of flexible goods. Equipment for electrostatic flocking consists of two electrodes with a high potential difference between them. A corona discharge ionizes the atmosphere surrounding the one electrode. As flock fibers are introduced into this atmosphere, they become charged and are attracted to the other electrode. An adhesive coated surface is placed in such position as to intercept these electrostatically impelled fibers (Fig. 22-4).

22—5. Vibration-type flocking machine.

COURTESY CELLUSUEDE PRODUCTS

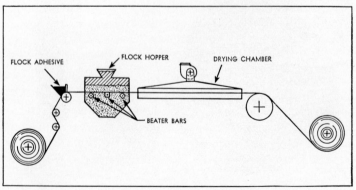

2. The Vibration or Beater Bar Method. This method is recommended for continuous flocking on yard goods and flat, rigid items such as greeting cards and fiber boards. In the general procedure followed in vibrator flocking, an adhesive is first applied to the article to be flocked. Next, the flock is sifted, screened, or blown onto the article while it passes over the square, rotating beater bars (Fig. 22-5).

In another method, the flock is sifted with one hand, while the article to be flocked is pulled across the single beater bar with the other hand. This action causes the flock to bounce and stand up vertically, imbedding it into the adhesive.

3. The Spray Method. This method is the most popular for all types of irregular-shaped items and small articles. Manufacturers of spray equipment now make special flock guns.

Spraying flock is somewhat similar to spraying paint. But flock, being a solid, is not atomized by the spray gun as in the case of paint or adhesive. As a result, the orifice on a flock gun must be much larger than that of a typical paint spray gun.

In spraying flock the operator holds the gun about 18 inches from the adhesive surface. This is to make sure that the flock particles are driven into the adhesive in an upright position. Also, from this distance, the air blast from the gun will not have such a quick-drying effect upon the adhesive.

The pressure necessary to spray flock depends upon the adhesive used, the atmospheric conditions, and the length of the flock. Recommended spraying pressure is between 25 and 40 lbs. If the adhesive is highly viscous, a higher pressure such as from 45-50 lbs. may be necessary to drive the fibers into the adhesive. In schools and home workshops where a limited amount of flocking is done, the flock can be satisfactorily applied with a simple hand-operated gun.

22—6. Christmas wreath coated with flock. Both the flock and adhesive are sprayed simultaneously by merging the two streams.

Types of Adhesives. The durability of the flock coating depends to a large extent upon the adhesive used. Adhesives include water-soluble glues, enamels, lacquers, and others. Water-soluble *glues* should not be used if the finished surface is likely to come into contact with water. Glue solutions also have the tendency to dry too quickly, allowing insufficient time for the proper application of the flock.

22—7. Materials and equipment needed to do simple flocking.

458

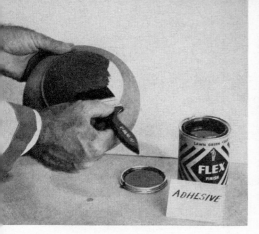

22—8. Cover the area to be flocked with adhesive. 22—9. After placing the object in its proper position, apply the flock with the gun.

A disadvantage of *enamel* as an adhesive is that it may crack and peel when dry. Although *lacquer* makes a good adhesive, it is difficult to work with because of its fast-drying action.

The method used for application of the adhesive depends upon the nature and design of the product being coated. For small articles, a spray gun or brush can be used. Before adhesives are applied, be sure that the surface is clean and otherwise properly prepared. Sharp edges should be rounded lightly, since flock will not stand upon a sharp edge. All obvious flaws such as dents, holes, and cracks should be filled and sanded smooth.

Normally, adhesives of harmonizing colors are used. On the other hand, it is possible to use tinted adhesives to enrich the shade of the flock. For unusual effects, flock and adhesive can be sprayed on simultaneously. In this method, two guns are used, with one gun spraying flock and the other adhesive. This method is widely used in the flocking of Christmas trees and wreaths (Fig. 22-6).

Procedure for Flocking with a Hand-Operated Gun:

1. Select the proper adhesive, which may be a thin water-soluble glue, enamel, or lacquer. Other items needed are shown in Fig. 22-7.
2. Fill the gun with the proper flock.
3. Using a brush or spray gun, apply the adhesive to those parts of the object that are to be flocked (Fig. 22-8).

459

4. Place the object in its proper position, and apply the flock with the gun (Fig. 22-9).
5. Allow sufficient time for all flocked surfaces to dry thoroughly.

SELECTED REFERENCES, CHAPTER XXII

Flock and Its Application

Black, George, "Flock Finishes." Edward A. Sheenan and Sons, Walpole, Massachusetts.

Bostrom, J. D., "Flock Finishing in a Custom Shop," *Industrial Finishing,* 23, pp. 41-52, March, 1947.

Cellusuede Products, Inc., "What is Cellusuede?" Rockford, Illinois.

Claremont Waste Manufacturing Company, "Flock Notes." Claremont, New Hampshire.

Deniston, G. L., *The Science of Modern Woodfinishing,* "Novelty Finishes," Chapter XIV, pp. 237-238; 1949.

Rayon Processing Company of R. I., "Rayco Flock." Pawtucket, R.I.

Schulze, A. P., "Flock Coating Practices," *Products Finishing,* Nov., 1948.

Soderberg, George A., *Finishing Materials and Methods,* "Flock," Chapter XII, pp. 91-97; 1952.

Chapter XXIII

Furniture Refinishing

With the high cost of furniture, it becomes increasingly important for the average person to know something about the techniques of furniture refinishing. Also, aside from the economic factor involved, many people find this activity of restoring furniture highly enjoyable and fascinating.

Regardless of the reason for restoring a piece of furniture, the work involved can be roughly divided into the following four categories:

Making the necessary repairs.
Removing the old finish.
Preparing for the new finish.
Refinishing.

Nothing will be said here about the repair of furniture, since it is outside the realm of furniture refinishing. Nevertheless, it is important for any piece of furniture requiring refinishing to be structurally sound and have all repairs completed before actual refinishing starts.

Removing the Old Finish. Before removing the old finish, examine it carefully to see whether its complete removal is necessary. A number of repair specialties are now on the market which are highly satisfactory in the removal of many finish defects. For example, so-called amalgamators can be used to restore checked varnish finishes. They work on the principle of softening up the finish and thus amalgamate or "heal" the checks. If such checks are the main fault of the finish, and if they can be eliminated through the application of amalgamators, the removal of the entire finish becomes unnecessary.

Only when the corrective possibilities of various repair specialties have been carefully surveyed should old finishes be removed in their entirety.

Old finishes are most satisfactorily removed through the application of some specially prepared solvents. Of these the commercially prepared ones are the most effective, and can be

461

23—1. Give the varnished surface a liberal application of varnish remover. 23—2. After the old varnish "curls" or "lifts," remove it with a dull putty knife. Wipe the knife on pieces of old newspaper.

purchased under various trade names as paint and varnish removers. Lacquer thinner is the most generally used solvent stripper for lacquer finishes. Solvents such as benzol, toluol, and acetone can also be used.

When using removers, certain *precautions* should be taken. It is necessary to have very good ventilation because of fire hazards and toxicity. The use of goggles and rubber gloves is recommended as a protection to eyes and skin. Follow the directions as listed on the container.

Removal of old finishes, at its best, is a messy and sticky job. A good supply of paper towels or old newspapers and rags should be on hand. A waste can should be nearby so that used papers and rags can be disposed of readily. In addition to these items, the following tools and materials are needed:

> Small can or jar to hold the remover.
> One or two old paint brushes.
> A dull putty knife.
> A small, stiff scrub brush.
> No. 2/0 steel wool.
> Denatured alcohol.

Before these removers are used it is necessary to know the type of finish. Tests: A drop of varnish remover will readily cause a wrinkled effect on varnished, enameled, or painted surfaces. A wax-free shellac finish can be softened and removed by rubbing with denatured alcohol. Lacquer thinner will have a similar effect upon a lacquer finish.

When removing an old varnish finish, proceed as follows:

1. Place the piece of furniture over some old newspapers to protect the floor or bench top.
2. Shake the remover well and pour a small amount into the small can or jar.
3. With a 2″ paintbrush, apply a liberal coat of remover. Do not cover more than about two square feet at one time (Fig. 23-1).
4. Let the remover stand for about ten minutes until the varnish surface shows a wrinkled appearance or "lifts."
5. Remove the old varnish with a dull putty knife (Fig. 23-2). Wipe the knife frequently on a paper towel or a piece of newspaper. Fold these papers and deposit them into the waste can.
6. Wipe off as much of the remaining finish as possible, using coarse rags or crumpled paper.
7. Scrub the surface with a stiff brush, dipped in denatured alcohol.
8. Wipe with a clean cloth.
9. Next rub with No. 2/0 steel wool, dipped in denatured alcohol.
10. Wipe with a benzine-moistened cloth (Fig. 23-3).
11. Allow this cleaned surface to dry 24 hours. Proceed to remove the varnish on other surfaces.

Inasmuch as possible, place surfaces to be cleaned in a

23—3. Wash the surface with a rag dampened with benzine. This will remove any wax left by the remover.

horizontal position. Clean crevices, grooves, and corners with an old toothbrush, and pointed picking sticks.

When the varnish has been removed and the surfaces are thoroughly dry, check to see whether any varnish spots remain. If so, remove them in the same way before continuing.

Sometimes painted surfaces will prove difficult to clean, especially on antique pieces. Often such furniture was covered with a paint containing skim milk or buttermilk. To remove it, apply a heavy coat of commercial remover to a surface. After letting it stand for a while, while the remover is still wet, scrub the surface with pads of No. 1 steel wool. After removing as much paint as possible, repeat this procedure as needed. Complete the process by scrubbing the surface with a fresh pad of steel wool dipped in denatured alcohol.

Another cleaning agent that often is used as a follow-up after paint remover is a solution of sal soda or tri-sodium phosphate. One pound of these materials dissolved in 5 quarts of hot water makes a good mixture. After giving a surface a good scrubbing, rinse and clean it thoroughly with hot water. Use rubber gloves for protection. Lye is sometimes used as a remover. This substance, however, is so potent that its use should only be attempted by those who have had experience with it. Its improper use may cause more damage than good.

As a rule the use of scrapers to remove old finishes is not recommended. Too often a scraper will dig into the wood, leaving rough spots which are difficult to smooth out. But very old varnish, at times, is found to be so flaky that it can be removed easily with a wood scraper without injury to the wood-surface. One should be familiar with the scraping action of this tool and the correct procedure for sharpening it.

Preparing For a New Finish. After the old finish has been removed, the article should be inspected closely for dark spots, small cracks, shallow holes and dents. These defects must next be eliminated.

Darkened or discolored spots can be lightened or entirely removed by the proper use of a bleach. Commercially prepared bleaches are usually of the No. 1 and No. 2 type. The No. 1 liquid does the actual bleaching, and the No. 2 liquid serves as a neutralizer (Fig. 21-1, p. 448). Follow the manufacturer's directions at all times. An inexpensive bleach can be prepared by dissolving 2 ounces of oxalic acid crystals in one pint of hot water. After applying this bleach with a brush, leave it on the surface 10-20 minutes. A second or third application may be necessary to obtain the desired result. Next wash the surface with a neutralizer prepared with one part of ammonia and ten parts of water. When a rather *weak bleach* is desired, many of the common household bleaches will work satisfactorily.

Discoloration. Often in the process of removing finishes, wood surfaces take on a gray or faded appearance. To avoid excessive discoloration, wash all surfaces down with a hot detergent solution. Do this before the remover has dried completely. Then apply a hot solution of oxalic acid. In about ten minutes this can be washed off and neutralized with ammonia or vinegar.

Removal of Grease Stains. Grease stains from animal fats can usually be removed with benzine or a commercially prepared spot remover such as that used on clothing. Vegetable grease spots often respond to the use of acetone. Apply these liquids with a small brush, and wipe clean with tissue paper.

Smoothing Surfaces With Sandpaper. Up to this point, a considerable amount of water has been used, and the grain of the wood has been raised considerably. This roughness must be removed by careful sanding. For the proper use of abrasives, see Chapter II, pp. 29-45. When all surfaces are properly sanded, the actual process of refinishing can start.

Refinishing. Unless a piece of furniture is to be finished in its natural color, the first operation in the refinishing process is staining. Stains are used to bring out the beauty of the grain or to emphasize the color of woods. For the proper selection of a stain and its application, see Chapters III, IV, V, and VI on pp. 46-83.

Depending upon the kind of wood used in a piece of furniture, wood surfaces should be filled with either a paste or liquid filler. So-called open-grained woods are filled with a paste filler; close-grained wood can be filled with a liquid filler such as shellac. For the proper selection of fillers and their application see Chapter IX, pp. 134-160.

With all surfaces properly stained and filled, the application of the final finish can start. Since the range of finishes is quite extensive, a brief description of the more commonly used ones follows:

Varnish Finish. This finish is partially or fully resistant to water, alcohol, heat, and acid, depending upon the kind of varnish used. For good results, special precautions in its application must be taken, such as the use of a dust-free room, proper temperature, and proper equipment. For a more complete procedure on how to produce a satin or gloss finish, see Chapter XII, on pp. 218-250.

Lacquer Finish. This finish is much quicker to apply than varnish. A spray gun for its application should be available. For more information on how to apply a lacquer finish, see Chapter XX, on pp. 402-443.

Shellac and Wax Finish. In furniture refinishing, this type of finish has been for many years the one most used and most popular among refinishers. It is highly satisfactory for chairs, desks, and such articles where surfaces will not come into contact with heat, water, or alcoholic beverages. For the procedure of producing a shellac and wax finish, see Chapter X, pp. 161-191.

Varnish and Oil Finish. By mixing a good grade of varnish with the proper proportions of linseed oil and turpentine, an excellent finish can be produced. This mixture, which can be applied with a soft, lint-free cloth, is especially well adapted to open-grained woods, such as walnut, mahogany, oak, and chestnut. For best results use a good grade of spar varnish, pure boiled linseed oil, and pure turpentine.

The general procedure for this finish is as follows:

1. With a lint-free rag apply a sealer coat made up of 50% spar varnish and 50% turpentine. Allow this application to dry. Sand lightly with No. 8/0 waterproof paper.
2. Next prepare the following mixture:

   25% spar varnish.
   25% boiled linseed oil.
   50% turpentine.

3. Apply this mixture with a rag, rubbing it into the surface for several minutes. Stop before it becomes sticky.
4. Wipe the surface with a clean, dust-free rag.
5. After giving all surfaces a coat like this, let dry for 48 hours.

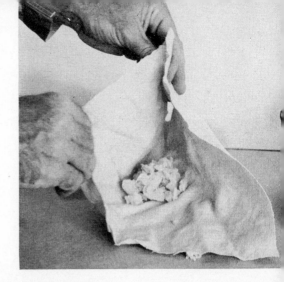

23—4. Make a wax pad by placing two tablespoons of wax in the center of a piece of heavy linen.

6. Rub lightly with No. 2/0 steel wool or No. 8/0 finishing paper.
7. Repeat steps 3, 4, and 5 until three or more coats have been applied.
8. Rub the last coat with No. 3/0 steel wool.
9. Apply two coats of wax, and polish with a soft cloth.

Waxing. Most finishers apply a thin film of polishing wax over all final finishes. Waxing gives a soft, pleasing luster and, if repeated from time to time as it wears off, will preserve the finish indefinitely. For best results use a paste wax, selecting a color that resembles the furniture. Directions for waxing:

1. Remove all dust from the surface to be waxed.
2. Prepare a wax pad by placing 2 tablespoons of wax in the center of a 10″ square piece of heavy linen. Fold the corners over the wax making it into a pad (Fig. 23-4).
3. With a circular motion, rub all surfaces, leaving a thin coat of wax (Fig. 23-5), page 468.
4. Allow it to dry for about 10 minutes.
5. Rub first with a soft cloth and follow up with a harder cloth. Be sure to remove all surplus wax.
6. Apply 2 or 3 coats for best results and rub as before. Avoid using too much wax.

Oil Finish. One of the oldest and most satisfactory of all finishes on hard and close-grained wood is an oil finish. This is produced by applying a mixture of two parts of boiled linseed oil and one part of pure turpentine.

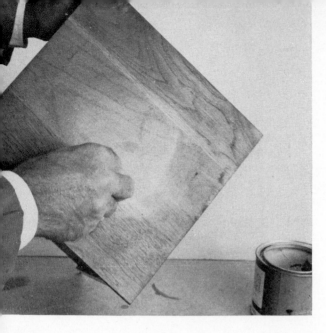

23—5. Rubbing with the pad in a circular motion, leave a thin coat of wax on all surfaces.

An oil finish should be attempted only when plenty of time is available and you are willing to do a considerable amount of rubbing. When properly applied, it makes wood surfaces impervious to water, heat, and scratches.

The procedure for putting on an oil finish is as follows:

1. With the surfaces to be finished properly sanded and dusted, apply the oil-turpentine mixture. Rub the oil in with a rag for 10 to 20 minutes.
2. Wipe off all excess oil with a soft lint-free cloth. Be sure to remove all oil from crevices and carvings.
3. Rub the surface vigorously with a hard polishing cloth for another 10 to 20 minutes. Rubbing with a hard cloth develops heat by friction and brings out a luster.
4. Apply oil to all other surfaces as indicated in steps 1, 2, and 3.
5. Allow the first coat to dry for at least two days.
6. Apply the second coat like the first and allow this one to dry for 2 days.
7. Apply from 5 to 20 coats of oil as directed above. Increase the drying time as additional coats are applied. The drying time for the final coats can be as much as one month.

Since oily rags are easily combustible, special precautions must be taken to avoid a possible fire. Either burn rags, or hang them up on a line in a well-ventilated place.

Penetrating Wood Sealer Finish. Penetrating, easy-to-apply finishes are especially popular among wood finishers who lack a satisfactory finishing room and other equipment.

Penetrating wood sealers were primarily developed for floors and panel work, but some of them can be used on furniture as well. Their application is simple, with a clean rag. Some of them produce a finish by repeating the application several times with the same preparation. Others are prepared in two or three different solutions, to be applied in the order suggested by the manufacturer. For best results, it is important to follow the directions for their application (Fig. 23-6).

Penetrating finishes have the following advantages over surface finishes such as shellac, varnish and lacquer:

1. No sanding or rubbing is required between coats.
2. They do not raise the grain of the wood.

23—6. Finishing a piece of walnut root with a penetrating rub finish. Three different applications are required.

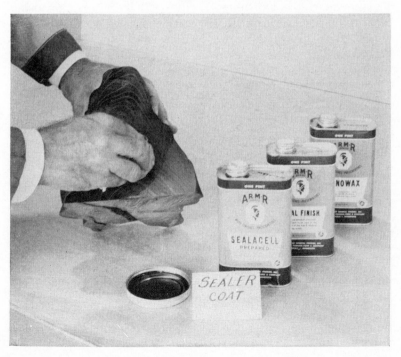

3. No finishing room is required.
4. No brushes or spray gun are required for their application. They are applied with a clean, soft rag.
5. Brush marks are eliminated.
6. Since the produced finish penetrates, rather than building up, it does not check or crack.
7. Some of them are highly resistant to alcoholic beverages, cosmetics, and hot dishes.
8. They can be patched successfully.

Finishing Repair Specialties.[1] When the finish on a piece of furniture is damaged only slightly, it can often be restored by means of certain repair specialties. A great number of these are now on the market, with some of them producing very satisfactory results. A few of them are listed here:

Amber glaze. The purpose of this liquid is to remove packing marks and imprints from the finish. It works on the principle of amalgamating or softening the varnish and smoothing out the impression. Amber glaze can be used in the removal of paper marks, hot dish spots, rings left by lamps, and other imprints in a varnish finish.

Ethereal varnish. This is a spirit varnish especially adapted for repair and touch-up work. It readily builds up places that have been rubbed through to the bare wood, or repairs places where the varnish has been scraped off. It dries almost instantly and can be used over any kind of varnish, shellac or lacquer.

French varnish. This is a heavy-bodied spirit varnish made by refining and dewaxing the better grades of shellac gums. Clear and almost water-white in color, it is one of the most widely used preparations for French polishing.

Touch-up lacquers. These lacquers have the advantage over other lacquers in that they will not lift the old finish. They can be mixed with prepared lacquer tints. Their application is most successfully done with an air brush.

In addition to these repair media for clear finishes, enameled surfaces can be repaired with so-called shellac enamels. Furniture polishes, scratch removers, stick shellac, and touch-up stains all help restore furniture without going through a

---

[1] Campbell, M. L., Instruction book, "How to Use Campbell Finish Repair Specialties," 1954.

complete refinishing job. It is well to investigate their possibilities.

SELECTED REFERENCES, CHAPTER XXIII

Refinishing Furniture

Campbell, M. L., instruction book, *How to Use Campbell Finishing Repair Specialties*, 58 pages, 1951.

Deniston, G. L., *The Science of Modern Woodfinishing*, "Repairing and Refinishing," Chapter XVIII, pp. 291-306; 1949.

Gibbia, S. W., *Wood Finishing and Refinishing*. New York: D. Van Nostrand Co., 1954. 255 pages.

Kinney, Ralph Parsons, *The Complete Book of Furniture Repair and Refinishing*. New York: Charles Scribner's Sons, 1950. 240 pages.

McGee, R. A. and Brown, A. G., *Instruction Units in Woodfinishing*, "To Refinish Wood Surfaces," Unit 14, pp. 98-102; 1950.

Pattou, A. B. and Vaughn, C. L., *Furniture Finishing, Decoration and Painting*. F. J. Drake, Chicago, Illinois.

Wright, F. E., "Refinishing Old Furniture," Bulletin 295. New York State College of Agriculture, Ithaca, N.Y.

Yates, Raymond F., *New Furniture from Old*. New York: Wilfred Funk, 1951. 253 pages.

Index